TRAVELLING LIGHT

— •*• —

• What are we - eternal, indivisible 'souls'
or a collection of qualities held together precariously
by some temporal process?

• How 'separate' are we from other human
beings and life at large?

• Can we loosen/dissolve our ego boundaries and expand
to include other life forms
- what other 'life forms', and how?

• Can we live other people's past and current lives
as if they were our own
- what might the implications be?

• What is space - where do we exist?

• What is time - are there 'actually' such things as
past, present and future?

• What is the real nature and function of sex
- recreation or procreation?

• Is sex the only means of procreation
(or has it always been so with humans)?

• How do we distinguish between dreams, hallucinations
and 'real' life
- can we be absolutely certain of what 'real' really is?
What is 'reality', anyway?

• What does memory have to do with truth?
What is truth?

Some comments on *Travelling Light*
(see more on the back cover)

"an engaging and absorbing series of dramatic encounters with an enigmatic and acute spiritual master...it opens up key areas of fundamental human interest and introduces us to new levels of consciousness and to multiple realities."

Arion Marsyas, PhD

"a gripping account of the author's experiences in being initiated into aspects of ancient Mystical traditions in which many of his cherished everyday perceptions of reality are turned on their head, and expansion and continuity of consciousness acquire a new and unexpected meaning."

Dr Rosemary Russell

"an engaging book that dares you to find your own enlighten-ment...fascinating and with a sense of humour...packed with tantal-ising gems of ideas and intimations of further Initiatory experi-ences..."

Gina Connor, psychologist

Dear Andreas,
I have thoroughly enjoyed re-reading your excellent book and have appreciated it even more this time. It is a wonderful book full of profound insights, intellectually and emotionally exciting and spiritually inspiring.

Thank you
Rob
Robert L. Paskin, group facilitator

TRAVELLING LIGHT

Glimpses of Modern Day Initiation

ANDREAS MAVROMATIS

- Thyrsos Press -
London

First published in paperback 2006
by Thyrsos Press
Reprinted in paperback 2010
by Thyrsos Press
57, First Avenue, London E12 6AW

A catalogue record for this book
is available from the British Library

ISBN : 978-0-9553052-0-7

Printed in Great Britain by
Park Communications Ltd
London, U.K.

By the same author:
HYPNAGOGIA
The Unique State of Consciousness
between Wakefulness and Sleep
New Edition in paperback 2010
by Thyrsos Press
ISBN : 978-0-9553052-1-4
First published in hardcover 1987
by Routledge & Kegan Paul Ltd
First published in paperback 1991
by Routlegde (Routledge, Chapman and Hall, Inc.)

Front Cover Illustration: *Horsehead Nebula* T.A. Rector (NOAO/AURA/NSF)
and Hubble Heritage Team (STScl/AURA/NASA).

This is the only published work dealing with the subject of Initiation in the Ancient Greek Mystical Tradition in a modern context - embracing connections with Egyptian and eastern traditions. It is a narrative record documenting an individual case, detailing the ups and downs, the shocks, fears, disillusionments and desperations as well as the elations experienced on this journey - led and guided by an incisive and inspirational Greek shaman-mystic.

The whole process unfolds organically, revealing how general rules are 'adapted' to fit the individual's personality and aptitude and how the person involved is allowed to grow within the system - often in leaps and bounds and repetitions.

Being a primarily Greek approach, the procedure is one of engaging the whole person - cultivating and promoting both intellectual doubt and intuitive certainty, challenging and guiding 'mind' as well as 'spirit'.

In more specific terms, this work delves into areas of crucial interest to all human beings and presents experiences that cast penetrating light on such fundamental concerns as the status of consciousness, space and time, the real nature of sex, the meaning and experience of 'assimilating' other people's psychological identities (including 'past lives'), and offers insights into the nature of reality and the function of memory in regards to truth.

Born in Cyprus, Andreas Mavromatis studied and worked as a journalist, actor, concert-organiser, script-writer, film-maker, teacher and lecturer in adult and higher education. He read philosophy and psychology, obtaining his Ph.D at Brunel University. He has been involved, since his teens, with the study and practices of mysticism and the 'paranormal' and has been holding classes and groups on these subjects.

His previous book, *Hypnagogia*, deals with the strange and wonderful experiences and mind-altering conditions of the unique state of consciousness between wakefulness and sleep.

Some comments on *Hypnagogia* (see more on page 402):
"This could easily become a cult book; it certainly deserves to be." Colin Wilson, *Yorkshire Post*.
"Anyone interested in altered states of consciousness simply has to read this book...it really is an excellent book." Dr John Rowan, *Self & society*.
"Mavromatis has revived the long-dormant tradition of true psychic science." Guy Lyon Playfair, *Light*.

Contents

Dedication and Acknowledgments   12

Preface/Introduction   13

1 The Timeless Doughnut Hole   17
(On Fear and Existence)

On a hot Greek summer afternoon - a 'doughnut hole' in a rock. Meeting old Yiannis: old and yet young. Strange behaviour, shocking language. Fear and panic and the childhood experience. Compassion and joy. Experience vs thinking. The dance of the crab. Is this a 'setup'? Is he a shaman? Fear re-experienced, intensified, then 'objectified'. Being 'beside oneself' - the physical body slows down the emotions. "Fear keeps you alive: physically, emotionally, intellectually." "Without fear you don't exist." Numerous deaths. The 'unit' of consciousness is made up of bits which are held together precariously - and they can function independently of one another, and they often do. An explanation of abnormalities.

2 Understanding and Knowing   40
(Logic and the Direct Method)

In a 'split' state: logic and direct 'perception' - understanding and knowing. 'Units' are made up of parts, and parts of parts... The ever-diminishing 'unit'. The 'fluid' amongst the parts. Observing the nature and mechanics of memory as it brings about the sense of 'ego': but 'I' does not exist. Plato's intentions. The old shaman's brilliant emanations. The beauty of it all! Do not indulge! The relationship between 'knowing' and 'understanding'. The personality gets in the way. Communicating vs understanding. Eliminating the 'it'. Types of memory. Eliminating the 'you'. Time is not a dimension. The 'Body of Light'. Definitions. The process of conceptualising and defining run amok. Yiannis and the Teacher - who is 'imitating' whom? "Go back". Go back where?

3 Yiannis the Evangelist (?)   59
(On Suspicion of Being a Healer)

At Bob's restaurant: All events in the 'doughnut hole' have taken place outside time! - stunned and disorientated! The 'Baptist' and the 'Evangelist'. Yiannis

6
the healer, the miracle-worker? Healing Bob's grandson, and other 'miracles'. On the way back: Beethoven's fifth symphony, taking stock of the day's events, failing to switch to the direct method when the occasion called for it. "Go back": Go back where? Deciding to begin by going back to relevant past experiences, evaluate and relate them to the current situation.

4   Searching for Answers   79
('Screams' and 'Coincidences')

Childhood experiences and adolescence. Looking for answers: the creation of the world is intimately connected with number, sound and colour. The music 'within' the body: the glorious symphony of colour and sound. There is nothing negative, there is no chaos. The Greek professor and Pythagoras. The guerrilla war - concealing ammunition. The newspaper editor, the poems, and Pythagoras' *Golden Sayings*. Establishing connections - the incident with the shattered bedside lamp. An intriguing conversation regarding 'coincidences'. Unaccountable feelings. New concepts and vocabulary. Who is this so-called Teacher - a mystic, a saint, a miracle-worker...?

5   Teachings and Practices   95
(Meeeting the Teacher)

At the Teacher's house. The two Brazilians, the trance, the 'communication'. Meeting the Teacher: tall and charismatic - the warmest 'homecoming' greeting, the Babylonian connection. More callers: the Greek parents and their downcast daughter. Not so much falling into trance as being 'overshadowed'. The Teacher's system: Absolute Be-ness, Absolute Beingness, the Monads, the noetic (mental), psychic (emotional), and physical worlds, the centres or chakras, the etheric energy, the Logos and the Holy Spirit, healing, 'elementals'.... Down at the Stoa: the "brothers" and "sisters". In the Stoa: the Teacher's talk on healing - real healing is achieved from within, every thing is energy concentrated to various degrees and at different levels, healing is the most spiritual of all activities. The "Researchers of the Truth". Back at the Teacher's house: the young relative with the 'romantic' problem and the Teacher's psychological trick. Invited to join the Inner Circle. The Seven Promises and Pythagoras.

6   Yianna the Twin   113
(On Being a Hue)

Welcome back - an animal welcoming committee! On the way to Yianna's, Yiannis' sister. The mongrel. Yianna the twin! - a very unsettling encounter. The walking stick/sceptre - the pharaonic experience. Yianna's appalling suggestion regarding the stick/sceptre! In the tranquility of a balmy evening. The guided visualisation: flying off the cliff, over the sea; the glorious sunset, Yianna the beautiful... In the Temple of Light: a vast variety of humans, the 'sourceless' light, a symphony of colour and sound; being a hue, a series of hues; merging, exultation...... Back at Yianna's house: more outrageous suggestions... Down the road by the church: overwhelmed by emotion; evaluation; the mongrel again.....

7

7 At Zeno's Taverna 134
(Athespodos - and something about Life after Death)

At the seafront: there's no such thing as Yianna the 'twin'! Shocked and dazed. At Zeno's taverna with Mike and Harry. Yiannis the dancer. The medallion. A meal with Yiannis and the boys. Some interesting linguistic/conceptual distinctions: making a 'thing' out of 'nothing'. *Caput mortuum.* The caterpillar, the chrysalis and the butterfly. Psychic 'revelations' regarding the death (and 'after-death') of Mike's uncle, and Harry's kidney condition. A distinction between 'physical' and 'natural'; a theory about 'theory'; a series of deaths after death... The old shaman is out the back talking to a dog called Athespodos!

8 The Mongrel and his Wife (?) 158
(On an Evolutionary Theme)

Up on the hilltop. "You never get answers to questions you've never been fired with." An internal struggle. Anubis: the vortex and the two flanking, entwining, columns of energy; the caduceus. An experience outside memory. Athespodos the mongrel again. Hermanubis. Dog the compassionate, dog the merciful! ... Entering the Anubis consciousness. 'Objective' love. The Mercy of Justice. "Nobody does wrong knowingly." Being conscious of Nothing. Phanes, the first light. Mercy: the balancing act of Creation. Hermanubis the equaliser, the facilitator. An experience repeated throughout the ages. Yiannis, the great consciousness. The mongrel and his wife(?). The idea made flesh. Prometheus and Epimetheus. The link between human and animal. The guidance of Hermanubis. The dog who aspires to becoming human(?). "You, too, are a mongrel." 'Exclusivity' and the new race. Making the grade or missing the boat. The 'personal' Hermanubis. Becoming empathic: the Teacher and the drama school. The laughing 'magicians'.

9 At Yianna's Again 185
(What was all that about?)

Yianna the what? - the twin?... 'Brothers' and 'sisters'. Oedipus' reasoning and his inability to cope with his 'reality'. The inapplicability of linear logic. States of dreaming. Different strands of consciousness, different logics. The walking stick/sceptre and its status and history. Too many Napoleons around: the danger of identifying with past personages. 'Raising the dampers' - insights and delusions. "Your attitude protects you." Like attracts like which attracts like which attracts like... The birdcatcher. A warning about a future abandonment - "you must become Light in order to survive the Darkness." The walking stick/sceptre/Rod of energy. We are not our thoughts, emotions, physical bodies. Emotions and incarnations - attachment and detachment. Ownership is common. "Be in the world but not of the world."

10 The Glory of Being Human 200
(We - the Storehouse of Everything)

Our magnificent commonality. The activities of intelligent entities. 'Sacrifice': a merely human conception. "You can be anybody and anything." 'Appropriating' personalities(?). Yiannis and the Teacher. Answers to calls. Teachers are everywhere. The drab little stone that turned into a sun. Socrates' midwifery. The disk-vortex of the heart. The vortex through the head - the science of love. Why many religions exclude reincarnation. Morality: consciousness itself is the moral law. 'Threatened' in order to develop consciousness. Expansion of consciousness - the hidden dangers. Certainty and bliss as the ultimate traps. "How fast does light travel when there is nothing for it to travel through?"

11 'Surviving' the Darkness 214
(Egotism and Love)

The struggle to develop egotism, to develop self-consciousness. Outside the bodies and the intellectual and philosophical levels. We develop self-consciousness as a prerequisite to surviving the Darkness. Pandora's vase. All incarnations can be mine - and yours: no exclusivity. Superconsciousness. The soporific nature of certainty and happiness. The irony of 'memory' of certainty and happiness. Plato's resort to metaphor. Yianna or Yiannis - the multiplicity of personalities and relationships. Aspects of love - Friendship at the top of the list. Shedding one's human nature(?). Love as the essence of creation, fear as an artifice. Self-consciousness from a human angle. Human and non-human perspectives. We never commit a 'wrong' act. The function of the Law. Confusing dreams. "Go back." Beethoven's fifth. The realities of head, heart, spleen, liver, etc. Listing events backwards. The holy man and his disciple. "Meet me at the 'brother's'."

12 Helen and Aphrodite - or was it Eve? 232
(Sex or Love?)

At the disco. Tricks of memory and recognition. At the Cove of Love with Helen. The poser, the impasse, and the rabbi's advice to his son. Sex or love? - the multiple orgasm(s) and the three columns of energy. The 'U' shape and the 'I' shape of merging energies. The elation and clarity of thought and emotion. Old Yiannis in the middle!? The shaman's 'takeover', the 'eviction'.... 'Inside' Helen.... Meditations on 'being' and 'existing'. Opening up to nature. 'Common sense', or synaesthesia.... The role of attention. Helen of Troy, Aphrodite the goddess of love, Eve... The Universal and the Particular. The splitting of the 'uniqueness' of Love. Guile and necessity - losing sight of the whole, the struggle to acquire individuality... The 'fall' and the 'resurrection'....

13 The Suicidal Girl 256
(A puzzling 're-enactment')

Tricking and diverting the mind. In search of the "brother's" place: 'Eavesdropping'. The suicidal girl - Yiannis the healer again. Healing by eliminating hatred and negativity and enhancing the capacity for love. The re-enactment of the healing event at the Teacher's house!! - different people, same details. Two languages in one. 'Indulging' in scruples - a waste of energy. "Poor woman;" "yes, but poor man" - pitying the perpetrator.

14 The Teiresias Dilemma 270
(On the Cusp: Male/Female, Existent/Non-existent)

Obsessed with sexual distinctions(?). A lesson in genital anatomy: not only mongrel but also hermaphrodite! The incident of the wise man and his disciple repeated: living a complete, detailed, female incarnation in a matter of seconds. Experiencing a past incarnation dissociated from present awareness. Back and forth. On being female: the Teiresias dilemma. A Turkish greeting - a clue? On the hillside: reflecting and meditating. Beethoven's fifth: not so much the music as the philosophy - Existence out of Non-existence, time that stretched, suspended..., on the cusp of Existence and Non-existence. Remembering backwards - 'Going back'? Returning to the birth experience. Different centres, different functions, different experiences. The no-man's land where time and space are...are not...are...are not.... Yiannis' Turkish greeting makes sense. At the "brother's" restaurant: meeting Yiannis; the donkey's kick and the woman's broken arm - a careless use of elementals.

15 At the Old Cypress Tree 294
(On Unconditional Love: an Exercise)

Under the cypress tree. "I am incapable of hurting anybody" and "nobody wants to hurt me": "Too much light". In constant consciousness expansion: pure, unadulterated, unconditional love and the burning desire to be of service. Healing and 'proper' healing: unconditional love and a knowhow. An attempt to heal the woman's broken arm: visualising and not being judgmental. The Will of unconditional love that holds Existence together. "I don't eat - except light." A simple exercise to see the sparkling, flickering light energy. The cypress tree's history and nature seen from within - time, time... The snake that ate cake, and other animals. The eagle that showed the way.

16 The Devil's Gorge 311
(Time and Space)

Paying respects to the devil's footprint(!?). The gorge. Time compression again. Washing 'in preparation'. The watery arches that turned into air, into solid matter, into fire, into translucent etheric energy. Questions concerning the substance of matter. Questions regarding time: difficulties in defining past, future, and present. Is past a logical impossibility? Are all concepts of time logically meaningless and experientially unattainable? When is the present the present? 'Inside' the walnut and the walnut tree: the impression of permanency in the cycle; the impermanent permanence... The beginning and the end and the beginning... Purpose? Dissolution into Non-existence, or expansion? 'Going back' and 'going forward': difficulties/inadequacies of the human mind.

17 A Dionysian Initiation 323
(Dionysos, Wine, and Sex)

Dionysos - the *thýrsos*, the ivy, the vine leaves and the grapes. Stage one: the enactment and the experience. Being 'enthusiastic': wings on my feet, raging urges in my loins, the whole of nature in my solar plexus - physical and through the physical; all manner of creatures; non-humans imitating humans; the nature and wisdom of the creatures of the solar plexus. The whirlwind at the spleen level. The turmoil of the heart. The 'liberation' of the head. Stage two: the myth as reality, becoming the journey itself... Evolution: from the feet to the head – non-humans, half-humans, 'lower' and 'higher' primates; pro-creation across the species: gods, humans, half-humans...; asexual procreation - past and future. The 'myth' of Dionysos the "twice born". Dionysos the 'liberated', the 'completed'. Dionysos the shaman: femininity/masculinity. Dionysos and wine. Wine and sex. The real function of sex: procreation or recreation? Sexual reproduction as the 'most recent' form/experiment in pro-creation - one of many.

18   The Tunnel of Truth and the Cave   339
(We: the Amnesiacs - Remembering and not Forgetting)

Entering the tunnel: going through the tight opening by 'merging' with the walls. Lines of energy. "Thoughts of failure are themselves a sign of failure." "A percentage of the result of any effort is always due to some other source." "If you must know the truth you must remember." Truth as absence of forgetfulness - as memory. The ability to hold the experience in one's consciousness as constantly transpiring in the present. Types of remembering. Recognition: "going back to the original knowledge, knowing the beginning and the destination." The Cave - a special place. The golden flower. The Cave as a temple. Listening to the quiet and watching the darkness... The gigantic egg-shaped diamond with the innumerable sides hanging up in the air.

19   The Cave and the 'Ancients'   353
(The Diamond Approach to Truth)

The diamond sides/'doorways'. Ancient Greek personages connected with Greek Mystery Schools. Omeros (Homer) and the *Odysseia*. Grades of Initiation. The *Odysseia*: multiple levels of comprehending. 'Identifying' with the hero, undergoing the experience according to degree of awareness. The Axis people. The task of the Greek priests/mystics/philosophers: disseminating the new approach necessary for the further development of consciousness - 'objectification', logic, and the scientific method. Thales: 'water', and 'gods' everywhere. Anaximenes: air - a matter of emphasis. Anaximandros: the earth floating freely in space, evolution, the *Apeiron*, the qualities. Introducing the method of rational debate. Substance and qualities. Inside a pyramid: the colour energies of the living, creative, entities. Empedocles: the four "roots" or elements, Love and Strife. Heraclitos: fire and the *Logos*, everything is in a state of flux and in balance, opposites are 'same'. Parmenides and the Way of Truth: the impossibility of movement and change. Anaxagoras and the Mind as eternal reality. Diogenes of Apollonia: purpose in creation, connections between microcosm and macrocosm. Democritos the 'atomist'. The great Pythagoras... Remembering the schools, the teachings... Orpheus and the *kratēr* with the *kykeón*... Yiannis as the Body of Light: a transfiguration.

20 The Medallion and the 'Lecture Hall' 370
(Humans, Non-humans and Gods)

The medallion and its symbolism: a state of health immune to illness. Attempting to enter the cave that houses the history of the planet(?): attacked by fear and nausea, the searing medallion; physical and psychological turmoil... Dissociating and applying will-power. Looking for a way out. In a cosy cave - falling into a hypnagogic state and studying basic issues: the fragility of Man, the unity of consciousness, the 'laws' that hold the 'bits' of consciousness together; *are* we before we *exist?*, the 'magnet', creation and re-absorption. 'I' the consciousness. Becoming 'disillusioned'. The possibility of ontological changes. Symbols, amulets and talismans. The medallion as a talisman: its power and reality entering consciousness. Hermanubis again: memories of wrong-doings, grandmother's advice. The lesson: continuity of life, the creation of expanded consciousness. The end justifies the means (!?). A new view on the survival of the fittest. The history of Earth - an ongoing experiment in consciousness expansion.... The cave becomes a 'lecture hall': a gathering of humans, non-humans, half-humans... In the middle of a 'lecture' being given by one 'of the light'. 'Hearing/seeing/intuiting' what is being delivered: "Listening: what is it, how is it done?" "Creation is imbalance." "The objective world is your creation." "Training the mind to understand what we already know." "There is no mercy." Yiannis, Pythagoras, Apollo - the youthfulness and brilliance of being 'completed', of 'becoming Apollo'. "You are god." Consciousness and conscience. The 'lecturer' and his/her effect on the thymus gland: a conflagration - feeling as if burning in the effulgence of Sun-Apollo; healing, purification, and exhilaration...

21 In Search of an Exit 389
(The Abandonment and the Way Out)

Knowledge, or service? - Buddha's dictum. Meandering through the tunnel seeking an exit. Tired, angry and frustrated - being unable to switch to the direct method! Abandoned. Fear of total existential annihilation. Falling into a dark, empty sleep... Remembering to dissociate - as if for the first time! .... At last, light. A tall, narrow chimney to climb. Dissociation is not enough: expansion - without the help of the direct method. Scaling the chimney and enduring the cuts - expanding and 'merging' with the sharp juts of the walls. And then, and then the singing of birds! Out, on a high plateau... The sun, the 'tube' and the pouring of energy, the eagle, Athespodos... Restored!... - ready to continue the journey....What next?

Appendix: Exercises 396

12

Dedication

This book is written for, and offered to, anyone who thinks they might benefit from it.

Some, no doubt, will identify very closely with its contents - the material and the participants alike. They may 'remember', and find themselves re-experiencing the 'adventures', and remember other 'adventures' not included here; they may recognise, decipher, and feel encouraged to 'perform' exercises of Initiation embedded in this work.

Others might find it a starting point, an acknowledgment and an impetus to embark on research into the meaning, status, and function of consciousness - joining me on the one and only journey for which the world came into Existence, namely that of *becoming fully conscious*.

Others still may prefer to read it as an intellectually challenging and, hopefully, uplifting story, which is sprinkled with a few tentative answers while raising a great many stimulating questions - to keep them busy for the rest of their multiple lives.

Acknowledgments

First I would like to offer my thanks to Denise Hollingbery and Robert Paskin who took extra care in correcting typing and spelling errors and pointing out my various contortions of the English language - whatever is retained of this misuse is, of course, entirely my responsibility.

I am also deeply grateful to Klaus Herold and Jeremy Cranswick for their moral support and extremely helpful editorial comments.

To Syed Safwan Ahdal I owe a great deal for his technical computer advice and actual help in transferring the material in this book onto the proper medium for printing. Similarly, I'd like to thank my good friend and 'fellow traveller', Andreas Kyrou, for his computer tips and technical help, and Colin Smith for the use of his invaluable skills in helping to design and print the cover of the book.

Last but not least, I would like to express my deep gratitude to my brother Nicholas for his all-round unstinting support in bringing this book back to print following unexpected public response.

Preface/Introduction

The 'central' material in this book, ie, the mystico-philosophical system and its integral practices, is the coming together of the teachings of two men: Yiannis, an itinerant shaman-mystic, and the Teacher, a mystic and healer known to some as the Magus of Strovolos. In point of fact, this material was originally intended as a text on the theories and practices of these two mystics to pass around to the various groups I ran at the time - and it was to be offered for publication in that form.

But then things changed. I was 'advised' to present the material in a narrative form, setting it down in context, unfolding it more or less as it 'happened' to me as opposed to giving it out in an impersonal, didactic, form. The rationale being that the most important aspect of any Initiation - the really 'central' part of it - is the series of experiences the person concerned goes through and the way he/she reacts to them, the theory forming a backdrop, an intellectual attempt - 'enlightened' though it may be - to understand and explain the experiences.

The result is a narrative in the first person, based on events and experiences that took place in Greece in the early 1960s. It is a modern day journey of Initiation along the lines of the ancient Greek Mystical Tradition - a two-pronged task bringing together 'mind' and 'spirit', intellect and intuition-inspiration. It details physical, but mostly psychological, 'adventures' crucial in the development and expansion of consciousness, alongside powerful philosophical questions and doubts.

Certain themes, concepts and ideas are visited more than once at various strategic points in the book. This is partly the old 'shaman's' technique of reiterating, of driving in important issues from different angles - making certain the message reaches home. It is also a psychological device for raising a particular type of understanding to a higher rung, affording the person a wider, deeper, perspective; to this effect, some fundamental experiences, too, are revisited.

Most significantly, during the course of this 'journey' many of my common, everyday beliefs, beliefs that I had cherished as essential to my functioning as a normal 'sane' human being, were profoundly shaken - to say the least: the 'normal', linear, *concepts of time and space*, for example, were shattered to pieces; *sex and its functions*, both on the personal level and universally, were also brought into question and investigated experientially, and so were *identity, memory* and *the status of physical and extra-physical experiences* - all of which I found myself viewing from new angles, as the direct result of the 'adventures' I had undergone.

Some of the ideas - and practices - contained in the book may appear controversial - not to say 'out of this world'! The crucial point, however, is that these ideas are not mere intellectual constructions but flow out of experiences acquired in expanded states of consciousness which make it possible to 'perceive' the world differently - precisely the sort of thing the ancient Greek Mystery Schools aimed at achieving.

The main implication of this process is the emergence of a new view, a new paradigm, based on very different laws of understanding from the ones necessary for physical survival: *It is a view of the structure, function, and possibility of continuity (survival) of consciousness as distinct from a view concerned merely with physical survival.* A corollary to this, is a further implication pointing to the possibility of ontological changes.

More explicitly, the whole approach revolves round the idea of 'Creation' consisting of an implicit, if only seeming, contradiction. This is to do with the way we are all 'constructed' and 'wired' with the express purpose of dealing with physical survival. In our automatic, but necessary, compliance with the 'laws of nature', however, we become totally enmeshed in needs and wants and absorbed and fascinated by the beauty and magic of physical existence to the extent of accepting that life *is* what *appears* to be - until, that is, we come to experience and appreciate the strong possibility that, in the long run, all this may only be a stepping stone and nothing else.

On a merely 'personal' level, it can be an extremely painful and frustrating realisation because it contains the notions of disentanglement from, and rising above, personal attachments - but, at another level, it may be survival as *consciousness* which has expanded to include all personal elements that are then viewed in perspective and become somewhat 'objective', while at the same time everything 'external' is drawn in and experienced as 'personal'.

Significantly, this expansion as *consciousness* affords the possibility of 'change', of a drastic, and dramatic, change - from a grub into a butterfly, to call on a much-used metaphor. In 'traditional' shamanistic terms, an expanded human consciousness can include many forms of life outside the ordinary, recognisable, human range - such as animal or even vegetable and mineral kinds; in terms of the ancient Greek Mystical Tradition, it can become a 'hero' or a 'god' or some other, even greater, consciousness.....

A few words of explanation regarding the terms 'Mystical' and 'Initiation': Mystical derives from the Greek verbs *mēo* and *meó* (μύω and μυώ) which carry two related meanings: that of occult, of hidden, of being covered or closed, and that of introducing someone to something hidden or occult. From that also derives the noun 'mystic' (μύστης), an Initiate, a person who possesses knowledge of the Mysteries, ie the hidden aspects of Nature. The words 'occult' and 'hidden' are, however, rather misleading here because of their negative connotations: nothing is actually hidden. One of the main tasks of an Initiate was (is) to learn to go beyond the evidence of the five known senses and ordinary logic and see/experience what these tools are not made to deal with.

Further, bearing in mind that the whole reason of Existence is the acquisition of full consciousness, two basic forms of Initiation can be pointed out - the 'active' and the 'passive'. The first kind is primarily the one practised in the Mystery Schools in which a person would undergo certain experiences and take active part in specific mental and physical exercises and 'experiments' designed to enhance him/her as consciousness with the express purpose of gaining knowledge of the inner workings of nature. In a more extended sense, we may also include in this group some mainstream religious and other similar rituals and 'attitudes', including prayer, as well as philosophical and scientific 'meditations'. In regards to this, the Greek approach has always been to usher the mystical into the rational and raise the rational to the mystical. The second kind of Initiation is that in which everyone participates in everyday life, that is, simply living. The former offers the possibility of 'survival', the latter.....

TRAVELLING LIGHT

– 1 –

The Timeless Doughnut Hole
(On Fear and Existence)

The 'first time' I met 'him' was in the middle of a hot summer's day in Greece. Or so I thought at the time. And it was a searing experience....

The sun was scorching. I kept submerging myself to cool off, but two minutes above the water and my hair would be as dry as a crisp. Who is complaining? I loved it. Why else would I be here, in Greece, at this time of the year? I filled my lungs with air one more time and submerged. I swam under water for as long as I could - one of my favourite hobbies. I came up and stood on the sandy seabed, with the water reaching up to my neck, and looked out as far as my eye could see: two shades of blue - the sea and the sky. And high above, the scorching sun.

I turned to face the land. The beach, with three people around at two o'clock in the afternoon, two small houses surrounded by orchards, and behind them rising up on the small mountain, the lemon and orange groves and then the undisturbed wilderness of the thinly wooded mountainside. A brief gentle but most welcoming breeze brought down the scent of resin from the cypress trees. A faint whiff of thyme descended from the low mound on the left. The cicadas were sizz-sizzing madly in the midday heat. "Thank god for the heat," I thought to myself, "it drives the tourists indoors and leaves the place to me and the cicadas and the aromatic bushes."

I swam ashore and climbed to the top of the mound. On the way up I crushed a little thyme between my hands and smelled it. Heavenly! I did the same with other aromatic bushes that grew on the hillside all around me, and disturbed a couple of lizards.

From the top I had a clear view: while the land stretched and rose behind me, in front of me lay the sea and the sea and the sea. Ah, and a passenger ship in the far distance. To the right stood out a big crag, like a small island, separated from the land by two metres of water. Someone had placed bits of driftwood and bridged the little canal so that one could, with a little care, cross over to the rock.

In the rock itself there was a sizeable hole, an opening like a doughnut hole about two and a half metres in diametre, and in it I could see two planks of wood lying opposite each other, resting on rocky protrusions against the sides of the hole and forming make-shift benches. "A welcoming refuge," I thought. Still, not certain if it belonged to anybody, I walked closer and called out in both Greek and English. No response.

I walked to another side which afforded me a better view of the opening and called again. Nothing. I could now actually see that there was nobody in the doughnut hole. There were other things though besides the makeshift benches: a newspaper and some items on a small shelf but I couldn't make out what they were. I was in-trigued, and very hot, and decided to investigate from closer quar-ters. After all, this was just a rock at the edge of the sea, I wouldn't exactly be breaking into somebody's house.

I climbed down to the driftwood bridge and clambered carefully up to the opening. I was grateful to get inside and out of the sun. It wasn't all that cool inside but I was at least in the shade, and being four or five metres above sea level in an open hole I caught some-thing of a draught-breeze. At the other side of the opening there stood a small rickety-looking wooden platform, supported on stilts which reached down to less than a metre above the lapping water.

On the shelf sat a first aid box, stocked with elastoplast strips, an iodine bottle, gauze bandage, aspirin tablets and some medicine for treating insect bites. In a plastic bag were biscuits and rusks. Under one of the benches rested a round, globe-shaped, narrow-necked clay pot with a gauzy cloth covering its mouth; it felt half-full of water. Next to it, lying upside down, was a plastic cup.

As I was so thirsty, I took a chance and availed myself of the water. Oh, it was fresh and cool, just what I needed. While I was drinking, I noticed a piece of paper attached to the shelf with some writing on it. I drew closer and read: "Welcome to the refuge and to everything in it. Use it but leave it clean for other visitors. Don't monopolise it. If you feel appreciative, please replenish or leave behind whatever you think might be useful to others. Thank you". It was written in Greek and English. What a lovely sentiment! I sat on one of the benches and looked at the newspaper. It was in German, and a week old. Presumably left there by some appreciative visitor.

What with the heat and the incessant sound of the cicadas, I felt a bit sleepy. I lay down on one of the benches using the first aid box and the rolled-up newspaper as a pillow. I don't know how long I lay there facing the mound and relaxing with my eyes shut. At some point I felt the sun on my face and half-opened my eyes.

And there, on top of the mound, fifty odd metres away, in the lull of the hot mid-afternoon, was the slim figure of a smallish man, about one metre seventy, in his swimming trunks, tanned to the whites of his eyes, with thinning greyish hair, smiling at me. He was in his sixties or maybe older. I opened my eyes fully. He greeted me with a wave of his hand and indicated that he wanted to come over. I returned the greeting and beckoned him to join me.

I wondered if he was the owner of the rock and prepared myself to thank him for his generosity. I sat up and watched as he climbed down the mound and up the rock. He was amazingly nimble and agile, moving with such delightful ease as if he were walking on air. His body was clearly old to look at but the energy and suppleness it displayed was that of a much younger man. He looked like a young actor playing the part of an old man with layers of make-up and lots of artificial wrinkles all over his body.

He emerged at the opening gasping for air, his whole body sweating profusely. What a contrast! A few minutes earlier, and at a distance, he was a youthful gazelle, now, at close quarters, he was a delapitated old billy goat! What happened? Were the brilliance of the sunlight and the heat playing tricks on my eyes? He stood at the entrance to the hole, still gasping, and greeted me in Greek with an explanation.

"Whooo! At my age! this is an adventure!" He stretched out his hand for a handshake. "Hello. Yiannis."

I reciprocated. "Andreas. Pleased to meet you."

We shook hands, or, rather, he shook my hand. I didn't have the chance to feel his hand as in a normal handshake - his grip was too sudden and powerful, and he was still gasping for air!

"Are you?" he asked, as he lowered himself slowly onto the bench opposite.

"Am I what?"

"Pleased to meet me."

I was still recovering from the handshake and trying to work out why such a forceful grip was also so warm and friendly. His tone wasn't hostile in any sense but, all the same, the question was not exactly what one would expect. Also, his use of language was a bit disconcerting.

He had introduced himself by giving his first name only, which I took to be his intention to show lack of formality as is the case with casual meetings on a beach, and to which I responded accordingly, but alongside that he used the plural which is the norm of formality. This form of greeting had its place in Greek social exchanges but was out of place here.

I smiled mechanically and explained that my response was just a normal social exchange.

"Oh," he said, and bent down to pick up the pot of water with a certainty of movement that indicated familiarity with the place. I suppressed my indignation and shifted the conversation. Maybe it *was* his rock and he wasn't very keen on visitors at that moment.

"Is this yours?" I asked in an as polite a voice as possible.

"What, the rock?" he answered dismissively. "Are you kidding? Who would want to own a rock?"

It was my turn now to say "oh."

I tried to understand what was happening while he busied himself with the pot and the cup. To begin with, I was in my early twenties and this was an old man joining me in this nice, comfortable, refuge. Nothing wrong with that but I could think of nicer people I would rather be with - like a pretty female tourist, for instance! Then, he was weird: rough, curt and yet pleasant. He climbed like a young man and yet gasped as if he were taking his last breath, his handshake was friendly and yet demanding - and commanding - and he asked me why I was pleased to meet him.

Ah, that was it! I'd been accosted by older men before. I had nothing against homosexuals as such but I'd rather they passed me by; I found the encounters so embarrassing. If that was the case here, his attempt at a display of youthfulness was just a pathetic showing off.

He was drinking from the cup while looking at me at that moment when suddenly he burst into a loud uncontrollable laughter, spitting and spraying water all over, and nearly choking himself in the process. It was a while before he began to settle down. As he was looking at me when this happened I took it that he'd seen something extremely amusing on my face or body that triggered it off.

"What? What?" I whispered, and checked my arms and chest and then began to wipe my face as if it were covered in a spider's web - which made him laugh even harder.

In between bouts of laughter he managed to speak. "You...you should see your face!"

I kept wiping my face, not knowing what else to do, a behaviour that seemed to act like a feeder to his inexplicable amusement.

At long last he managed to bring himself down to small hiccups of laughter and spoke again.

"What - you think I want to fuck you?"

Ahm.... Ehm... I was stunned. He stopped laughing but there was still the feel of mirth on his face. And the glee in his eyes. He had dropped the formal plural and was now speaking to me in the singular, which he kept to from then on.

"Or is it the other way round?" he added.

I didn't know what to say. I needed time to recover. It was too much of a shock. I mean, I was not used to this kind of encounter: the directness and the vocabulary! He kept looking at me. And I couldn't think straight.

The look in his eyes changed. As if mesmerised by his stare, I sat there looking back at him, practically immobilised. Like his handshake, there was both power and warmth in his eyes. Maybe it had been there all along but I hadn't noticed it before. His face turned into a mask of severity and gentleness rolled together.

As I continued to stare back at him in a semi-hypnotic numbness, I began to enter into a state of panic. It was totally out of my control and I felt it physically around my abdominal area, in my gut. It was a feeling I had only experienced once before in my life, as a young child of about four.

At that time, our family lived at the outskirts of the town next to a big orchard owned by an old Turk and his son. I watched the two men many times with fascination from a distance as they tended to their fruit trees and other plants and vegetables. One afternoon, I watched them planting and watering seedlings. When they had finished and returned to their house at the other end of the orchard, I decided to get into the field to investigate, to find out exactly what they had been doing.

I crawled in through some border bushes and went over to the beds where the seedlings had been planted. Although I had watched the two men many times, I had no idea what they'd actually been doing - I'd simply been fascinated by the activity. And now was my chance to find out. So I proceeded to pull the seedlings out of the ground and examine the parts that had been buried, that is, the roots.

While I was absorbed in my investigation I became aware of a big shadow cast right over me. I turned and looked up and saw this giant of a man, the son, standing close behind me looking very menacing. I knew right away that I wasn't supposed to be doing what I had been doing, and that this giant was about to eat me alive.

He swore at me and my whole family in Turkish and told me in terrifying terms how he was going to finish me off and give me to the carrion crows to pick my little bones clean. And right on cue I heard a crow cry hoarsely and threateningly in a tree close by. And that was when I felt this panic for the first time, and that was when I knew for sure that my little life was coming to an untimely end.

Then, this enormous horrifying Turk bent over me and was about to grab me by the seat of my shorts but instead he swore again and changed his mind - presumably because my pants and my legs were soaking in urine - and picked me up by the scruff of the neck and threw me out. Being thrown out of the orchard through the bushes and getting scratched and blooded all over was nothing. It was the fear which accompanied the panic that stayed with me. And now it was back again.

I sat there staring at him, transfixed. But this time, the fear, although very similar to the one I had experienced in my childhood, was somewhat different, and more severe. It felt unattached. Even though I found the old man weird and intriguing, I certainly did not fear him. And I did not feel afraid for my life or safety, as I had done on that other occasion. This was pure fear, unprovoked and undirected, coming from nobody and nowhere... My mind, my intellect, could not engage or participate in any way. This feeling-sensation continued to grip me, and it intensified into sheer paralysis.

And then, another feeling-sensation began to set in. This time, it was in my chest, around my heart. And it was the opposite of fear that I felt in my gut. It was a feeling of warmth and security that began very gently and grew more and more powerful and changed to a mixture of compassion and joy. A strange combination and yet there they were both of these feelings. And as with the fear they were unattached and unprovoked, and as they grew, the fear slowly dissipated and disappeared. At first I felt the joy radiating from my chest in waves and reaching out to everything around me. And then it changed in source and direction. It felt as if it were coming out of everything else - including the old man - and reaching me instead, before becoming a continuous reciprocal activity.

And there was this compassion for everything, as if everything were in what I felt to be 'pain of ignorance' and needed my compassion. It grew to a paralysing feeling of pity that brought tears to my eyes. And then it was pity and anger, anger at what I perceived to be a universal joke in very bad taste. But, eventually, both fear and anger subsided and gave way to pure compassion, a compassion that included myself and it was genuine and had no trace of condescension in it. Everything began to sing with joy, and my heart felt that it was about to burst.

I began to recognise a tinge in this joy and compassion that made me want to embrace everything, everything without exception. And just as this uncontrollable need came over me, I was already embracing everything. The love I felt - pure, unattached love - was too much. My body couldn't contain it. I began to shake violently under a series of shock waves, and tears were now running out of my eyes and streaming down my face and dripping on my chest. Oh, the joy and love!

And, again, as with the panic and fear, some of these feelings were not totally new. I had similar experiences before. The operative word here though is *similar*. Not the same, but similar. There were differences both in the context and the content between this experience and those of the past. This one, as with the fear, was free-floating, not attached to anything in particular, uninvited and seemingly uncaused. But why? Why now and in these circumstances?

My thought processes were detached from me, as if they belonged to someone else. I felt split: there was the thinking and there was me. The thinking - and it was minimal - that began to take place towards the end of this experience, was not central to me. During the experience there was no thinking whatsoever, it had been completely obliterated. Towards the end of it, however, I could 'hear' the thinking taking place, as if coming from outside me. And it sounded so silly. There were serious questions posed by the thinking process. Philosophical questions of existence, scientific questions of the structure of matter, theological questions of the nature of divinity and its relation to the world at large.

As on a cinema screen with multiple insets each one unfolding its own story, there was a succession of people of all ages and from numerous cultures and races asking genuine, sincere, questions concerning the world, the universe, and their lives, the meaning of their lives. I could sense pain in these questions, but it was not my pain. All this was outside of me. And although it felt genuine it also felt irrelevant. As if all these questions were missing the point. *What* was the point? I couldn't tell. The thinking that was trying to make sense of things was also part of the irrelevancy. Somehow I knew there was a point but I couldn't see it.

And then I did: it was the manner in which these questions and concerns were expressed. Within the frame of the thinking process they were extremely important and vital questions, but outside this process they were childish. It was the seriousness with which they were posed that made them appear silly. They were important and relevant but only within that particular framework. Like a house in which one lives and keeps warm and protected, but when this house is viewed from outer space - if it can be seen at all - is totally insignificant. Was life insignificant, irrelevant? It seemed so.

But then I began to drift into the thinking process, almost like putting on a coat, being enveloped by something. And I saw how important and painful these questions were. They were questions that I, too, had raised many times and with great intensity through most of my young life.

Next thing, as if taking off the coat, removing the envelope, I was outside the thinking process once more and the questions were unimportant. I wanted to stay in that 'outside' state because it was wonderful but I couldn't. I was 'pulled' back into the envelope of the thinking process. Now, however, I knew: the questions were extremely important and the desperate search for answers painful, but only within the framework, only within the framework!

Ah, but was I not in the framework myself? Was I not, perhaps, the framework itself? I was pulling myself up by my own boot-straps....

I heard him laughing. It was a raucous, loud laughter - but a 'disembodied' one. It was definitely *his* laughter although it was coming from all around me, and reverberating all around me - his face was straight, perhaps the suspicion of a smile on his lips, but nothing else. And yet he was laughing!

Gradually, the laughter became less loud, more of a chuckle, then a gentle giggle, and was synchronised with his face which now exuded gentleness and the feeling of expansive affection and sibling love. He was the older brother I never had. He giggled like a happy child, like a gurgling brook welling up with pure, refreshing water. I felt ashamed for having had those thoughts concerning his intentions towards me.

He stood up and beamed a full smile at me.

"Right. How about some figs? Would you like some figs?" he said straightening himself.

"Ehm...." I nodded "yes" but with some reservation. Funny offer, I thought. Figs? In the middle of nowhere? Where would he get figs from, inside this rock off the coast? Then a creepy thought crept into my head: 'figs' and 'fig trees' were words often used by Greeks as slang terms for gays and gay activities. Oh, god, not back to that again!

He laughed as if he knew what I was thinking and made his way to the outside of the rock opening facing the sea. He climbed down one side of the rickety little platform and approached a protrusion at the waterline. I watched him as he bent down and dipped his whole arm into the water. When he pulled his arm out he was lifting a basket. He brought it back to the hole dripping with water and put it down by the bench. In the basket was a plastic bag tied firmly at the neck. He bent down again, picked out the bag, untied it and placed it on the bench, next to me. And there they were: big, luscious-looking figs, fresh and cool out of a natural cooling system!

He picked out one, peeled it back a little, and put it in his mouth. He ate it with relish. His demeanour was relaxed, as if nothing had happened, apparently oblivious to my roller-coaster experience. The right edge of his mouth stretched a tad back and upwards into a cheeky smile, exaggerating the creases on that side of his face.

"Well, aren't you going to have any?" he said, as he reached into the bag for another one. "You deserve it."

I deserved it? Why? What did he mean by that? I picked a fig out of the bag and began to peel it. What did he mean by it? Was he aware of my experience? I looked up at him.

"What do you mean I deserve it?" I said with a degree of anticipation.

"Well, you managed not to piss yourself this time!" he said reaching for another fig and breaking into a roar of a laughter.

I felt embarrassed. But he was right, I managed not to piss myself this time. I smiled nervously trying to conceal my embarrassment.

"But the second part was better, wasn't it? Much better," he continued.

Yes, of course. I felt so elated, so happy, so loving-.... Wait a minute! I'd been nodding and agreeing with him without it ever occurring to me that he couldn't have known these things: my childhood experience, the experience I'd just had.... I turned to face him.

"Don't worry," he said reassuringly, "we'll talk about them in a while. The important thing is that you love me. Have some more figs. They're good for you. And you can drop the formal plural - we don't need it."

He sat on my bench, the other side of the bag, and picked out two more figs. I followed suit, and nodded in agreement.

Strange and weird do not sufficiently express what I was feeling. This old man that I had never met before, walked into my life a short while ago, and was now telling me that I loved him! Stranger than that was the 'fact' that he was right. Not only that. The way he had said "you love me" implied reciprocity, as if he were also saying "I love you, too". I felt warm and secure. He was not a stranger. I could have sworn I had met him before. I knew the feeling because I had had experiences of 'recognition' in the past. My mind began to drift....

"Okay, okay," he said, pulling me back from what looked like the start of a light trance. "Let's do this properly."

A shiver ran down my spine. My whole body tingled as if electric current had shot through it.

"Have another fig," he suggested gently.

What's with the figs?! Why is he going on?

"They're good for you. Buddha ate them, didn't he? He found enlightenment sitting under a fig tree and eating figs." There was an air of mischief in his voice.

"No," I said, correcting him, "he did not find enlightenment by eating figs."

"Maybe not; but he liked them, all the same," he quipped, "and so did your Greek ancestors with their sacred figt ree orchards. And so did Jesus who was so fond of figs that when he was hungry and couldn't find figs in a fig tree, he cursed it and killed it. Oooh, that was going a bit too far!"

Mischief was now apparent all over his face. I joined him with a similar smile and picked out another fig.

He got up and went over to the other side to fetch the water. I watched him as he returned with the pot, poured water in the plastic cup and offered it to me. I thanked him and washed down the sweet-ness of the fig with the coolness of the water.

"Don't thank me," he said casually, "I didn't make the water. It came from the spring."

Yes, it came from the spring, but why dilute my appreciation and polite response? He had done the same earlier when I said "pleased to meet you". In fact, he had been behaving in this manner ever since I met him: every now and then, when I felt a sense of close-ness towards him, he would throw a little spanner in the works, make me stand off a bit. It felt like being put through an emotional churning pot, one emotion raised then succeeded by, or checked against, another. No matter. I still liked him. I liked him a lot. He was sharp, awake, independent. He put a check on my sentimental-ity and meaningless politeness.

He drank a cup of water with the same relish he ate the figs. This man did nothing by half. He reminded me of Zorba in the eponym-ous novel: full of life, devouring life with passion. He left the pot and the cup at my feet and went and sat on the other bench, facing me.

"Now, let's talk." He spoke with gentle authority.

I didn't know what to say. I straightened up and tried to collect my thoughts but they were too scattered.

"What, you have nothing to say? No questions?" he prodded teasingly.

Oh, I had lots of questions alright, lots and lots of questions. I just didn't know where to start.

"Are you happy with your life?" he asked me unexpectedly.

I was beginning to adjust to the shock of his questions. No beating about the bush. Still, it made me take a deep breath. Was I happy with my life? Well, I was a happy-go-lucky kind of person with a thirst for knowledge. There were many things I wanted to learn and just as many that I wanted to do. Happy? Yes, but I wanted more.

"You move in leaps and bounds," he said. "Like a grasshopper. You don't stay in one area long enough." He stopped and reconsidered. "No, more like a butterfly or a bee."

I wasn't sure what he meant at first. I lived at home most of the time. I was not a globetrotter. Then I realised he was not referring to physical movement. A while back, someone else had called me an "itinerant", meaning that I kept moving from one area of interest to another, not staying long enough to exhaust any particular subject.

"Or is it a crab? Yes, yes, a crab. Two steps forward, three steps back, two to the right, one to the left."

Yes, yes! I got the message. I turned towards the sea to organise my response. And it was my turn now to burst out laughing. He joined me in the merriment. A metre or so away from me, at the curve of a protrusion on the rock, a sizeable crab had just made its appearance and began to move gingerly in all directions: to the left, to the right, to the front, to the back. It was a dance. I could practically hear the beat. And the melody, a mocking melody. I couldn't stop laughing. 'The dance of the crab!' Surely, this would be my epitaph.

After a while the crab stopped dancing and stood still facing us. It seemed to be waiting for something. I turned to the old man. He shrugged his shoulders and opened his hands in front of him indicating ignorance. I stood up and walked towards the crab. The edge of the rock where it stood looked risky to approach, wet and slippery.

"Be careful," shouted the old man. "Remember the fig tree."

I stopped in my tracks, took a deep breath and, with great effort, managed to erase the imagery that had suddenly sprung to my mind. As I did that, the whole scene acquired a dreamlike quality which I immediately recognised and which filled me with confidence.

I approached the crab and, against my instinct and my considerable experience with these crustatians, I stretched my hand and
stroked its back. I held back my natural apprehension. I was in
control. The crab did not even attempt to use its claws on me. But
as I removed my hand and straightened up, it turned its back to me
and lifted its hind legs - well, some of its legs! - in what looked like
a gesture of defiance before jumping clear off the rock and into the
water. It made a splash that was underscored and enhanced by the
old man's laughter. I couldn't hold back a chuckle or two myself.

As I made my way back to my bench, I was amazed at, and
pleased with, my behaviour. Under any other circumstances I would
have grabbed the crab and made a meal out of it, cooked or otherwise - a childhood habit. But instead, I caressed it! And it didn't
attack me with its claws!

By the time I was back inside the doughnut hole I had returned to
my normal 'waking' self. The old man clapped his approval.

"Bravo! Bravo!"

I decided not to stop inside the hole, and walked over to the other
side. I needed to arrange my thoughts. The old man seemed to
relent. He was not putting pressure on me with disconcerting questions, for the moment. All the same, I had to take stock, analyse the
situation, and decide how and where to start with my questions. I
had found myself in the unenvious position of having thrust on me
answers to questions I hadn't raised. And my questions would not
be formulated to elicit explanations on 'how' certain events took
place so much as to 'why' they happened: 'why' to me, and 'why'
now.

I always found that my thinking was clearer in daylight and
especially in plenty of sunshine. So I stood at the edge of the opening, facing the sun, allowing it to drench me with its light and
warmth - scorching heat, actually.

Now, for the first time since I met the old man, I believed I was
able to think clearly. I began to put things into perspective. To start
with, I was certain the old man was not what he appeared to be on
the surface. I was not sure that he was 'real', in fact. The whole
setup - and it was beginning to feel like a *setup* - including the old
man and my reactions to him, felt as if they belonged to another
realm of reality. It was as if I, the old man, and all the events that
had taken place, were 'staged'. My thoughts, my feelings, my re-

actions, my behaviour in general did not follow my normal patterns
- there were times when, I could have sworn, they were not 'mine'.

I was ready to accept that the old man was some kind of shaman.
There were rumours that various psychics or mystics or 'magicians'
lived in the area. And my personal experiences in the past prepared
me in that direction. I was more than keen to meet such people, but
if this were such a case I was not prepared for it, not the way it was
thrust on me. My past experiences were gradual, and more or less
explicable when set against some 'metaphysical' system. But these
present occurrences were in a class of their own, or rather, they did
not seem to belong in any class. There were no coherent, consequen-
tial, metaphysics that I could fit them into. They were random and
sometimes contradictory, especially when it came to the emotions I
experienced. I needed to make a list, a catalogue of inquiries.

I began at the beginning, when I first laid eyes on him. I noted,
as I had done earlier, the contradiction between his display of youthfulness and his gasping for air, his contradictory behaviour: being
friendly and caring and yet curt and distant even sarcastic; saying
that I loved him (and its effect on me), his knowledge of events in
my past, his apparent ability to read my thoughts and emotions, the
event with the crab and his shouting out to "remember the fig tree"
which had a special place in my childhood memories, the experience
of fear and then security, and, most important of all, the fantastic
and wonderful experience of being 'in' and 'out' of the world (had I
really been 'out' of this world?). And --

"Well?" He spoke softly as if to avoid breaking into my thoughts
too abruptly.

He was standing right next to me. I sighed and huffed quietly in
an effort to cool myself.

"Too hot," I said. "Let's go back in."

"A very good idea," he agreed.

We returned to our benches and sat opposite each other. I pondered for a few seconds.

"How...ehm...Why my childhood experience in the orchard?" I
began.

He smiled cheekily. "What, your pissing experience?"

I was determined not to be ruffled. "Well, yes, if you must put it
that way."

He continued to smile. "I see you are jumping in at the deep end.

As usual. But you're learning."

"What do you mean?" I asked, genuinely not knowing what he meant.

"You nearly asked me *how* but then you managed to veer off. Why?"

I had a ready answer to that. "Because had I asked you *how* you knew you would have said that you had psychic vision and were able to see that way."

"How do you know? Are *you* psychic? Could you have seen my response?"

I was thrown a bit. But I stood my ground.

"Not in a literal sense. But it is obvious from your behaviour that you are capable."

He laughed and shook his head.

"I can see that I'll have to take it back. You are not learning."

"What?"

"You're using logic. You're making inferences. You're observant, which is good, but you're still relying too much on inference. You are inferring from observation, you are not using the direct route." He was making a statement of fact.

I knew what he was talking about but I still felt compelled to justify myself.

"I was not prepared."

"Not true. You *are* prepared. You have been preparing long enough."

He was playing with words, deliberately twisting my meaning.

"You should have switched within seconds. You were given plenty of opportunities," he insisted.

I did not react. I reflected very quickly on the events of the afternoon and concluded that he was right. I already knew he was right.

I looked around me once again organising my thoughts. It suddenly occurred to me that if somebody was listening to us at that moment he would think we had escaped from some mental institution. I was now taking it for granted that the old man was one of those psychics I'd heard about living in the area and so I decided to face the whole situation with its numerous separate events at a different level. I took his criticism on board and followed his advice.

And, lo and behold, this old man was no mere psychic, there was a much wider dimension to him. Whether he was 'real' or not I couldn't tell, but now I knew that my 'hows' and 'whys' had to merge into a single-pronged inquiry. I wasn't quite certain why I had to do this but it felt right, although rather embarrassing that I had to raise such questions with him.

"How did you know about my childhood adventure in the orchard and why was it brought up?" I began asking him.

"Because it was there, all around you. Because it *is* there all around you," he said emphasising the present tense and opening his eyes wide to add to the emphasis.

He blinked once as if deliberately then opened his eyes wide again and was about to blink once more. I saw his eyelids beginning to come together.

Suddenly, I was back at the scene in the orchard. But with a difference this time. Earlier on it was a memory, an adjunct to the panic and fear I was experiencing, an association practically. Now, it was the real thing. I was in the orchard and I was a child. I experienced the whole thing in real time, moment by moment. I even felt the urine running down my legs. At some point in this process I felt myself screaming with fear and anguish, somehing that was not part of the original experience. There was a further, more pene-trating dimension to this that was absent from both my 'memory' of the event and the original childhood experience. And then, just as suddenly, I was back in the doughnut hole. I was shivering with fear, with terror.

The old man was still staring at me just as he was right before I shot back and relived the orchard scene. His eyelids were in the same position as before and about to close, to complete the blink he had started. He blinked. I continued to shiver a while longer. Al-though his eyes showed symphathy for my predicament, he did not move. Somehow I wanted him to come over and comfort me, but I did not expect him to, and he didn't. He continued to look at me until I stopped shivering and began to compose myself.

The fear continued to reverberate for a while but now it acquired a different character. It was objectified. I knew I could go back to the scene whenever I wanted to, and re-experience it in all its sens-oreal detail and emotional pain, but it was now under my control. It was an experience I could get in and out of at will. All of it, phys-ical and emotional, could be invested with or divested of reality. I could make it as powerful and real or as faint and unreal as I wanted to. Be in it or stand beside it. I began to get an inkling of 'why' this scene, with its concommitant emotions, had come up the way it had both the first time and also just now. But I was not sure. It was only an inkling.

He was smiling at me like a father proud of his child for passing some exam, maybe getting marks a little above average or simply managing to avoid failing abysmally! I wanted to turn the tables, to find out about him the way he knew about me, but I couldn't. There was something in the way, as if someone had thrown up a barrier that prevented me from finding out. Intriguingly enough, it didn't feel like a hard barrier but more like a net curtain that allowed my intuition shadowy glimpses. I had a certainty that this curtain was going to either pull itself aside or just dissolve away in due course. I could almost hear him say "Not yet, not yet". I gave up for the time being. It would be better to pursue my other line of inquiry for now.

"Why?" I asked him, returning to my inkling.

"Why? You mean to say you don't know why?" he responded with an obvious pretence at surprise.

"I'm not sure."

"What is it that you *are* sure about?"

He did not only turn my statement round but he also avoided answering my question and put *me* on the spot. I had to think.

"No, don't think," he said, cutting into my thoughts. "Don't think," he repeated.

I knew what he wanted me to do. I tried but couldn't get into it.

"Okay," he said. "Give me your conclusions. Your *thinking* conclusions," he emphasised.

That was easier. I took a deep breath and told him how I perceived the differences in the two experiences in the orchard I had undergone that afternoon. That the second time, even though more 'real' and painful, in the end I was able to control it, to call it up fully and at will and re-experience the events bodily and emotionally and know that it was only an experience, its power and reality depending entirely on the way I invested it with energy.

"Good," he said. "Anything else?" He sounded more eager now.

"Well...," I stumbled. "Well, if I were to extend the principle to other experiences, if I could do this with all my experiences then I'd have nothing to fear."

He broke out into a loud chuckle.

"Yes?" He was expecting more.

I felt encouraged. "Ehm. By the same token, I could live my everyday life as well as my memories and my daydreams in full power, with total energy, as if it were the only thing that mattered in the whole wide world and, at the same time, treat it as a mere inconsequential experience and place it right outside of me."

Nothing could stop me now. I'd found my flow. He chuckled away.

"And then the men in the white overalls will come and get me!" I joined him in a chuckle of my own.

"Good, good. You're on the right track," he said. "We'll make a Pythagorean out of you yet."

I half-understood the obscure reference to Pythagoras but he did not allow me the opportunity to ask for clarification.

"What else?" he prodded further.

I couldn't think of anything else to add relating to that particular experience.

"Go back to the fear," he said.

I suddenly remembered. "Oh, yes. Why the fear and why now?"

"You tell *me*," he said, throwing the ball back into my court.

"I understand the fear," I retorted, "because it was part of the experience in the orchard."

"How?"

"Because I was afraid I would be hurt. In my childhood perception, in fact, I thought I would die."

"Ah, now we are getting somewhere. The fear of injury to your physical integrity, even total loss of it. Right?"

I had to agree with him. He waited for me to expand on my agreement, to go into detail, but I didn't. The issue was obscured by its complexity. I could feel many ramifications but I couldn't pick out one in isolation from the others and unfold it. He sensed my difficulty. He leant forward a little, resting his hands on his knees.

"Okay, let's see how we can unravel this." He looked me up and down slowly, examining me - for what? "Tell me about the fear again. Was it the same on all occasions this afternoon?"

"No, it varied."

"How?"

I reflected and tried to grade the different kinds of fear I had experienced that day in terms of severity.

"Well, it ranged from remembering that I felt fear, to fear invoked by the childhood experience, to fear as I re-experienced the incident, then to fear invoked by re-experiencing the event but enormously amplified, to horrendous fear that was not connected to any memory of any incident. Ehm....." I stopped, wondering whether what I had just said was the expected response to his question. And then added: "I am not doing this chronologically, you understand. Not in the order in which they came up. I thought I--"

"That's fine," he interrupted. "There's no need to apologise. You presented it that way because that's how your mind works: logically - in bits, in pockets, in pigeon-holes. That's fine. In fact, it will be useful for what you'll have to do next." I wanted to ask him what he had in mind for "next" but he quickly moved on. "Now, is there anything else you want to add?" he said, and waited.

I didn't want to add anything to that particular theme but I needed answers to an earlier question.

"No, but I would like to know why this particular experience would come up, why now, and why fear of all other emotions? What's the rationale, what's the purpose?"

"Ah, good. Let's do this your way then. Fear. What is it? What is fear?"

"An emotion?"

"One aspect of it, yes. But what is its function?"

"Survival. We are afraid of what might hurt us."

"Right. Which may lead to our taking steps to check against possible threats to our survival."

"Yes."

"Such as turning round and fighting, when we are threatened, or running away."

"Yes. Fight or flight, as they call it."

"Ah, but you didn't do either of those, did you? You just pissed yourself!" he said, and gave in to another bout of laughter.

He wasn't going to give up humiliating me at every and any opportunity. I wondered if all his questions were not just a ruse leading up to such punch lines. Otherwise, what was he driving at?

"Seriously now, why do you think you pissed yourself?" he continued amidst occasional chuckles.

"Because I was too scared."

"Yes, but shouldn't you have fought or fled?"

"I couldn't. I was stunned. The fear paralysed me completely."
I'd read somewhere that in situations of real or perceived extreme danger the body empties its bowels in preparation for fight or flight - emptying one's bowels apparently renders one's body more capable to fight or run; it also redirects the blood to much needed and more important muscles. Fainting is also another possible reaction which indicates to the enemy that one is not a threat any longer. I told him all this. He opened his eyes and mouth wide in mock astonishment at my erudition. But he did not mock me otherwise.

"We mustn't forget the psychological aspect. Fear at a purely physical level is no more than a reaction to a sensation, a knee-jerk reaction. Fear, as it is generally understood, is a perception. It is psychological. Don't you agree?"

"Yes."

"A few minutes ago you mentioned fear invoked by re-experiencing the event but enormously amplified. What did you mean by that?" he asked.

I was certain he was quoting me verbatim. I went back to it and tried to explain.

"What I meant was that it wasn't only a full revival of the incident - you know, being there as a child as it happened. Suddenly, it became much more frightening. I let go, and my mind, my imagination, enlarged it out of proportion."

His smile was that of a primary school teacher dealing with a pupil who got an answer nearly right, not quite but nearly, and was ready to goad his charge towards the full answer. Under normal circumstances this sort of behaviour I would have called condescension and it would have raised my hackles, but these were not normal circumstances, and he was not a 'normal' person.

"Tell me, where were you when this happened?"

Was he joking? "What do you mean? I was here. Next to you."

"I don't mean physically."

Ah, yes. "I was here and I wasn't here. I--"

"You were *beside yourself.*"

He hit the nail on the head. That's exactly how it felt. I was familiar with the process but not in relation to fear.

"And that's why it felt so powerful," he continued. "Your body, your physical body, everyone's physical body, slows down the impact of emotions and obscures the clarity of thought. When you're beside yourself, however, it's a different story. But you know these things, anyway."

I did, but he was not answering my question. I was about to ask him again when he obliged me, right on cue.

"Now, you want to know why this particular experience came up, why fear, and why now."

I nodded with some relief. He was coming round to it at last.

"Your childhood experience in the orchard was the best and easiest to bring up. Of all the fearful moments in your life, and you've had a few, this was the purest, strongest and most appropriate."

Appropriate for what? I formulated the question in my head and waited for him to respond as he had done so many times during the afternoon. But he didn't. He seemed to be waiting for me to digest his explanation. I ran through my mind very quickly some events in my life that could be classed as fearful: I had nearly drowned twice, I'd fallen off a cliff once, I'd been shot at once, I'd become paralysed once as a result of a diving accident...ehm... What else? Oh, yes, I'd fallen off a roof once. But he was right, the orchard incident was the purest from the point of view of fear. Why fear?

"Why fear?" he verbalised my mental question. "Fear keeps you alive: physically, emotionally, intellectually. It secures you against the dissolution of your integrity on all three of these levels. There is fear of injury or death to your physical integrity, emotional integrity, and integrity of thought, or, as is better known in Greek, noetic integrity: integrity of the *nous*."

He waited for a beat or two and then repeated the idea more concisely. "There are physical, emotional and noetic deaths, and injuries to these entities. You know these things instinctively through fear. Without fear you don't exist. Fear is wired into your system. You *are* the system and you are held together by fear."

He dropped these ideas like bombs. The last one, especially, was the most shattering. I was a system held together by fear?! And he was not laughing now. He seemed aware of the effect the things he had just said were having on me. Or, maybe, the serious look on his face was merely there for a theatrical purpose, to hold my attention and impose emphasis.

He remained silent. He straightened up, waited for a beat and then lent gently backwards and rested his back on the wall of the rock behind him. His face was straight but I could have sworn there was a suspicion at the edge of his mouth waiting to develop into a raucous laughter. A few minutes went by without anything happening. I couldn't wait any longer.

"What you're saying denies both unity and unit," I said, hoping to call his bluff.

"No, there is unity, alright, but unit is a fabrication," he retorted.

"What? What about the *I*, the ego," I said, pointing to my chest, "the sense of being a unit, an entity? And what of the con-tinuity of memory and consciousness?"

"Ditto," he said unflinchingly.

"Ditto? Is that all? Ditto!?"

His response to my reaction was a calm question. "What do you mean by *unit*?"

"What I just said: the *I*, the ego, the sense of being a unit."

"Fine. But you should listen to yourself: 'the sense of being a unit' you said. The sense of being something doesn't necessarily make you that thing." He leant forward a little, closer to me. "Consider the concept of unity for a moment: this implies a process, a state of affairs perhaps, which brings and/or keeps together apparently individual bits to make up a whole."

We were both using the Greek word 'monad' for 'unit' which is also an equivalent of the word 'atom' meaning indivisible - a word applied both to the physicist's atom and to the 'person': individual, 'indivisible'. I was getting the impression he was leading me into a wordgame.

"So?"

"So this whole is your unit, which is made up of parts. There is no such thing as an indivisible unit or 'atom'. These are invented concepts, convenient, in fact necessary, for the survival of the amalgam called ego, 'I', or individual consciousness. They are dictated and held together by fear. They are self-perpetuating constructions created at the very inception of this amalgam - which is what makes it so difficult to go beyond it."

He had my head spinning.

"Are you saying that I as consciousness I am not an indivisible substance, that I'm made up of parts?"

"That's precisely what I'm saying, and these parts are held to-gether precariously, and they can function independently of one another. And they often do."

He waited for what he had just said to sink in and then went on. "What do you think 'survival instinct' stands for?" It was a rhetorical question which he proceeded to answer. "It stands for a routine expression of fear, fear of injury to or extinction of the fabricated unity. Many times the reaction in support of this imagined unity, otherwise known as a 'person', goes over the top. Everything you might call a bad action, emotion or thought is just that: an overreaction in defence of a person's imagined integrity."

He offered me another short pause before he continued.

"And what are physical and psychological abnormalities - of which there are millions - or even demonstrations of genius? What are they if not overdeveloping or overcompensating aspects of this collective, out of control efforts to keep it together, bits working and developing independently sometimes at the expense of other bits?"

He stopped, straightened up and waited. And then he leant forward again and lowered his voice.

"Can you see now how fear lies at the root of everything, and how it works?"

– 2 –

Understanding and Knowing
(Logic and the Direct Method)

I found myself in a split state again. I was following what he was saying intellectually, step by step, making logical connections and seeing implications and inferences, but at another level I was taking in meanings directly, without the intermediary of language. This latter level was a state in which the experience pointed out the rules which themselves flowed out of whoever was having the experience - in this case, myself. I alternated between these two states which were similar to those I had entered earlier that afternoon. I could see endless ramifications as if they were rolling off an assembly line. These ramifications were not inferences, they flowed naturally and unquestioningly, like water out of a mountain spring.

As I went back and forth between these states I came to 'understand' more clearly some of the concepts the old man used. It was a strange process. When I was in one of the states *I knew* and when I was in the other *I understood*. In the 'knowing' state there was just that: knowing, a certainty that things were the way they were and had to be so.

In the other state, there was a very delicate intellectual activity in which simple concepts panned out into enormous complexes, all interconnected and one flowing from the other. I could understand very clearly how this logic worked. And it was part of the old man's logic. I understood more widely his use of the term 'monad' which now opened up to reveal some other meanings: it did not only carry the sense of 'unit' but also those of 'alone' as well as of 'lonely'. This much could be easily extracted from its etymology, but it suddenly yielded features which were not readily there to be seen.

The concept of 'alone' within the 'unit' carried a sense of arrogance, of standing apart, of being unique (which, in Greek, is derived from 'monad'). The concept of 'lonely' was attached to the concept of 'alone' as a consequence and had a strong emotional accompaniment. So now it appeared that the 'unit', which was made up of parts, acquired the sense of uniqueness and arrogance, of being apart and bigger than the parts it was made up of.

There was a strong feeling of insolence arising from this epiphenomenon, from this tenuous 'unity' of tapestry. It was as if the 'monad', the 'unit', were personified and felt itself apart and unique and independent instead of realising that it was a construction, a put-together of parts which themselves were not unique but merely units made up of parts which were made up of units which were made up of parts..... Every unit dissolved into increasingly smaller parts, and the process went on and on like a physicist's atom under a powerful microscope.

The most amazing thing was that the parts or units were connected into a bigger whole by the same substance that they themselves were composed of: like ice cubes and icebergs floating in water - the same substance in different forms, different appearance. The 'fluid' substance that moved amongst the parts and kept them together as a unit was the same that produced the sense of uniqueness and individuality, the feeling of the ego and the 'I'. But this came about through a particular type of activity: the fluidic form of this substance moved and vibrated and gave rise to an impression of continuity, sometimes simply by vibrating and other times by concentrating these vibrations into images - which were, at times, accompanied by 'feelings'.

These undulating images and 'feelings' appeared and disappeared as if on crests and troughs of waves, but they were always connected somehow. As I watched them, I gradually came to realise that I was observing the nature and mechanics of memory - how memory is created and how it functions. And the mere fact of connectedness, of unity, of continuity in terms of memory brought about the sense of ego, of 'I', of self-consciousness, of a unit that believes in its own uniqueness, indivisibily, indestructibility - a state of affairs that gave true meaning to the word hubris!

I was at once devasted and liberated! The uniqueness of my individuality was no more. In fact, I did not exist as an ego, as 'I'. *I did not exist, I did not exist!* I felt unburdened, relieved, liberated! All of a sudden, I had no fear, no fear of anything. How could I have any fear, any fear at all, if I did not exist? That's it! Fear is the result of existing! He was absolutely right: fear was wired into existence. I felt inundated by a rush of brilliant cleansing energy that swept away everything that I called 'me' or 'mine' and lifted me into...into what? I was not lifted, I simply became weightless, non-existent...No, no, I existed somehow but I had no consistency and no boundaries. I was that substance that vibrated amongst the parts and the units and turned itself into all those parts and units....

"Enough! Enough!"

I heard his voice reaching me from somewhere and pulling me back. I resisted. I fought. I could have won and stayed where I was but I was not strong enough. I knew that all I needed was more strength, more willpower. If only I had that, if only I *were* that and nothing else - just be the willpower, that aspect of the substance that escaped me.

Another, more distant, voice was saying "not yet, not yet". And I was back, still inundated with the energy, still very light.

He was sitting there as before, looking at me.

"A few minutes ago you said you were not ready. Now we can't pull you back," he said teasingly as he smiled at me. "But it's a matter of degree," he continued. "We cannot allow you to go too far. The mind is a delicate contraption." I was staring at him, still in a daze. "We want you to stay sane. Don't go crazy on us."

What's with the royal "we"? But, no, intuitively I knew what he was talking about, I needn't ask.

"Remember Plato," he added.

Plato? What Plato? Oh, yes, of course, Plato. The philosopher, the mystic, the teacher. People thought he was referring to geometry when he had a sign chiselled outside his Academy which read "No admission to those who cannot do geometry", like an entrance requirement. But to him geometry, and mathematics in general, had one very important function that escaped most: to exercise the mind, to sharpen it, to ground it safely in logic; and, when properly prepared, to move it up to more abstract practice until it was capable of functioning somewhere outside 'earthly' logic where the other 'geometry' held sway and in which Pythagoras' 'divine mathematics' were applied. Yes, Plato. My Plato. I knew what he was talking about alright.

I stood up. I had this uncontrollable impulse to jump into the sea. But I felt dizzy. Maybe because of the way I got up so abruptly. I wobbled a little, then steadied myself, looked around and found my bearings and made for the water. But before I took a step I was already in the water. I felt the water all around me. In fact, I felt the water throughout my body, as if all the cells in my body had become detached and spaced out and the water penetrated the spaces between them.

And then I felt this hand grabbing my arm.

"Don't be silly. Be careful. You *will* drown yourself this time. Come and sit down."

He was next to me holding my arm and I was standing in front of the bench. I hadn't moved an inch. For a moment, I felt I was drowning, the water was choking me, and then I was back on dry land. I was disorientated again but I followed his instructions and sat down on the bench behind me.

And as I did that I found myself looking up my backside! There were two of me, and the one standing in front of me was being gently pressed by someone backwards and downwards and into me who was sitting on the bench. I had a distant certainty that the person who was doing the pressing was the old man, except that I could not see him.

Instead, I saw this beautiful figure which was radiating brilliant colours that extended throughout the opening in the rock and beyond. I could sense it was the old man but, like a Russian doll, it contained within it a number of other figures. I was drawn to it and wanted to see these other figures but something like mist was thrown in front of me and obscured the view. I could still see the brilliant main figure very clearly. Then I heard a creaking sound and the two of me became one again.

"Stay there," the old man said practically ordering me. "Get back in and stay in."

I took a deep breath and felt myself becoming more solid, more cohesive. I wanted to lie down on the bench but he stopped me.

"No, don't lie down. Sit upright. And stay with me. Don't drift," he said firmly.

I straightened up and took a few deep breaths, holding each to a certain count then exhaling slowly to another count using my diaphragm to control the length and depth of each cycle of breathing - something I had learnt a while back. Slowly, I regained my balance. He was smiling at me again. He went back to the other bench and sat down. My first thought was: "were the figs drugged?" He continued to smile either not picking up my thought or just ignoring it. We sat there quietly for a while.

I looked out to the open sea. The deep blue and the light blue and the faint line of the horizon where the two met, they were all there. Oh, God, how beautiful they were! How immensely beautiful they were! I turned my eyes to the other side, to the land, to the mound and the countryside with the orchards and the rising mountainside beyond. My heart was fluttering with happiness. The beauty of it all! Even the rocks and the sparse soil at the edge of the mound where the promontory sloped into a small precipice radiated with beauty. Then a realisation struck me: all this was ephemeral, temporal, it would disappear one day. I wanted to weep for its loss. I thought of the Persian king gazing out over the beauty of Bosporus and weeping for the same reason more than two and a half thousand years ago.

"Don't do that!" he called out. "That's self-indulgence. Stay with the beauty. Nothing dies."

"But isn't everything temporal? Isn't everything an illusion?" I retorted.

"So is death," he responded with aplomb.

It worked almost immediately. The sadness was strained out and happiness was enhanced, as though energy was transferred from one to the other. Everything was simply beautiful.

And then, out of the blue, he said: "You saw me, didn't you?" And before I had time to get back with a question he continued. "Now tell me--"

He stopped and looked at me searchingly, like a physician looking for signs in a patient, except that he did not so much look at me as through me. I waited.

"Do you understand now?" he whispered as if to make me draw closer to him in order to hear him. "Do you understand?" he repeated.

Was he playing with words again? Understand what? There were two ways I could have taken this. The first one was--

"Or do you think you know?"

Ah, he was after the other possible interpretation. I talked to him about my experience regarding 'understanding' and 'knowing'.

"So, what's the relationship between the two," he prodded.

I couldn't tell for sure. "I know the difference between them," I said, hoping that I was on the right track.

"Not the difference. The relationship," he insisted.

I told him I didn't know.

"You do," he said. "But right now you are on the side of the *understanding* so you are unable to know. And that's only because you don't know how to, you don't have the technique to get there by yourself, under your own steam." Then he put it in a summary form: "You don' have the *knowhow* and you don't have the *willpower*." He waited for a beat or two and added. "Not yet, anyway. Though sometimes you get close to it momentarily. Almost spontaneously."

He stopped to let me reflect on those experiences he was referring to, and then moved on. "We'll talk about this later."

He stopped again and waited. I began to recognise this waiting bit. It was his way of telling me that he was expecting me to ask a question. And I obliged him with the obvious.

"*What* is the relationship between knowing and understanding?"

He chuckled gently. "You're very perceptive," he said, with an almost imperceptible trace of sercasm in his voice. "Yes, as perceptive as a rhinoceros when a fly lands on his horn." And he burst out laughing.

Why did he always have to spoil it? Such a lovely atmosphere and he goes and....

"Don't let your personality get in the way," he went on. "It's only a glove you put on to clean the toilet. You discard it at will along with all the shit it's been dealing with."

Nice imagery! I tried desperately to hold onto the beauty and elation I was feeling.

"Not easy, is it?" he continued.

No, it wasn't. I found it especially difficult because not only was I feeling so elated that I did not want to deal with anything as mundane as that, but the imagery evoked by his words was also too strong, lifelike. I mean, the faeces were floating in front of my face, for crying out loud!

"Ah, that's the price you have to pay. The more perceptive you become the greater the need for willpower. If you can see beauty, be utterly blissful, and deal with penetrating, world-shaking intellectual insights while you are swimming in shit, well, you've made it."

Another bout of laughter. I waited to see where he was going to go with this. It was a tall order. A very very tall order.

"Anyway, this is the target. Let's get back to the practice," he said, returning to the subject as if all this were a mere parenthesis, something you could relegate to an appendix.

"Right. Knowing and understanding. What do you understand by *understanding*? What does it mean to you?" he asked.

I pulled myself together and plumped for definitions. "I understand what you are saying by understanding the concepts you are using. I understand the concepts because of their definitions. We agree on the definitions and so we understand each other."

"That's not understanding. That's just a form of communication."

"Yes, but you can't communicate without clarity of definition."

"Be that as it may, this is not understanding."

I was baffled.

He continued. "What if someone is unable to communicate clearly? How do you understand this person?"

Now I could see where he was heading. "I feel, I empathise, I put myself in that person's shoes," I said.

"What happens to the concepts? How do you come to understand concepts and abstract ideas?"

"By means of their definitions," I ventured.

"But definitions are made up of words, and these words themselves have to be defined, and so on and on."

I was thrown again.

He leant forward and looked me straight in the eye. And I saw it. Ah, yes.

"By understanding the other person's *understanding*," I said reading his mind, understanding his *understanding*!

He clapped his hands in confirmation.

"So," he concluded rather pleased that I was getting somewhere, "so, to understand a concept, an idea, you must understand how a person uses that concept."

Although this insight was somewhat pleasing it also sounded a bit counter intuitive. I had always taken it that objective, consensual, definitions were the *sine qua non* of understanding and communicating. Was Socrates' insistence on clear definitions wasted, then? I voiced my concerns.

"You're talking about a necessary but elementary stage, an effort to avoid misunderstanding that, unfortunately, creates more of the same. Precisely because no matter how far you go with so-called objective definitions, the interpretation of these definitions is always subjective. You need to break the circle. By going to the person directly."

I not so much followed intellectually what he was saying as I felt the flow of his meaning.

"Eliminate the *it*," he added.

"The what?"

"The *it*," he repeated. "Think of grammar: the personal pronouns I, you, he/she/it. Eliminate the third person. Why are you so happy when you love, why do you think the world appears so beautiful to you right now? Because you have eliminated the third person, the *it*. You should know this by now. You've been practising it. Perhaps without realising it."

I had to admit he was right. We don't really communicate by means of definitions but by understanding the other person. Even when reading someone's work we must go to the writer's understanding in order to comprehend their meaning, at which point they are not a 'he/she', a third person, but a 'you', a second person.

"What about objectivity, then, and the objective world outside?" I inquired.

"Now you really disappoint me," he said, and he did sound disappointed. "How can you ask such a question in the state you are in now? Are you sliding out?"

No, I was not. I was playing devil's advocate.

"You're using the word *objectivity* which means you're facing the world as an object. You're sliding out."

I remonstrated, and he laughed.

"By eliminating the *it*, by eliminating the idea of the object or third person, you enter into a personal relationship with whoever or whatever you're dealing with," he continued. "You said it yourself: to put yourself in the other person's shoes, to be that other person. By doing this you are doing more than simply understanding the other person on a one-to-one basis. You open the gates to their whole personality. And the same applies to ideas: they suddenly flood you with meanings." He was describing my earlier experience of 'understanding'!

"Take Plato's ideas, for example," he went on. "They are found in the upper regions of *understanding*. Just below *knowing*."

He looked at me as if to say "you know where I'm going now,

don't you?". So I asked him.

"What about *knowing*?"

"In *knowing*, the possibilities are literally endless. Everything resides in it. You reside in it, I reside in it. *Understanding* is merely the application of one particular kind of logic emanating from *knowing*, one amongst many, one universe amongst many some of which are spatially co-existent. All of them flowing from *knowing*. When we are training our minds to understand we are working towards *knowing* of which we are, albeit unconsciously most of the time, integral parts. To put it another way, we get to *understand* what we already *know*."

"This sounds like Plato's argument of knowledge as memory."

"It's more than that. Plato's partially right about memory, but there is more than one kind of memory. There are two kinds, with the first one divided into two parts. Earlier, you talked to me about the parts or units and the spaces amongst them. Well, there is memory at the level of the parts: this is ordinary memory, including remembering past lives - albeit mostly erratically.

"Then there is memory relating to what you described as spaces, the glue so to speak that keeps the parts together, the *I*, the consciousness that links, *coherently* this time, present and past lives. This is what gives people, intuitively, the sense of eternity, of continuing for ever and ever as a unit.

"And the other kind of memory?"

"The other kind is a very different type of memory: it is not temporal, sequential, in a strict sense with a *normally* understood beginning and end. In it there is no past or future as you understand it - it is beyond *understanding*. You can call it eternal present, if you like, but, as there is no commonly understood temporal sequence of events, calling it anything which implies time is misleading. As an example, there is memory of the future, *knowing* the future as if it has already taken place, but it hasn't, it is simply there."

He waited for me to take it in before continuing.

"First, then, we get rid of the third person, the *it*; now, at this stage, the *you* disappears as well."

He stopped again and waited, perhaps for a question on my part. But none was forthcoming. I was struggling to get back to an earlier state in which what he was now saying made perfect sense.

He continued. "The question now is: can you have an *I*, an ego, in the absence of anything outside of it?"

This was not rhetorical. It was a real question requiring an answer. An answer, however, was impossible given the logic in which it had to be formulated.

I ventured a proposition. "I know you dismissed time in the second kind of memory, but could time, assimilated somehow, be an extra dimension?"

"No, no. Time is not a dimension. Philosophers and physicists are terribly confused. Time is an accompaniment, a perceived effect if you like, of the logic dictated by the kind of space one is in and dealing with. In the logic of the three-dimensional world, for instance, there is time which we understand as past, present and future. In worlds of other spatial dimensions, a different logic is functioning and time is experienced differently."

He stopped, straightened himself and looked out to the sea awash with the bright sunlight, waited for a beat and then continued.

"Supposing your body was made of pure light and never grew old, the world around you was, similarly, pure light, there was no sun to rise and set, you moved instantaneously by simply thinking where you wanted to be. Wouldn't time then apply differently and the logic of existence be different?"

He leant back against the rock and looked at me, waiting for me to rise to the experience. Somehow he knew that I knew about the 'Body of Light'. Why else would he bring this up? It was not a coincidence, it was deliberate. He smiled at me cheekily and waited.

Suddenly, I heard this shrill angry voice:

"So you're still here you fucker, you son-of-a-bitch, you arsehole!!"

It was like an electric shock! My body shook and rattled. I could feel this piercing attack cutting through my whole being. I had already begun to rise to the occasion, lifting myself into a state of light obviously intended for me by the old man, and then I was shot to pieces. What was he up to this time? Why lift me up, elate me, and then shatter me?

The shieking voice continued. "You fucking arsehole! You're not getting away with it this time!"

As I began to pull together the shattered pieces of myself, I saw the old man turning towards the mound. I followed his gaze. And there on top of the mound was this middle-aged man shaking his hand in anger. He was wearing sandals and baggy trousers but no shirt, and his head was protected from the midday sun by a ridiculously large hat - an oversized sombrero that could have been made by a Mexican who wanted an undesirable tourist to look as stupid as possible. But under this hat there was definitely a very irate face.

"Hi, hello there. Nice to see you again," Yiannis called out, greeting the man in a friendly voice. "How are you today?"

"None of your fucking business how I am today or any other fucking day, you faggot!" came back the response.

The man went on to hurl more abuse at Yiannis - most of which defies translation not only because of its rudeness but also because of its florid and explicit imagery that would baffle any non-Greek speaker - before turning to leave in an angrier mood than when he had arrived.

"Goodbye for now, and God be with you. See you again soon." Yiannis' greeting sounded genuine enough although I couldn't help sensing a smidgeon of sarcasm.

"Yes, see you in court, you sicko!" And then as if to himself: "Fucking pervert!" And he walked away mumbling more abuse, with flailing arms and gesticulating digital rudeness.

"What was all that about?" I managed to inquire in my utter confusion.

"Oh, nothing of any significance," came the dismissive answer. "The man owns the land, and he also thinks he owns this rock."

"Does he?

"No. Not really. Sometimes."

"What do you mean 'sometimes'? He either owns it or he does not."

"Well, apparently he does sometimes. Look. You see the water that separates the rock from the land, down there?"

"Yes?"

"Well, there are times during the year when the tide goes out and the two are bridged by a bit of dry land. Then the rock is part of his land. But right now it isn't - the water separates them. As you can see."

"But, surely, when the tide is low it can be easily established that the rock is a continuation of his land, and therefore part of it," I countered.

"Surely. And if you empty the Aegean you'll see that Turkey is part of Greece." He laughed at the thought. "The Greeks would love that."

"But if the rock doesn't belong to him, who does it belong to, then?"

"The State. Which means anybody and everybody. It's part of the sea. Mind you, he did try to steal it once."

"Steal it!? How? Did he tie it to a boat and try to float it away?" It was my turn to laugh now.

"No, on the contrary. He doesn't want the rock to be floated away. He wants it joined to his land. So, he tried to do that by preparing concrete with the intention of pouring it into the gap between the rock and his land thus raising the level of the bottom of the sea there and creating solid ground which would remain permanently above water."

"What happened?"

"The villagers got wind of it and stopped him. And things got worse when I put these benches in and turned it into a refuge from the sun."

"What happens in the winter?"

"Nothing much. The sea gets rough, the waves wash through it and over it, the wind dismantles the rest and blows it away. In the summer it's put back together again."

"What did he mean when he said 'see you in court'?"

"Oh, he's threatening to take me to court for trespassing. For squatting, actually."

"Can he do that?"

"Nonsense. Empty threats. I offered a compromise but he can't get his head round it."

"What do you mean? What kind of compromise?"

"I offered to use only the hole, this opening we are in now, and if he ever catches me on his land or on the rock outside the hole, I'll give up and never come here again."

"But you used his land to get here, you walked on it, I saw you."

"Yes, you saw me. But he didn't. He never has and he never will. He can't see me outside this hole."

"What, you make yourself invisible?" I was intrigued.

"To him. He's obsessed and his obsession has blinded him. And I make use of it."

"How?"

"Some other time." He dismissed my inquiry without explanation.

I pressed him from another direction. "I suppose you could climb into this rock from the side of the sea - when he was not looking."

"Oh, yes? Try it - be my guest."

I glanced over to that side only to confirm how dangerous such an enterprise would have been.

"Anyway, he could've seen you when you went to get the figs just now."

"Ah, but you are wrong. First of all, he couldn't have seen me because the figs were on a side of the rock which was out of his view. And then, was I really out of the hole?"

"Of course you were!"

"Okay, show me."

I was puzzled. I didn't know what he was driving at. I'd seen him get out of the opening to get the figs.

"Go on. Humour me."

I got up and walked to where the figs used to be kept, then turned round to face him, standing outside the opening in the hot sun.

"Good," he said. "Are you in or out of the opening."

"Out, of course."

"Show me," he insisted.

"What do you mean? How?"

"Show me where the inside finishes and the outside begins."

I walked towards the opening and looked around its edges searching for some more or less defining boundaries, some indications on the rock that pointed out the mouth of the opening. It wasn't as easy as I had thought it would be. Had it been a man-made opening, such as a doorway for instance, there would be clear edges, like a door frame. But this was an opening created by nature. The wind and the waves that made this hole also worked on its edges, if ever there were any, and rounded them off.

I fumbled around, stood back and then approached again. I did this a few times but every time I thought I was getting there I could see that my judgment was arbitrary. I could not find exact signs to help me decide, to be absolutely certain of the boundaries of the opening. I could see him out of the corner of my eye smirking but being patient. After a while I made a decision, fully aware that it was arbitrary. I wanted to see his reaction.

"There," I said, sweeping with my hand down one side at the edge of the opening.

"Where?" he asked, and walked over to me. "Where?"

"Here." I brushed with my hand down on the rock in a curved movement to indicate the edge.

As my hand came to rest on a small protrusion on the rock at the end of the gesture, he placed his hand on mine and asked:

"Are you sure it's here and not here?" and moved my hand a few centimetres to the right. "Or here?" and moved it a little to the left. "Or here?" and moved my hand quite a distance to the outside.

He took a step back and waited. I could see that any one of those positions was as good as any other, so I gave it one more try.

"Well, approximately around here," I said pointing to a mid-point between the left and right positions he had picked out with my hand.

"Pooh," he exclaimed. "This is a cop-out, and you know it. You are supposed to define the boundaries of this opening not offer me an approximation."

I stood back and took another look.

"Well I can't," I admitted, and followed him back into the hole.

It was beginning to dawn on me now that the landowner's claim to the rock was not really important, not even relevant. The landowner himself and all his arguments and swearing may have been a figment, a ruse, a trick like some of the other tricks old Yiannis had been playing on me. Was I getting paranoid?

"So, have you given up already?" he turned and asked me as we stood close to the other end of the doughnut hole facing the mound. He was smirking again.

"Who gives a damn about it?! It's just a hole in the rock, for crying out loud!" I exclaimed, betraying my frustration.

"Oh, yes, it's easy for you to say, but if the landowner accepts my challenge I must be able to argue my case."

He appeared serious about it but I could feel him giggling to himself underneath. He was pushing me and I didn't know how to respond.

"Come on. You're the one with the definitions."

Ah, that's what he was driving at: definitions. I pondered for a beat or two and then went and sat on my bench. He stood facing me from outside the opening.

"There are definitions and definitions. Some are more difficult than others," I responded, hedging my bets.

"Another cop-out," he said, and returned to his bench.

I thought of giving him examples but he spoke before I did.

"What's a definition?" he asked.

Now, I could do that. That was easy. "Definition is the distinction of one thing or concept from others, stating the nature or meaning of something."

"Good. Now, what's this?" he asked and slapped gently the bench he was sitting on.

"A bench."

"Define it for me."

"A flat surface on which you can sit."

"Okay. But I can also use it to sleep on. Right?"

"Right."

"Or eat from, as a table."

"Yes...?"

"Or I could break it up and use it as fuel, or throw it in the sea and use it as a raft, or place it down there below and use it as a bridge to cross over to the mainland. Right?"

"Okay...?" I could see where he was going.

"So this plank of wood which you have just defined as a bench for sitting on is also a bed, a table, a raft, a bridge as well as fuel to keep me warm in the winter or cook my food."

As I said, I could see where he was going. "True. What's your point?"

"My point is that definitions, like the boundaries of the hole in this rock, are convenient concepts arising from usage. Concepts themselves are convenient tools and so are definitions. They are loose, transformable, expandable and expendable. They are constructions for our use, they are our tools, we are the masters who use them. We can alter them or dispose of them."

He stopped and waited for me to say something. I didn't feel the need to contribute, I was happy to follow his line of argument. Seeing that I was not responding, he picked up again.

"But instead of using them as tools, people in general allow the process of defining and conceptualising to run amok. So much so that it takes over their lives. The world becomes populated by things and concepts, we ourselves become *things* and *concepts*."

He stopped again as if to gather his thoughts, to direct his explanations in a way that I might be able more readily to follow. For the first time I thought I sensed a whiff of sadness in his demeanour, or maybe I was projecting my own feelings.

"It's an aspect of the human condition," he continued, "part of the need to itemise, pigeonhole, separate, make individual and unique. Which is fine, imperative in fact, for survival in a three-dimensional world, but it gets out of hand and people end up being obsessed with and by it - which is undoubtedly a hindrance when it comes to loosening one's boundaries, to breaking up one's ego, the ego itself, of course, being another construction, and obstruction."

I felt the need to interject. "What about natural definitions?"

"Like what?"

"Like species. Humans, for instance, and the variety of animal and plant species."

"Fine. But are you sure their boundaries are clear and well defined, and their functions unique to themselves? And they're not constructions of the human mind which itself is a construction?" He looked at me and waited for a beat or two. "Go back to *knowing*," he added.

Was he brushing me off? It was easy for him to say that but would it be possible for me to do it, to go back to 'knowing' under my own steam, unaided? I caught him glancing over to the mound.

"Poor guy."

"Who?"

"The landowner. If he doesn't snap out of it while he is still alive, after he dies he'll end up haunting this rock. And he'll be haunted by his own obsessions, his very own Erinyes."

Then, all of a sudden, he asked me the time. I looked at my wrist watch. It was two o'clock in the afternoon. No, surely that couldn't be right. It was two when I got in the water, and that was ages ago. Automatically, I shook my wrist, although I could see clearly that the watch was working. It must have stopped at some point while I was in the sea. But it was waterproof, and I had swum with it many times before. Then I remembered hitting it against a rock as I climbed down from the mound to the small makeshift bridge. Oh, well, whatever.

"I'm sorry but my watch is playing up," I said apologetically.

"No matter," he said and glanced at the open sea. Then, in a decisive movement, he slapped his thigh near the knee with his right hand saying "Enough" and stood up. "I don't know about you but I'm dying for a cup of coffee," he added, and walked towards the rickety platform.

I followed him outside wondering what he might be up to this time.

He stood at the edge for a second or two and then dived in. As before, when I saw him climbing down the mound, he was supple and agile like an athletic teenager. He made a most wonderful dive. He bent his knees and sprang into the air, making a beautiful arc as he angled his waist inwards and then stretched outwards, with arms and legs closed and pointing, and hit the water with the quietest of entries. Olympic divers would have been envious.

I waited for him to surface in a straight line from where he had dived but he didn't. Instead, he came up somewhere to the left, towards the promontory and at some considerable distance. As he surfaced he waved his hand and shouted "Go back". He waved his hand a few more times in a way that seemed as if he were pointing to the other side of the mound, to the beach. I wasn't sure. I watched him swimming for a few more seconds before returning to my bench.

I needed to sit down. My knees were shaking and my solar plexus shimmering with a mixture of excitement and apprehension. I felt I should have stayed out there and watched him, making sure he did not just swim away and disappear into the open sea, but my knees couldn't hold me. And I was not certain about his saying "Go back". Did he mean that I should go back to the beach, perhaps to the restaurant at the end of the beach to have coffee with him, perhaps a meal? Or, did he mean that I should try and return to the 'knowing' state?

Another possibility rose in my mind, or, more accurately, in my solar plexus and my heart, a possibility that was turning into certainty. It had begun when he slapped his thigh and said "enough" and that he was "dying for a cup of coffee." His voice was different, and the whole scene at that juncture was the signature of the Teacher, a man of amazing spiritual and healing powers who lived back home, on an island in the Mediterranean, and was well-known for his abilities and teachings. It wasn't as if old Yiannis were imitating him. It was more like the one inhabiting the body of the other, although I couldn't tell who was inhabiting whose body?

As I reflected on that, the shimmering in my solar plexus began to turn into a pleasant tickling sensation that rose up towards my heart, and I started to shake with a full, gurgling, childlike laughter. In my head I could also hear old Yiannis laughing and saying teasingly "who's inhabiting whom?" and "mind your definitions!" I lay back and laughed and laughed. I was strangely happy, and filled with love, love that came to me by the sheer presence of the Teacher. Was Yiannis telling me to "go back" to the 'teachings', perhaps re-examine them? He'd made enough references, albeit oblique most of the time, by saying that I was 'ready' and that I 'knew'.

There were stacks of questions I wanted to ask; I had to catch up with him, hopefully on the other side, and bombard him with them. I picked myself up, still laughing, put the remaining figs back to their cooling place in the sea and headed for the beach and the restaurant.

As I climbed to the top of the mound I saw the landowner sitting under a tree high up on the hill that stretched beyond the mound. He was looking towards the mound and the rock, shaking a hand threateningly. Ah, was this perhaps the reason why old Yiannis had taken to the sea instead of walking over the mound? Was the landowner taking the old man's challenge seriously? I found the whole thing so ridiculously funny that I had to watch my step to make sure I didn't trip and fall down the cliff - I was laughing so hard!

At the foot of the mound, at one end of the beach, I picked up my shirt and trousers from where I'd left them and slipped my sandals on. The sand was as hot as ever, maybe hotter than when I'd left the beach earlier. The sun didn't look like it had moved from its zenith, and it was beating down mercilessly on those three tourists who were lying on their towels in the same position they were earlier. Somebody ought to tell them about skin cancer. Or maybe they were already toasted dead. They lay there motionless.

As I walked past them on my way to the restaurant at the other end of the beach, one of them showed signs of life; she moved, and asked me the time. I glanced at my watch out of habit and told her that it was ten minutes past two but that she shouldn't take it as gospel truth since my watch was on the blink. She thanked me and said that the time sounded about right. I asked her if she'd been in the sun too long and whether she had a sunstroke and lost track of time. She laughed and said that she'd only been on the beach a few minutes but she wanted to know when the little ferries which carried people to and from the island were coming. (These were small motorised boats carrying about ten to twelve passengers at a time). I said at four o'clock and moved on.

She was very attractive and I was tempted to stay and chat - a national obligation for young Greek men in the summer! - but I wanted to get to the restaurant to wait for old Yiannis and pick up where we'd left off.

– 3 –

Yiannis the Evangelist (?)
(On Suspicion of Being a Healer)

I went up the few steps from the beach and sat at a table under a tree in the bare-ground courtyard of the restaurant. There were a few other customers having a meal, mostly foreign tourists. I was surprised by the fact that the restaurant was serving lunch this late.

A boy, most likely the son or nephew of the owner, was tending to a couple at a nearby table and when I caught his eye I waved him over. I asked him how late they served lunch. He said they would be stopping pretty soon, at two thirty. I asked him the time, he looked at his watch and said it was quarter past two, which was the same as my watch!

I felt disorientated. It couldn't have been quarter past two. At two o'clock I was still swimming in the sea. From there to the doughnut hole it would have taken five to ten minutes. Then I walked down to the beach on my way back and when I told the tourist girl the time it was ten minutes past, according to my 'faulty' watch which now turned out not to be so faulty.

Even if I assumed that going to the hole took only five minutes and coming down to the beach after my meeting with Yiannis another five minutes, which was really pushing it, it would have meant that I spent no time at all in the doughnut hole!

I began to take deep breaths to stop myself from falling apart. The boy became concerned and asked me if I was alright. I didn't want to draw attention to myself so I said I was fine and quickly ordered a Greek salad and a coffee. The boy left with a puzzled look on his face.

I continued to take deep breaths, timing carefully the four parts of the process: slowly in, hold, slowly out, hold, all to a particular count, using the diaphragm with as much control as I could possibly muster. Eventually, I brought myself together. Luckily, the tourists were too involved, lazily drinking their cold beer in the shade of the restaurant trees and talking among themselves, to pay any attention to me. After placing my order, the boy got busy clearing the tables for the afternoon break. Everything looked normal. And I was pretty certain I was fully awake.

Or was I? How could I tell? One way would be to wake myself up. Ah, but there's the rub. Waking up might only mean waking into another dream that looked and felt like wakefulness - not the first time that such a thing had happened. But I always woke up in the end, and it never lasted very long. Perhaps I should wait. It had only been fifteen minutes since..... What was I saying?! If I were in a dream, clock time couldn't be relied on as evidence for anything - it is notoriously elastic and could be made to fit any series of events.

I searched desperately for an answer. Then I hit on an idea: in a dream I could make things behave in a way that I could not do when awake. Human beings were not always easy to affect but I could do lots of things with so-called inanimate objects and with plants and animals.

Right. I didn't have to look far. The restaurant cat was meandering under my table hoping for a morsel. I concentrated on him and tried to make him grow bigger. In a dream this would be accomplished in no time. But the damn cat wouldn't oblige. In fact, after a while, he looked at me with some disdain, hissed, turned his back, raised his tail and moved to another table. Was I not in a dream, then? Not necessarily so.

Perhaps for most people so-called wakeful reality and dream reality are fairly well demarcated, even though there are situations when the boundaries are breached and blurred. Very vivid dreams intrude into wakefulness in extraordinary ways. You may wake up from such a dream and carry its vividness with you all day to the extent that it becomes accepted by your wakeful reality as an integral part of it; I mean, to a degree that it is incorporated as wakeful memory, not as memory of a dream.

On other occasions, the dream reality continues into wakefulness with the same intensity that it displayed in the dream, in which case it becomes wellnigh impossible to dismiss it as mere dream; in terms of reality sense it is on a par with wakefulness. And what of those occasions when both realities are running in parallel and you end up dreaming while awake and being awake while dreaming? As for reality testing, well--

"Excuse me, mister. Would you like potato chips or boiled greens with your fish?"

It was the boy from the restaurant cutting into my reverie - dream, daydream, whatever? He was asking me if I.... What on earth...?

"Sorry. What did you say?" I asked very puzzled.

He repeated his question. I couldn't understand what he was talking about. I hadn't ordered any fish, and I told him so - only the salad and the coffee. He insisted that I had. Earlier on, he said, fifteen minutes ago. And he went in to get his uncle, the restaurant owner. I shrugged my shoulders dismissively. Was he drunk? He didn't look it. He was only about ten years old, anyway.

The uncle came over to ask me why I had cancelled the order. They'd gone to a great deal of trouble, he said. Apparently, I'd ordered fish but because they'd run out of fresh fish they offered me frozen fish which I accepted. I was then told that it would take a while to defrost it and grill it, and so I decided to go for a dip in the sea while they were preparing it. I sat on that very same chair that I was sitting on now when I ordered the fish.

I was confused. I had no memory of such things but I didn't want to argue. It was a very small restaurant, more of a local taverna, really, family-run which in all probability functioned only a few months in the year to cater for tourists, and the fish they cooked for me would have been a rather costly item to them. Besides, with everything else going on, I could easily have forgotten, although I wouldn't dare admit it to myself. But it would have been embarrassing to insist that I had no memory of ordering a meal fifteen minutes earlier!

I apologised and said that I was only pulling the boy's leg and that I would like boiled greens with my fish, please. We all laughed that the boy had fallen for such an obvious practical joke (!).

They went back to their duties and I sat there feeling devastated. How could I possibly have forgotten? I racked my brains trying to remember but to no avail. I had a go at word and then visual association. Nothing. Of course I knew that trying to remember something by exerting excessive effort is exactly what you shouldn't do when you want to remember. But when you panic you don't always do the right thing. Such is the nature of panic: jamming the circuits the wrong way.

So, I calmed down and changed my approach. I relaxed. I fixed my sights on the trunk of the tree in front of me, concentrated my

attention to where I was at that moment and filled it with my presence. I stayed in that position until my vision changed.

Swirling clouds of colours obscured everything in front of me. I
closed my eyes and the colours continued to swirl. All the sounds
around me, including the conversations of the tourists, became crisp
and clear. I concentrated on the swirling colours and emptied my
mind of all concerns. Various pictures and sounds popped into my
head which I ackowledged and then ignored.

After a while I opened my eyes and cast a look around casually,
without intent, without purpose, keeping my mind relaxed and undirected. People were still sitting at their tables eating, drinking and
chatting. The cicadas continued to sizz-sizz as before. I turned and
looked at the sea and let my eyes drift aimlessly on its calm surface
until they came to rest on a chair to my left, almost behind me.

There, on the chair, lay my snorkle and mask. I'd left them there
before I went for a dip because I wanted to swim for a while and
then get to where I had left my clothes on the beach. I did that instead of walking along the beach because it was more pleasant that
way. I needed to go to my clothes in order to get the money for the
meal.

But I was enjoying the sea so much, swimming on the surface
and underwater, delighted by the view of the land and the sea and
the sky.... The sun was scorching. A gentle breeze brought down
from the mountainside the scent of resin from the cypress trees, a
whiff of thyme descended from the mound....

Aaah, my memory was being restored! Yes, I had ordered fish,
and they had had to defrost it. Oh, I felt ever so apologetic for the
hassle I'd caused. But more important than that, I needed answers
both to my temporary loss of memory - and severe it was - and to
the fact that I had an experience which, according to clock time, had
not taken place. Normally, dreams and hallucinations of a particular
type might fit into that category. And I hadn't decided yet that I was
not dreaming or hallucinating.

I looked out to the sea in the direction of the promontory to see
how far out old Yiannis still was. In addition to those pending from
the doughnut hole, I would now have to ask him questions concerning dreams and hallucinations - provided, of course, that he himself
was not a hallucination! I couldn't see him anywhere. The promontory wasn't that long. He should have been not far from the restaur-

ant by now, if not here with me already - if by shouting "go back" he had really meant for me to return to this place and wait for him.

I was diverted from these concerns by the arrival of the boy who brought my food. He carried all of it in one go on a big tray. He looked as if he wanted to finish with serving lunch as soon as possible. I was his last customer and he surely didn't want anybody else turning up after me. Some of his friends had already arrived and gathered around a table under a tree, sounding very excited. I heard them talking about the boat they were taking out to sail to the other side of the island. They were between the ages of ten and sixteen. I apologised to the boy again for the joke. He said that it was okay but he also threatened to pay me back in the same coin. He laughed and went to join his friends.

As I began to eat, it occurred to me that these kids, being local, might provide some information about Yiannis and his activities. They might also act as some kind of check against the theory that I was still hallucinating! Unless they themselves were also... Oh, no, I had to stop this paranoia!

I cast one more searching look towards the sea and then dug in. The fish was worth waiting for. The boiled greens, known as "mountain greens", are a Greek speciality. They grow wild in the countryside , and the villagers simply go out and gather them - nice with olive oil and lemon. I suddenly discovered that, along with my memory, I'd also recovered my appetite. I was starving: I hadn't eaten anything substantial since seven that morning, and even that was only a slice of cheese and toast. I should have waited for Yiannis, but cold boiled greens and cold grilled fish would have been a waste - well, that was my justification, anyway. He would be welcome to my Greek salad.

I beckoned the boy to come over, which he did, but I could tell from the look on his face that he wasn't particularly thrilled to be torn away from his friends. He'd undoubtedly thought he'd been finished and done with me for the day. I explained that I didn't call him over for more fetching and carrying but simply to ask him about old Yiannis. He said that he knew of the man but that the older boys could tell me more, and he called them over. A sixteen year old was quite forthcoming with information.

"Oh yes. We know him, alright. He's a right old bastard!"

And they all broke out into a scornful sort of laughter.

I was very surprised both by their lack of respect for someone so much older than themselves and because I couldn't see how they could justify this kind of judgment. I'd grown to like and respect old Yiannis. Had they called him strange or weird I would have had no argument, allowing for the possible fact that due to their age they wouldn't have known him that well.

"Why did you call him that?" I inquired.

"Because that's what he is. Ask anyone."

"Yiannis the bloody Baptist!" shouted one of the other boys, and they all had another bout of laughter.

Now, this was going a bit too far. The name 'Yiannis' is Greek for John, and for a boy in a closely-knit Christian community to call someone "John the bloody Baptist" was shockingly irreligious, and I querried that with him.

"It's not me, mister," he retorted, "it's the grown-ups who gave him the nickname."

"Why?" I asked.

"Because of what he does," he answered.

And before I had a chance to ask what it was he did, one of the boys volunteered that information.

"He throws them into the sea. Off the cliff."

"Throws whom off the cliff?" I asked really puzzled now.

The sixteen year old explained. "Whoever he catches on his land. Over there," he said, pointing to the mound and the promontory. "He chucks them over and they get baptised in the sea."

"Mind you, he has to catch them first, the nasty little squab!" said the restaurant boy.

"Lucky he's not around that much. He's abroad a lot," added another boy and then stood up and started imitating a bullfighter using a paper napkin to provoke an imaginary bull and calling out "Torro! Torro!"

"Mind your hat, mister!" a boy called out, addressing the 'bullfighter'.

"And watch out for the birds that nest in it!" added another.

The merriment was contagious. We all laughed. It was obvious now that they were referring to the landowner with the mean character and the big sombrero who, to my confusion, had the same name as the old man I'd met in the doughnut hole.

I explained to them who it was I was actually asking about, and described him in some detail.

"Oh, you mean Yiannis the Evangelist," exclaimed the sixteen year old. "Well, that's a totally different Yiannis. He is a very nice old man, nice and pleasant and friendly, not like the Baptist."

"Why is he called the Evangelist?" I asked.

"I'm not sure. Like the other one, he is not around a lot. I've only seen him twice myself. But when he is around and people happen to have fights or arguments he always reconciles them. He talks a lot about loving your neighbour."

"But not like a priest," another boy added.

"That's true," agreed the sixteen year old. "When the priest talks about loving your neighbour it's like, you know," he glanced around furtively, leant forward and lowered his voice before completing his sentence: "bullshit." The other boys giggled cheekily. "But when the Evangelist says the same things, it's different. You believe him. And you understand exactly what it means to love your neighbour. He's a bit strange, but nice."

The other kids nodded in agreement. I was quite impressed, and moved, by this testimony, and glad to agree with them.

I told them that I'd met him a little while ago in the doughnut hole but I gave them no details of the meeting except for the encounter with the Baptist and the latter's threats. They laughed.

"A lot of barking but no biting," said the sixteen year old. "He's scared shitless of the Evangelist. I bet he wouldn't go near you either because he saw you with him."

"Why is he afraid of old Yiannis?" I asked.

"I don't know. I don't think anybody knows," said the boy, shrugging his shoulders.

"My uncle might know," ventured the restaurant boy.

His uncle was standing at the door of the restaurant leaning against the frame, relaxing and looking casually across the courtyard, taking the air one might say. I said that I would like to talk to his uncle about this, and then looked out to the sea again and told the boys about old Yiannis swimming round the promontory and taking so long to appear on this side of it.

They all showed genuine concern and spontaneously decided to get in their boat and go search for him. I agreed, thanked them and encouraged them. They were brimming with youthful excitement at the prospect of adventure for a good cause.

The uncle looked on smiling benevolently and understandingly at the exuberance of the boys and called out to them to be careful around the reef. I caught his eye and beckoned him over.

"Kids!" he said as if to justify their effusiveness, and then looked at my salad with some surprise as he approached my table. "But you haven't eaten your salad. Something wrong?"

"Oh, no. No, there is nothing wrong with the salad. It's just that...ehm... Would you mind joining me for a few minutes?"

"No, of course not," he said, eager to please a customer. He cast quick glances towards the restaurant door, the other customers and then at the boys who were clambering enthusiastically into the boat, before sitting down opposite me.

"You've just lost a good waiter," I said, "and it's probably my fault. I'm sorry."

"No, don't say that. He's a lovely boy and enthusiastic but not much of a waiter."

"I'm sorry but I must disagree. He's a marvellous waiter," I said, not wanting to put the boy down and trying to repair some of the damage I thought I'd possibly caused earlier.

"Oh, yes?" he said with a reprimanding smile. "D'you know what he did yesterday?"

"No, what?"

"Listen to this. I'm out at the back tending to the animals - you know, we have a goat and a couple of pigs, nothing much - and two customers come in. They want fried eggs. He doesn't call me, he decides to do them himself. Do you understand? - enthusiastic. So, he fries the eggs, serves them, here at this table," he says, tapping at the table, "and then goes and joins his friends over there," he says pointing to the other end of the courtyard. "A few minutes later the customers are spitting and calling him over. When he arrives they complain to him that they found eggshells in their fried eggs. D'you know what the little rotter said to them?"

"No, what?" I responded with some anticipation.

"He said: 'You called me all the way down here, away from my friends, just because of a few eggshells?' and he turns and goes back to his friends! Now, I ask you, do you call this being a good waiter?"

We stared at each other for a few seconds, watching each other's face to see who was going to go first, and then, perfectly synchronised, we burst out laughing.

He was a good-natured man, the uncle, middle-aged, totally bald, of average height with a developing waist. He introduced himself as Bob. His actual name was Thrasyvoulos, a perfectly good Greek name, which, because it was too long for them to pronounce, the northern Europeans of Australia changed it to Bob. After a spell in Melbourne, he repatriated but the new name had stuck with him mostly because his friends and neighbours back home found it extremely funny. We agreed on that.

It's a Greek thing; monosyllabic names are very unusual in Greece and quite amusing, and 'Bob' had an extra funny ring to it. We laughed at the sounds of some other ordinary monosyllabic English names like 'Pat', 'Dick', 'Jill', 'Jack'. It's a Greek thing. Greeks often isolate the sound from the meaning by repeating the name thus making it sound funny. Take 'Pat', for instance: it becomes pat-pat-pat-pat-pat-pat which is made to sound like someone tapping on a window or an engine chugging away. Or dick-dick-dick-dick-dick.....

Anyway, after this elementary sort of bonding, Bob asked me why I thought I was to blame for his nephew taking off with the other boys the way he had done. When I explained to him the situation with Yiannis he agreed that the boys were doing the right thing but that I shouldn't be too worried about the old man.

"The old boy has the habit of doing that. Appearing and disappearing in front of your very eyes. You get used to it. He'll surface somewhere." He sounded so casual.

"What do you mean? Where?"

"Ooh, I don't know. Somewhere. In the village, perhaps. Or in Athens. On some island. Who knows? Eat your salad, my friend, he's not going to turn up here."

"How do you know? How can you be so sure?"

"Because that's what he does." He stopped and looked out to where the boys were sailing. "It's good for the boys, though. It concentrates their energies and hones them morally. I shouldn't be surprised if he did all this just for their benefit."

"What?"

He turned back towards me again and spoke to me as in confidence.

"Look, you've just met him, you don't know him. Actually, nobody knows him, come to think of it. As I said, he appears and disappears. Sometimes while you're talking to him. You turn your back for a second and, poof, he's gone."

I was getting confused again. These people seemed to know Yiannis and yet not know him. I wanted to find out more about him, where he came from, where he lived, what he did for a living if he was still working, if he had any relatives....

"Yes, I believe he still works. Buying and selling something or other. Up in Athens. But nobody knows where he comes from for sure. Some say from up north, others from Crete or Egypt or somewhere else. We don't even know if he is Greek. If you ask him he'll probably say that it's not relevant, and leave it at that. He's got a sister in the village."

"Ah, that's great! Maybe I should pay her a visit. D'you have her address?" This was great news. I felt really excited about it.

"I'll tell you where she lives, but I don't think she's going to be much help either. She's just as dismissive when it comes to personal information."

"But why? Why so secretive?"

"I don't know. They're not really secretive, they just don't care about personal chit-chat."

"Is that where he stays when he's in the village?"

"Sometimes. Rarely, actually.

"Where does he stay, then? In a hotel?"

"Oh, no. People put him up. Other times, we don't know. You see him in the day, but as for the night it's anybody's guess." He leant forward and whispered. "Maybe he's got a secret mistress."

"Really?" Whether he was being serious or not he got me intrigued now.

"Who knows," he said, shrugging his shoulders. "Half of the men in the village are away at sea most of the time. Maybe... Who knows?" He was smiling cheekily.

"You're kidding, aren't you?"

"I told you, I don't know. He looks old but...." He hesitated for a beat or two and then straightened himself, sat upright and went quiet. More intrigue.

"What? But what?"

He leant forward again.

"He stayed here once," he whispered and indicated his house behind the restaurant. "He's a healer, you know." He said this as if he were letting me into a very important secret.

"What do you mean - like a doctor?" I said leaning forward to join him in this 'conspiracy'. Why conspiracy?

"Oh, no. He's not a doctor - he's a healer, a spiritual healer."

"Ah, I see. Like a priest or a psychiatrist."

"No, no! None of that. He's a healer, laying-on-of-hands kind of healer."

"Oh, I get you now."

The penny dropped at last. The problem was that the Greek for healer, like the original English, encompasses all types of healing, from physical to psychological to spiritual, whatever the latter might mean. It all sounded very exciting but why the conspiratorial behaviour?

"Are you kidding? If the priests got wind of this he'll be excommunicated."

I recognised the threat. The Teacher had the same problem back home and had to watch his step.

"But why? He's not doing anything untoward, is he?" I inquired.

"No, but...but..." He stopped and glanced around furtively. "Look, you're a stranger in these parts. You met him once, you may not see him again. Would you promise to keep it under your hat?"

"Keep what under my hat?" The man was not making sense.

He drew closer and whispered again. "He's a miracle-worker. He performs miracles. Right?"

"Miracles? What kind of miracles?"

"I told you, he's a healer. Look: last year my grandson, my daughter's child, nearly died. He had cancer in the liver. My god, he's hardly four! We'd been everywhere. There was nothing anybody could do. The doctors in Athens gave him only a couple of months to live. The whole village was devastated by the news, not to mention the family. I persuaded my daughter and my son-in-law to come and stay with us. They have nobody else in Athens - that's where they live. We...."

He stopped. I could see he was getting emotional. He sniffled, took a deep breath and continued.

"Anyway, to cut a long story short, Yiannis happened to be around. He popped in to say hello. Nobody in the village had seen him for weeks, months I should say. We were having coffee in the restaurant and the child walked in. He was not supposed to, he was feeling so bad he was bedridden.

"But there he was. He walked in and when he saw Yiannis his face lit up and went straight to him greeting him with 'Hello, uncle Yiannis', as if he were expecting him to be there. You understand we are not blood-related, the *uncle* was just courtesy. And the child had never met him before. He went and sat on Yiannis' lap and introduced him as his 'best friend, uncle Yiannis'!"

He stopped to bring his emotions under control with a couple of deep breaths before he continued. For my part, I was thrilled. I wanted to ask him a few questions but I didn't want to interrupt the flow of his narration. I just eased him forward a bit.

"What did Yiannis do?"

"Nothing much. He chatted with the boy for a while. They laughed quite a bit, like old friends, and then he said that there was nothing wrong with the child. I couldn't believe it. I said:

'What do you mean there is nothing wrong with the child? He's got cancer in his liver!'

'No,' he says. 'He *had* cancer in the liver. Not any more. He's okay now.'

'What do you mean?' I say. We all wanted to believe him, but how?

'Your love saved him,' he says. 'You have all paid your dues,' he says, 'including the child. The doctors will call it spontaneous remission. Whatever. It doesn't matter.'"

"What happened? I asked with obvious anticipation.

It took him a minute or so to respond to my question. He had to wipe the tears off his eyes first.

"Next day the child went back to playing with his friends. Two days after that we took him to the hospital for a check-up. The doctors thought the records had got mixed up. They couldn't find any trace of cancer in his liver. We left them arguing among themselves about spontaneous remission."

The smile returned to Bob's face, and he apologised for being so emotional. I said it was understandable, but I also pointed out to him, as gently as possible, that there was indeed such a thing as spontaneous remission.

"Are you kidding?" he said dismissively. "One minute the boy is condemned to death, unable to even get out of bed, the next minute is up and running as if nothing had happened. Spontaneous, my foot! What do they mean by it, anyway? The child wasn't cured because of any medical treatment. It was a miracle. And Yiannis performed it."

He stopped and cast another quick glance towards his customers. It wasn't clear whether his glance had to do with wanting to keep an eye on his clients in case they wanted more service or to make sure that nobody was within earshot. He returned to whispering again.

"Besides, I watched him. And I saw what he was doing." More intrigue?

"What did he do?"

"While the child was on his lap and they were chatting and laughing, he placed his left hand just above the middle of the child's back and with his right hand he kept rubbing the boy's front between the heart and the tummy. He was tickling and playing with him but I could see he was doing more than that. Ask my daughter, she was there."

He stopped, and seemed uncertain as to whether he should say anything else; but he couldn't contain himself and so he continued with some hesitation.

"You may think I'm crazy for saying this, but I believe I saw his right hand melting into the child's body."

"Did you say *melting*?" This was becoming more exciting than I expected.

"Well, it sort of more or less disappeared inside him. The boy gave a little jolt and lay his head on Yiannis' shoulder looking a bit drowsy. That's when Yiannis said there was nothing wrong with him, and then we decided the child was getting tired and we took him back to bed."

He looked rather uncomfortable for having said this last bit about Yiannis' hand melting into the child's body and he reminded me that I should keep it under my hat.

"You see, if Yiannis was a priest or a bishop or a monk or even a hermit, and he began performing healing miracles, the Church wouldn't have minded, they would have been very happy about it actually.

"But he's not particularly religious, you see. He's got nothing against them, don't get me wrong; in fact, I'd say he's rather friendly with our priest. But he's not a church person. And sometimes he says things about them which can be misconstrued. He's only taking the mickey. And the villagers love him. Both, for what he does for them and for sending up the priesthood."

He chuckled at the memory of something or other.

"Oh, I could tell you stories!" he said.

But much as I would have liked to hear stories about Yiannis and the priesthood - and I could well imagine the character of the stories judging by his behaviour at the doughnut hole - I wanted to hear more about his healing practices, and his possible whereabouts. At the hole there was no direct indication of any healing activities, save for my intuitive, if momentary, attainment of bliss and the direct conduction of love radiating from Yiannis. And, in particular, the sudden connection with the Teacher.

There were interesting, if tenuous, similarities between the two personalities, especially in their ambiguous relationship with the Church. They both avoided confrontation, but whereas the Teacher sought conciliation and compromise, Yiannis, from what I'd heard, avoided too close a contact and even poked fun at the clergy, albeit under the guise of good-natured humour.

The Teacher's approach was designed to prevent confrontation which might have led to alienating the people he was aiming to help. Yiannis seemed to have chosen to keep his distance. Was his admonition to love one's neighbour perhaps an attempt at keeping the Church happy and out of his way? He seemed to have enough tricks up his sleeve and I wouldn't have put it past him to entertain the clergy with a pulling-the-wool-over-their-eyes kind of joke. But that would have been cruel, and cruelty wasn't something I detected in his character. Besides, the love and affection he engendered was clearly genuine.

And now, the revelation regarding Yiannis' healing activities brought these two people, Yiannis and the Teacher, closer together - in addition to Yiannis' 'imitation' of the Teacher at the doughnut hole which had already created an early connection and an extra puzzle for me to solve.

But my immediate concerns were to find out how extensive Yiannis' healing practices were, and how he justified them. And where I could find him. I also needed to know how genuine his healing was. I shelved this latter question for later, not wanting to appear too critical at this stage or give the impression that I was casting aspersions on Yiannis' character - seeing that Bob was so convinced of Yiannis' miraculous healing abilities.

So I began by asking him if he knew of other healing cases involving Yiannis. He hesitated. He wanted to make certain I did not lump Yiannis together with all those so-called psychics, channellers, magicians, new-agers and the other "charlatans" that happened to be infesting the area. I assured him that the idea couldn't be further from my mind.

He proceeded to enumerate various cases of cancer - breast, throat, skin, prostate - as well as ulcers, eye and ear diseases, and accidents in which bones were broken. Most of these were children but there were also adults. All of them cured by the miraculous powers of Yiannis. Interestingly enough, all could be explained by spontaneous remission. All, that is, except for the instantaneous reconstruction and healing of bone fractures. It was hard to account for the instantaneous mending of broken bones by invoking spontaneous remission! Bob said he'd witnessed one such case.

"The child fell off his bicycle and broke his leg. You could see the bone sticking out. He fell down right in front of me. Yiannis was sitting outside the café having his coffee when it happened."

"What did he do?"

"I dropped the shopping I was carrying and went to the boy's help. I could see the bone sticking out. I touched it. It was almost coming through the skin. I didn't know what to do."

"What about Yiannis? What did *he* do?"

"Yiannis jumped across from the café, went down on one knee, grabbed the boy's broken leg, one part of the broken bone in each hand, pulled them out and then brought them back together and joined them. Then he ran his hands over the leg a few times, like he was stroking the child's leg. Like this."

He turned to one side, cocked up a leg and began to stroke it by way of demonstrating Yiannis' action.

"*Then* what happened?" I asked, being more interested in the event than watching Bob stroking his hairy leg!

"He helped the boy up, patted him on the head, smiled at him and sent him off."

"How did the boy behave?"

"Got back on his bike and rode off. As if nothing had happened." He stopped and looked at me momentarily before adding a dusting of sarcasm: "Spontaneous remission!"

I ignored the small dose of sarcasm and continued with my questions.

"Are you sure the bone was broken?" I said, not realising he might take offence.

"What do you mean? Am I making this up?!"

I had to explain that no offence was intended, that I was simply making sure. He reassured me that there was no doubt about the boy's broken bone, and added that he himself had a leg broken when he was a child and knew very well what a broken bone looked and felt like. And he proceeded to cock up the other hairy leg to point where the fracture had taken place. I conceded that he was right, and thus cut short the hairy leg display! And pressed on with my inquiries.

"How does Yiannis explain these miracles?"

"He doesn't call them miracles."

"Okay, but what does he say about them?"

"All kinds of things. Sometimes he says that such things happen because the dues have been paid - I don't know what he means by that, and he doesn't bother to explain. Other times, he talks about love, that love burns up the debt. I'm not sure about this either, but I understand that the love of one person can lift the pain off another person - like the love of a parent can lighten the pain of a child."

"As in the case of your grandson?" I asked.

He stopped to reflect for a moment.

"I suppose so, yes. But only to an extent; the cure itself was a miracle. Nearly always he talks of love when he does such things. Sometimes he tells people to watch out because the illness will return if they don't love, especially if they fill themselves with hate. The priests can't get a handle on this. He says that to heal the body you must heal the mind. But he doesn't push people, he just tells them and leaves them alone to work things out for themselves."

"Has he ever had any failures? You know, cases where his healing didn't work?"

He appeared to be thinking for a few seconds, trying to remember a case, then he shook his head.

"No. I can't think of any. There might be but I personally never heard of any."

Some customers at a table were trying to draw his attention, they wanted to pay their bill. He told them he'd be with them in a second and then asked me if I needed anything from the restaurant because he'd be finishing for now, for the midday rest. I didn't want anything and so I settled my bill and asked him for the address of Yiannis' sister.

Before giving it to me he made me promise again to consider all he had said as confidential and not to pass around any of it. He said that he was now doing this as a request from Yiannis who didn't want journalists seeking him out, pestering the villagers with stupid intruding questions and ruining their lives. I understood his concern and gave him my promise. Yiannis' secretive attitude began to make more sense now, much more sense than the reason given earlier regarding the Church and the priesthood.

Only, it made me feel guilty for having to conceal from him the fact that I myself was a journalist - well, freelance. But I comforted myself with the counter-fact that I had no plans to send anything to the newspapers - and, after all, it was Yiannis himself who had approached me first.

"The same applies to the address of the sister, Yianna," he added. "He doesn't want journalists and other strangers descending on her and disturbing her privacy. You promise not to pass it around?"

"I promise."

I felt as if I were taking an oath, 'cross my heart and hope to die' in a literal sense with all its serious repercussions! And the address proved to be no address at all! Being a small place, there were no street names, something I hadn't noticed before. Her house was at the other end of the village. It was now a matter of following directions, like turning left at the kiosk, going up to the square, turning right at the third tree on the left, past the barber shop!.....

I thanked Bob, shook hands with him, and promised to see him again soon. He said he liked my company and his door would always be open to me. And I think he meant it, not merely as a customer but as a friend. When I said I'd decided to walk along the shore back to the village instead of waiting for a boat, he gave me a bottle of water and a hat to protect me from the sun. I left with a feeling of warmth inside me, and it wasn't because of the heat.

The walk back turned out to be longer than I expected. I was tempted to veer off to the left, away from the shore and into the lemon groves, perhaps go up to the café at the top edge of the groves on the mountainside. I'd gone there once before and had a most wonderful experience. But it was a long way and it was too hot, and even the donkeys that normally took tourists up there were given a break. I saw the poor things resting in the shade of a tree.

I walked for a while admiring the view on my right. Beyond a few hundred metres of water there rose the island. Picturesque, with its traditionally white houses nestling on the hillside and its attractive little coves following one another like jewels on a necklace.

The hotel where I was staying with my two travelling companions was itself on the island - I'd met these two guys in Athens a while back, we hit it off, and decided to travel together, but they'd gone off on a hike of their own for the day to round off their holiday as they were flying back home the following day. Most of the tourists stayed on the island, where the majority of tourist hotels and guest houses were to be found, but made occasional excursions to the mainland in the little boats. The locals advertised the place as the Greek Venice, and there were times, especially in the evenings, when it looked a bit like Venice. But not now. Not a boat in sight.

On my left, as I moved along, were olive trees, carob trees, fig trees and the occasional house nestling on the mountainside. I looked for a tree with a good thick shade to sit under for a few minutes. The only ones that fit the bill were fig trees but the ground under them was too messy with fallen and splashed figs - and I didn't exactly fancy the idea of having figs dropping on my head as I sat under a tree!

I found a good-sized carob tree laden with fruit, some green some dark brown, the latter indicating that they were ripe. I picked a couple of the ripe ones, cleared a patch of ground near the trunk of the tree and sat leaning my body against it. I snapped one of the fruit and revealed its harsh, sugary contents. I chewed on it with relish, raising in my mind childhood memories when we went carob picking.

The locals don't think much of this fruit - it's fodder for their pigs. I was reminded of the parable of the prodigal son who ended up eating this stuff to survive. I looked at a neighbouring fig tree and found myself smiling at the thought of being a prodigal. For, there I was, choosing a tree to sit under which was associated with the prodigal son's story, whereas I could be sitting under a fig tree associated with Buddha's enlightenment.

Was my choice of tree subconsciously symbolic, was I perhaps drifting into self-exile, away from the path I had been safely treading? The fig tree was only a few metres away, maybe I should go and sit under it. I mused on the idea for a spell.

Yiannis' last words rang in my ears: "Go back!" This time, however, for some reason I could not fathom, they were accompanied by the opening bars of Beethoven's fifth symphony: ba-ba-ba baaaam, ba-ba-ba baaaam! I had no objection to that as I liked the symphony, one of my favourites. I always found it invigorating and uplifting. Was there a connection?

I was already struggling to see a possible connection with the restaurant and all that had transpired there: the kids and Bob and all they had said about Yiannis' behaviour and his healing activities. Was there a musical clue somewhere? I was aware that those opening notes had stood for fate hammering on the door, an awakening, the force of destiny in action. But I couldn't see the link in my case.

I lay back and enjoyed the symphony as it unfolded. I jumped to the second movement which I'd always been fond of - it touched my finer emotions so deeply. But the opening bars of the first movement kept coming back. I followed the development and relaxed in the shade of the tree, in the middle of the summer, in the heat of the day. After all, tunes pop into your head for no apparent reason, nothing unusual, nothing to be particularly concerned about.

I drifted back to the events of the day, most of which did not even have the status of events seeing that they appeared to have transpired in 'no time'! I had already decided to put out of my mind the possibility that what had taken place in the rock was a dream or a hallucination - I shelved the idea for later consideration, to discuss it with Yiannis when I found him. It seemed that it would serve no purpose at the present, it would merely increase my paranoia. So, I set out to examine the events as facts that had taken place in real time in the physical world.

I made a list, as was my habit, and then ascribed relevant importance and a preliminary explanation to each item. As I did that I utilised psychic insights and forms of understanding I'd already been employing through my previous training in these matters. Yiannis kept reminding me that I was ready, that I should be using the direct method, that he was disappointed when I did not latch on to what he was doing or saying.

I knew what he was talking about, and when I said at some point that I was not prepared what I meant was that he'd taken me by surprise. I was a bit like a soldier who had done his basic battle training and then found himself in a totally unexpected urban guerrilla war. But he was right, I should have been able to switch immediately to the required mode.

Be that as it may, there were occasions when I managed to do just that. But what bothered me were the parts that I could not penetrate. I understood his joke with the crab, even the sensation of seawater coursing through my 'body' when, in fact, I was not in the water. However, I did not understand his ambiguous behaviour towards me; the ambiguity of his own character - being detached and yet caring; my inability to learn more about him even when I was using the direct method - was it inability on my part or great ability on his whereby he blocked my efforts, for whatever reason?

He did say that I lacked the capacity of will and concentrated attention, but, on the other hand, I had no doubts regarding his capabilities: he caused fear as well as warmth and security in me and unbelievable clarity of thought and understanding, and bliss. And now 'Yiannis the healer' added another layer to the man's character, and a tenuous lead to the unravelling of his unconnected exhortation to "go back".

I now felt that I should take this 'admonition' to "go back" as meaning that I should go back to my own experiences and the teachings and activities I had garnered from the Teacher and other sources.

So, I set about retracing some of the key experiences in my life and sought to evaluate and relate them to the present situation.

– 4 –

Searching for Answers
('Screams' and 'Coincidences')

One of my earliest experiences in this area was falling off a cliff unharmed. I was seven years old at the time and we lived for a short spell in my mother's wine producing village, which lay on the higher side of a mountain. We had a large backyard full of vegetable rows and fruit trees. A big fig tree grew at the end of the yard, literally on the lip of a cliff, jutting upwards and outwards over the cliff. I loved climbing up into the fig tree and picking the big delicious fruit.

On a long branch that hung over the cliff were two enormous figs which grew bigger and more delicious-looking by the day. I lusted after them, and one day, I climbed up the tree very carefully but, as I reached out to pick one of them, the branch snapped and tumbled down the cliff with me riding on it. It hit a protruding rock on the cliffside and ejected me.

I found myself flying through the air which, somehow, triggered in me a feeling of invincibility. I had had, you see, numerous 'flying' dreams in which I'd felt unlimited freedom and a sense of empowerment. As I flew through the air down the cliff, I entered this 'dream state' in which I was invincible. The air around me acquired the feel of gentle, caressing and supportive viscosity so that as I hit various rocky protrusions on the way down I felt as if bouncing securely on rubber surfaces. Instead of being scared I was filled with joy and elation for the fact that I was flying.

As I came to land at the bottom of the cliff I chuckled to some invisible but felt company of friends and treated the whole incident as a childish prank. I stood up, dusted myself and went my way home to wash some minor scratches, and find a way to justify to mother the tears in my shirt and shorts.

And when old Yiannis called out to me to remember the fig tree and be careful not to slip and fall on the sharp protrusions of the rock as I got up from the bench and walked over to the crab, this is what he was referring to. His mere call triggered the whole scene in my mind but by checking the imagery I managed to block the event while I retained the 'dreamlike' state of mind which enabled me to stroke the crab without its turning to dig its claws into my hand or scuttle away. The crab raising its legs at me was old Yiannis' joke!

Our family moved around a fair deal those days. Because of this constant move which took us to various inland locations, away from the sea, at the age of eight I was still not proficient at swimming. As we settled, hopefully for good, at a seaport I discovered my true love for the sea. And I was determined to become an expert swimmer. However, it hadn't occurred to me that in order to become a good swimmer I had first to master the art of staying afloat. Again, this probably had something to do with the fact that in my dreams I swam and breathed naturally under water - in the same gentle, caressing and supportive 'viscosity' in which I so often flew.

So, one day I simply jumped off at the deep end of the pier where the depth of the water was twice my height. I dog-paddled, splashing with both arms and legs, but I was clearly no natural canine. I made for a rock, four or five metres away, which reached in height to about thirty centimetres below the surface of the water. As I approached the rock I lowered my hands to grab hold of its top. Unfortunately, I miscalculated my proximity to the rock and found myself half a metre too short of it.

As I began to sink I splashed violently with my arms and legs, but everybody thought I was simply playing at drowning. There were mostly kids of my own age around, and they paid no serious attention to an old 'prank'. Luckily, a much older boy happened to be there, who dived in, pulled me out and threw me face down on the worn planks of the pier, to cough out the sea water I had swallowed.

This, again, was an incident that Yiannis made reference to when he stopped me from going into the sea, saying: "Don't be silly. Be careful. You *will* drown yourself this time." As he said that I was flooded with the live imagery of the scene and felt that I was drowning. He stopped me, however, from going into the water since he, presumably, knew I would really have drowned myself in the state I was in.

These and various other incidents were like extensions of the peculiar, dreams I used to have. In these dreams I not only flew but also had experiences that involved encounters with strangely wonderful entities, visits to 'exotic' places (for want of another word), precognitions, feelings of being loved and protected, and the sense of attending 'lessons' - and, occasionally, I had clear recollections of people, places and 'classrooms'.

When I was about sixteen I became obsessed with some peculiar assumptions whose foundation in reality I could not justify. They were simply unjustifiable intuitions. I had the conviction that the creation of the world was intimately connected with numbers, that numbers themselves lay at the heart of creation, and that music, and sound, in general, was intrinsically involved in this.

We must bear in mind that at the time I had no training in formal philosophy, and my musical knowledge was limited to singing in the school choir - in which everybody had to participate at some point or other irrespective of whether they sang in or out of tune. I had no idea how exactly number and sound/music were involved in this but I was determined to work it out.

I would sit and stare out at the open sea, gazing at the infinity of the clear blue sky and the seeming infinity of the water for hours on end. I would stroll along an empty pebbly beach ostensibly collecting shells and interesting looking stones, and return home empty handed. Then I would stare at the sea and the sky again for hours racking my mind and heart for an answer.

My basic problem was this: Assuming that the world came about from something, this something must be a unit - *the* unit - outside which nothing existed and within which there were no subdivisions. Such a concept, however, implied the denial of all concepts, including those of space and time - in this unique (only one) unit you could not possibly have space or time. But how do we move, then, from this One to Two, not to mention Three and Four and so on? It was logically impossible.

This problem bothered me so much that it put me off my food. And then I made the conscious decision to stay off food until I solved it. Desperate problems required desperate actions. A bit over the top, you might think, but each to their own way of solving problems. In fact, I found, many years later, that this kind of obsession or obstinacy is a human trait that a person can employ to advantage by turning it into psychological 'blackmail' on oneself in order to enhance creativity and achieve intuitive insights.

On this occasion, I lived on water and orange juice for four days at the end of which period I began to see the arrival of some solutions. I continued to hold onto the idea of the Unit steadfastly but as I looked around me I saw multiplicity. How did the One become the Many? (I did not know at the time that this philosophical question was not new - many others had grappled with it before me and come up with varying answers).

My insight into this was as follows: The One always remains the One but the One also *appears* as Two or, more accurately, as Three. (Since in the One there is neither space nor time). Within the One there arises movement or vibration - this is the Two which now gives rise to Three, *the appearance*. Why vibration comes about I could not explain, nor understand, but there ought to be vibration or movement in order for anything to exist - the One is beyond existence, it does not exist logically; in fact, to all logical intent and purpose it is a fat zero, it is Nothing. Why call it One? Because like zero it is and it is not – a bit like the god Janus with the two faces. We can call it zero before creation but in creation it is the One, the ground, the essence, the source, the Unit.

With movement we have Two, which is still One but a vibrating One. Vibration (Two) gives rise to forms which are an *appearance* of the One, that is, the vibrating One (Two) gives rise to appearance (Three). Four presented an additional problem. In arithmetic you can add one to anything but here the One is not something you could add, say, to Three to make Four - the One is not external, it is within everything, it is the essence of appearance as well as appearance itself. I was stuck for a while.

Then, I felt that since Three was the first appearance, the first form of existence, the One in existence, I could now start with Three, consider it as the One then move to a new vibration (Two as Four), then to another appearance (now as Five), and so on. I was also fascinated by the observation that Four was the only number that could be arrived at by both adding Two to Two and by multiplying Two by Two - no other number had that feature. Four felt very solid. My mind was on fire when I realised that if I added the numbers one to four I would get ten ($1+2+3+4=10$), the complete, the perfect number, after which numbers were repeated.

All this may sound unimportant to many people, and even daft to most, but for me it was as if some sluice had opened or some obstructive skin fallen from my eyes. The ramifications and consequences flashed through me so fast I could not get my brain into the right gear to catch them.

Throughout this episode I could also see some musical scheme in which every note was accompanied by an enormous orchestra of harmonics. There was only one note in fact but every harmonic above it acted as the key note creating its own harmonics and so on. Some of the sounds occasionally felt as if crashing or overlapping one another, but they were extremely pleasant, and vibrated all through my body. Certain harmonics, with their accompaniments, were each like a new world, a new creation. A new level of being. Visually, the experience was indescribable in terms of everyday colours and shapes - fantastically brilliant hues in unimaginable combinations, fluid abstract shapes that flowed into one another.

The whole thing was taking place within my body or mind, or me - what was *me*? I could not tell. At some point I felt all my consciousness concentrated on my breathing, not so much the inhaling as the exhaling. I was in my lungs and moving towards my throat. My mouth opened slowly and automatically and I began to float out in a slow, delicious blaze of a glorious harmony of colours and shapes as the whole area from my lungs to my lips exhaled the alphabet - slowly, the letters flowing one into another accompanied by their, practically innumerable, harmonics. I felt as if I were present at the moment of creation, as if I myself were the Creator.

I tried frantically to jot down as much of this fast flowing information as possible. The task seemed impossible not only because of the sheer mass, complexity and speed of the information but also because of an understanding that writing it down was totally irrelevant, as if I were trying to catch a grain of time in a vast, timeless field.

I could sense a spatial and temporal order in all this but it seemed irrelevant, as if order itself were not relevant, as if order were merely an effect, an appearance, and that behind it lay something whose essence rendered order meaningless - meaningless in the sense that meaning was both not relevant and unavailable. I felt as if I were breaking into a world devoid of meaning - not in a negative sense but rather in the sense of a void which lay beyond meaning, beyond mind. A void that was somehow full.

I was suddenly in the middle of a contradiction: I was filled with awe and reverence and at the same time with jocular irreverence, as if the whole of creation were a joke. The words "divine comedy" sprang to mind. Was creation simply a gigantic joke?

Whatever the answer to that might be I had no doubt that the created world was in order, in a very precise if complex and unfathomable order - albeit an appearance, an 'effect'. The order was such in fact that there was nothing conceivable outside of it, that is, there was no room for disorder. I thought of the word 'cosmos', a Greek word which is generally translated as the 'world' but which also carries the meanings of order as well as those of 'proper' and 'beautiful'. Very fitting, I thought. I had been taught at school that Cosmos (order) came out of Chaos, that before the world (Cosmos) came about there was Chaos (*dis*-order). This did not sit well with what I was experiencing. Disorder had no place here, had no place anywhere.

Suddenly, all negative meanings were shown to me for what they really were - meaningless, in the normal sense of the word. The word Chaos originally meant infinite, boundless, 'empty' space, and denoted a state before 'Creation', the One as Zero - Cosmos being an orderly stage in the process of Chaos becoming 'apparent', 'revealing' itself as the One. There has never been Chaos in the sense of *dis*-order, and there will be no Chaos in that sense ever.

This insight gave me a great sense of joy and liberation but at the same time it chained me. If everything was, is, and will be in order there was no way for me to stand outside of it and evaluate it since I myself was in this order. Was my young mind perhaps too immature to comprehend the complexity of the structure or were the laws governing this order truly and precisely the way I experienced them, in which case, being part of this order, I was inescapably conditioned to experience things the way I did?

I spent a number of days trying to take in the experience and work out some of its ramifications. Something that had begun as a youthful, if searching, inquiry into numbers and creation led into an unexpected experience that shook me profoundly. I was walking constantly on air with my mind still on fire.

Two events/shocks that followed soon after, and looked at first sight unconnected with each other and with what followed, brought my enthusiasm down a few notches, at least temporarily. They also opened up new areas of experience and research.

The first shock came when I spoke to my Greek professor about my ideas concerning numbers - I left out the more subjective aspects of the experience for fear of sowing doubts in his mind regarding my sanity. He, nonchalantly, brought me down to earth by saying that my theory was very interesting but that someone else had already thought about it before me.

"Bravo, bravo", he said, as we walked in the school corridor towards the classroom. "It's a brilliant idea, but Pythagoras has already come up with this a little while back".

Pythagoras? I'd only spoken to one person about my ideas - Chris, my closest friend, intellectual companion and confidant. Did Chris speak to someone else about it? This was a clear case of plagiarism. Who is .... ? Surely, he is not talking about....

"You don't mean Pythagoras, the one with the hypotenuse?!"

He chuckled. "Yes, the very same."

"But he lived ... ehm..."

"Over two and a half thousand years ago. He's probably dead by now", he said, delivering the briefest ever obituary for a great man, while grinning at my stunned face. I must have looked very amusing to him at that moment.

He was a nice person and had been very good to me, my Greek professor, but what he had just done was unforgivable. As if to make up for the shattering he had caused, he directed me to the municipal library where I would find out more about Pythagoras.

On my way there I began to adjust myself psychologically. After all, Pythagoras was a great thinker. I was in good company here. Was this a case of great minds thinking alike or what?!

This event, incidentally, was to set a pattern that would repeat itself throughout my life: I would invest a great deal of time and energy thinking and working something out only to find that somebody else had already thought about it. Or, worse still, I would plan a venture, procrastinate for some reason or other and before I knew it someone else would go ahead and put the very same plan into practice. I needed to talk to someone about this.

At the library I began my research into Pythagoras and the Pythagoreans. Fascinating stuff. All of which felt very familiar although I could not find everything that would match my experience.

The next event initiated a series of other events that led to some remarkable situations which culminated in coming into contact with the Teacher, his teachings and his amazing feats of healing.

The whole thing unfolded against the background of a guerrilla war in which I, as a young teenager, was also involved. One of my functions was to receive, store, and make available to the guerrilla fighters various types of weapons. On this occasion, I and Akis, my 'comrade-in-arms', had orders to pick up a box of guns and ammunition and store it safely until, as usual, it was required by the guerrillas. We had to find a place in town, central if possible for easy access, as a big attack was being planned in the near future.

We spent a whole afternoon cycling around looking for an appropriate location. Eventually, we found the perfect spot. It was an empty plot of land, a neglected orchard with a few trees in it, which nobody bothered to tend, and lots of overgrown weeds. We had never seen anybody go into it. Rumour had it that the owner lived abroad. A low wall and some barbed wire separated it from the road. Likewise, the far end and the left hand side were separated from the gardens of the adjacent houses by walls of at least two metres high. On the right, a low wall, stretching halfway down the length of the plot, separated it from the neighbour's garden, and for the rest of that side, all the way to the back of the plot, lay the side wall of that neighbour's house.

An external staircase led from the neighbour's garden to a small balcony and to a door which opened into the first floor of the house. The main entrance to this house stood round the other side, facing a gate to a small narrow street, and it was obscured by trees and bushes.

Under cover of darkness, around ten or eleven at night, Akis brought the box on his bicycle - heavy stuff, but Akis was a muscular guy, a body-builder. We loosened a couple of barbed wires and took the box into the enclosure, along with a pick and a shovel. It was pretty dark and nobody saw us moving into the orchard although we had to take extra care not to trip on anything. We chose a particularly overgrown spot near the back wall of the house and dug a hole big enough to place the watertight box in after we had wrapped it in cellophane for extra protection against water and dampness. Then we began to cover it with the soil we had dug up.

Suddenly, there was light on the balcony. We stopped shovelling soil and watched carefully.

Someone came out and puffed on a cigar. He paced up and down on the balcony for a while and then came over and stood at the edge facing our side. We could not make out his features for certain but as he continued to smoke his cigar he was clearly staring in our direction. We crouched motionless and waited. After a few minutes he went back in but must have left the door open because the balcony remained lit as before.

"Let's finish covering it up!" I whispered urgently, and picked up the shovel.

"No, wait!" Akis whispered back, and stopped me from using the shovel. "He's gone in to phone the police! Let's go!"

"Where?"

"To stop him! Come on!"

He brushed the soil off the top of the box with his hand, tore the cellophane, opened the box, took out a handgun and bullets, and moved quickly to the dividing low wall. I followed close behind him. We didn't know for sure whether the man had gone in to phone the police, but Akis was right - we couldn't afford to take any chances. We jumped over the wall and rushed up the staircase to the balcony.

The room the man had gone into was an office with a desk, shelves covered in books, various magazines and newspapers, lots and lots of newspapers. A middle-aged man was leaning over the desk, a cigar in his left hand and a pen in the other, making marks on a newspaper. He was absorbed and did not notice us. Akis recognised him.

"He's a traitor!" he whispered angrily and, before I had a chance to query his accusation, he lunged forward, grabbed the man by the throat, pushed him against the wall and shoved the handgun into the man's side.

"You phoned your friends yet?!" Akis grunted threateningly.

The man struggled to breathe. Akis relaxed his grip a little and repeated his question with greater force and urgency.

"Have you phoned your friends?!"

"What? Why?" croaked the man as he managed to take in a much needed breath of air. "Why should I phone my friends? Which friends?" he said in obvious puzzlement.

"The Special Branch!" barked Akis.

"What? What are you talking about?"

"You saw us, didn't you!" continued Akis in the same threatening tone.

"Yes. But why should I phone the Special Branch?" retorted the man.

"'Cos you're a traitor! I know who you are! You consort with the enemy! You're a traitor!"

Despite Akis' stranglehold and the obvious threat to his life, the man had the courage and presence of mind to challenge Akis' accusation.

"No I'm not! How dare you?!"

"We've seen you! We have photographs of you talking to senior army officers!"

"So what?" said the man in obvious indignation. "I'm a journalist. It's my job".

"Wait a minute," I cut in. "Let go of him for a minute".

Akis continued to stare the man in the face threateningly, but he released his hold on the man's throat and moved his hand away.

"Look," said the man, in a conciliatory tone, "why don't you pull up a chair, the both of you, and let us see what the problem is?" He sounded genuine.

Akis was still pointing the gun at him. "Don't you try anything stupid!" he warned him as he began to sit down.

"Why should I? I'm as Greek as you are. I'm fighting the enemy, too, in my own way."

The man offered us soft drinks. We sat down and talked for a while and the situation was gradually diffused. He was a soft-spoken person and even Akis eventually relented and was prepared to accept that the man had been misunderstood.

Moreover, I was pleasantly surprised to hear that he was the owner-editor of my favourite weekly newspaper, which had a section comprising two pages dedicated to new poetry and young people's ideas. In fact, I had only recently sent in some of my poems for publication. I told the man about it. He asked me my name. Akis glanced at me in obvious concern.

"Look," said the man, "you either trust me or you shoot me."

Akis stared at me for a bit, then looked away and shrugged his shoulders. I gave the man my name. He smiled and beckoned me to approach his desk. There on the desk lay the poetry section of his newspaper in proof form, the very page he had been marking with the pen when we burst in on him.

"Take a look," he said to me.

There in front of me lay two of my poems in print.

"I like them," said the man softly. "They're full of mysticism."

I asked him to elaborate because I was not all that certain as to what he meant exactly by the word "mysticism". He kindly obliged me and ended with a suggestion.

"Why don't you go and have a chat with Mr Manolides, one of your professors. He'll take you to the capital to meet the Teacher, a real mystic. You'll get all the answers you need from him."

It turned out that this man also knew a great deal about Pythagoras. He was, indeed, kind enough to lend me a book with the title *The Golden Sayings of Pythagoras* - which did not exactly throw light on my original questions but, nonetheless, pointed my research in a direction that proved fruitful in another important respect.

Mr Manolides was not, in fact, one of my professors although he did teach at my school - the girls' section. I only knew him by sight - a thin, short, middle-aged man. I called round to his house one afternoon without an appointment. He opened the door and asked me politely what I wanted. A sad smile hung on his face. I introduced myself, apologised for my unsolicited call, and stated the purpose of my visit.

His face lit up and he invited me in and offered me a soft drink. He wanted to know how I "came" to him. I told him about the ammunition cache and the incident with the newspaper editor. I knew I was breaking security regulations but, somehow, I felt I could trust him. Besides, we had already moved the ammunition to another location as part of a routine safety measure. My eyes kept drifting to a black band he was wearing round his arm, a sign of mourning. His wife had died recently, he told me, and I could see his eyes moistening.

"That's how I met the Teacher," he added, as if letting me into a secret.

"How was that?" I probed with unconcealed interest.

He confided in me that he loved his late wife very dearly and that her death did not mean she was lost to him - in fact, he assured me, his wife was much closer to him now than when she was physically alive. He felt that she was constantly with him, and various incidents strengthened his conviction. The Teacher consolidated this conviction with further communications from his wife.

"So, this... Teacher is some kind of medium who communicates with the souls of the dead, then," I concluded, a little uncertain about the whole setup.

"Oh, no, no!" he objected. "He's more, much more than that. He's a Master."

I became rather confused at that point. I was not familiar with his use of the term "Master", which he delivered in English, a language of which I had only a smattering. I, also, misunderstood his use of the word "Teacher". Naturally, I thought he was referring to some school-teacher who was very proficient at his job. He laughed at my misconception. Apparently, the two terms, "Teacher" and "Master", were interchangeable, and their use applied to a person who was knowledgeable in spiritual truths and adept in the use of mystical or psychic powers. He reminded me that "Teacher" was a word we often used in Greek when we spoke of a spiritual teacher, and that we also used it sometimes when addressing a priest - something like 'rabbi'.

He went on to talk with great respect and admiration, bordering on awe, about the Teacher's amazing psychic abilities which included telepathy, clairvoyance, psychokinesis, ecsomatosis (out-of-the-body activities) and materializations - terms which, with the exception of telepathy and, to an extent, clairvoyance, I was not familiar with at the time.

This Teacher appeared to have an enormously deep knowledge of the inner workings of nature, and he was also known for his diagnostic and healing abilities. Was Mr Manolides describing some saint or, perhaps, a sorcerer? I was impressed by his overflowing enthusiasm and asked him to tell me what kind of things the Teacher had done to demonstrate his abilities in regards to Mr Manolides' departed wife. For instance, did he show him that his wife survived physical death as a soul - whatever that might mean?

"Oh, yes," he responded, "he gave me masses of proof about my wife's psychic survival after death. We've had many communications, but most of it is personal."

"Oh," I said, clearly disappointed.

"But I can give you one example which is not so personal," he added. "When I was first persuaded to go and see him - I was not very keen at the time, and I was still totally devasted by her death - he said to me straightaway that my wife was always with me and looking after me. 'What do you mean she's looking after me?' I said. He looked me straight in the eye and said: 'Who do you think protected you from the flying glass when your bedside lamp exploded?' I was dumbfounded. Nobody knew about this incident."

"What incident? What bedside lamp?" My interest was rekindled.

He reflected for a moment or two and then stood up decisively.

"Come," he said, "I'll show you."

I followed him into his bedroom where he demonstrated to me what had happened and related the incident in detail. He was sitting up in bed one night reading a book, with only his bedside light on when, all of a sudden, a framed photograph of his wife, which had been standing on the mantelpiece, came tumbling down to the floor. Nothing else fell, and there was no draught in the room to justify the sudden movement. At the same time, he thought his wife was calling him, and he felt her presence very powerfully. He dismissed the possibility that he was dreaming, and rose from the bed to pick up the photograph from the floor.

As he moved away from the bed he heard a loud explosion and the room was plunged into darkness. He dashed to the door and switched the ceiling light on. His bedside lamp had exploded, and bits of glass were scattered on his pillow, the bed and the floor. He sat at the edge of the bed shaking, realising that, had he not risen from the bed to pick up his wife's photograph from the floor, the flying glass would certainly have cut his face and injured his eyes - very likely, blinding him. He looked at me almost triumphantly, as if to say 'is this proof or what?'.

He went on to recount more occurrences, some of which were anecdotal reports of people he knew and which included healing feats - miracles, I thought - that the Teacher was said to have performed through the years.

As we returned to the sitting room to refill our glasses with orange juice, I pointed out to him that, impressive though it was, the whole incident with the exploded bedside lamp could be put down to mere coincidence.

"But how did the Teacher know about it, then? I hadn't told anybody about it. How did he know?" he retorted.

Telepathy was a clear possibility. This would have involved no theories of survival. But he would have none of that.

"The Teacher told me things about my wife that I myself didn't know and had to confirm afterwards. Some of them practical things, like where she kept certain documents I didn't even know she had."

He sounded very convincing, and I had a real problem finding a reasonable rebuttal.

"And how about *your* case?" he challenged me, and his whole face stretched into a broad mischievous grin, certain that he had turned the tables on what he must have perceived as scepticism on my part.

"*My* case? What do you mean *my* case?" I said.

"You don't seriously think that this was a coincidence, do you?" he prodded.

"Ehm..." I wasn't sure what he was talking about.

"Look: this is an answer to a scream, a desperate scream, can't you see?"

"A scream? What scream?" I said, even more baffled.

"*Your* scream, of course, for answers to your questions," he responded.

I slowly began to see what he was getting at.

"Can't you see?" he continued. "You've been asking questions, spiritual questions, about the world and human nature. And what happens? A series of events leads you to where you're most likely to get answers. D'you follow me?"

I nodded slowly a few times while making those tenuous links in my head.

"And how did it actually happen?" he posed another question, and proceeded to answer it. "You're burying weapons, this man sees you, you jump up and grab him by the throat--"

"No, no, *I* didn't grab him by the throat. My friend did." I objected.

"Well, whatever. Then it turns out this man is publishing your poetry, and he sends you to me to take you to the Teacher with your stack of questions. Do you really believe these are mere coincidences?" he said, opening his arms and hands to emphasize his point.

I had to admit that I hadn't thought about it that way. And I was more than intrigued.

"When am I going to meet this... Teacher, then?" I said, feeling infected by his surge of enthusiasm.

"Well," he said, after some hesitation, "I can't take you there this evening. Wednesday evenings are reserved for the Inner Circle. But you can come with us on Saturday. Saturdays are open to everybody."

I was delighted to accept the offer. The meetings took place in the capital, an hour and a half drive from where I lived. Mr Manolides drove there twice a week accompanied by another middle-aged gentleman called Leonidas. I was to be at Mr Leonidas' house early Saturday afternoon where Mr Manolides would pick up both of us. The meeting wasn't until the evening but Mr Manolides had to be there in the afternoon for a personal rendezvous with the Teacher - I understood it had to do with more 'communications' with his wife.

As I was about to leave he asked me a strange question. He looked me in the eye, smiled and said:

"How do you feel about me?"

I didn't know what to say. It was such an unexpected question. Nothing had been said beforehand to lead up to it. It came out of the blue.

"Well...." I mumbled.

"Go on," he coaxed me. "How do you feel about me?"

"Well, I think--"

"No, no. Don't think. I didn't ask you 'what you think' but 'how you feel'. *Feel*," he insisted.

I wasn't sure what exactly he wanted me to do. Feel? Feel what? I couldn't work out what I was supposed to do. Eventually, however, with more coaxing on his part, I told him an obvious truth, that I had filial feelings towards him, like a son normally feels towards his father. The age difference and the way he seemed to be taking me under his wing were clear factors in arousing such feelings.

But what I did not tell him - dare not tell him - was that I had an almost irresistible urge to hug him. Something about his appearance and general demeanour felt very familiar, and aroused in me feelings of affection and terms of endearment. But I couldn't say these things to a man I'd just met - too embarrassing, and could be misconstrued.

I left feeling a little confused, but intrigued by the discovery that I could have such feelings of affection towards a person who was a total stranger to me. Such considerations, however, were soon over-shadowed by the mounting excitement at the prospect of meeting this mysterious miracle-worker referred to as the Teacher.

On Saturday, I was all geared up for the planned journey to the meeting. I walked to Mr Leonidas' house where I was greeted by a lively man of a similar build and age to Mr Manolides. Married, with three delightful daughters, all below the age of ten, whom he introduced as his "three Graces", Mr Leonidas was full of questions regarding my interest in the "teachings" and the circumstances that led me to Mr Manolides.

I was, justifiably, a little disconcerted when I found that he worked in an abattoir. Somehow I could not imagine this jolly little man going around slaughtering poor innocent animals. Besides, didn't this clash with some spiritual principle or other? When I raised this question, during our drive to the capital, I discovered that it was a sore point for Mr Leonidas who had been trying desper-ately to find another employment, more in keeping with his prin-ciples, but who also could not give up his present job because he had a family to support.

It was also a subject that Mr Manolides would use in order to tease his friend almost incessantly, telling him that he was storing up bad karma for future incarnations. Since I was a novice in this area of thinking, I had to ask them to explain the meaning of the word "karma", and some other concepts they used. The two men went on to half-explain them, and concluded by saying that more would be revealed at the meetings.

I began to sense an air of secrecy around these meetings. In spite of the fact that the Saturday ones were open to the public, the way these two men spoke about them - the manner in which they were conducted, the teachings, and the activities that took place during them - made me feel both intrigued and uneasy. They made repeated reference to the admonition that one should not speak openly about "these things" for fear of ridicule, but more importantly, of an over-hanging threat from the Church, the threat of ex-communication.

Teachings and Practices
(Meeting the Teacher)

We arrived at the Teacher's house mid-afternoon. The actual building where the meetings took place was about one hundred and fifty
metres away, in an otherwise empty plot of land at the end of a dirt
road. It was a longish rectangular bungalow, called the Stoa, the
door of which was surrounded by vine and jasmin. I could just
about make it out from the veranda of the Teacher's house.

We were welcomed by his wife who invited us into the small hall
and offered us coffee and soft drinks. She was thrilled with Mr
Manolides' present - a pot of geraniums he'd carried in the boot of
his car and which he'd apparently promised her a while back. But
she asked us to be as quiet as possible as the Teacher was in the
lounge with visitors. The door of the lounge was half-open and we
could hear voices coming from inside, but couldn't make out the
language - it was clearly not Greek. In a low voice, Mr Manolides
asked Mrs Katina, the Teacher's wife, what the language was.

"How should I know?" she whispered back, shrugging her shoulders. "They're from Brazil. They spoke English when they came
in."

"How many are there?"

"Two. The father and his teenage boy. His wife died recently and
they're both inconsolable. You know," she said, nodding her head at
Mr Manolides in a knowing look.

"Only too well," he responded, with sadness returning to his
face.

"That's Portuguese," said Mr Leonidas, listening to the voices in
the lounge. And then, turning to Mrs Katina: "Wait a minute, you
said father and son, but I can hear three voices speaking Portuguese
in there."

We listened in for a bit.

"Oh, well, your Teacher is speaking in tongues tonight," she said
dismissively. "So long as he speaks Greek when he talks to me,"
and she made to go for the kitchen to get the drinks. I asked her for

a glass of water and she said I should follow her into the kitchen.

Passing by the lounge door, I glanced in and saw a middle-aged man sitting on a sofa and next to him a boy whose head was slumped backwards and his eyes practically shut. They had similar facial features and I assumed they must be the father and son visitors. I was dying to stop and watch but that would have been improper. As I continued to the kitchen, a girl of about eleven, the Teacher's younger daughter, passed by me with a slice of bread and jam in her hand and said nonchalantly:

"He's in a trance. And so's my dad," and moved out to the veranda.

I couldn't see the Teacher who must have been sitting on the opposite side of the lounge.

I went to the kitchen for my glass of water and then carried the tray with the drinks for Mrs Katina and we all moved to the veranda.

After a while, the Teacher emerged from the lounge accompanied by the two Brazilians who looked very emotional and clearly pleased with whatever had taken place in there. They shook hands with the Teacher, thanked everybody, including me and my companions, and left.

"Good," said the Teacher, rubbing his hands with satisfaction as he turned to us.

He took a quick look at my companions and then at me.

"Right. Who do we have here?" he said, but before Mr Manolides had a chance to reply, he continued. "Ah, you're back! For good this time, I hope!" he said and advanced towards me, opened his arms and gave me a very warm hug.

I felt confused by his unexpected demonstration of affection but very happy, so much so that I could hardly keep my tears back - I was so flooded with love. It was the warmest 'homecoming' reception I could ever imagine. 'Homecoming?' Why should I feel such strong emotions, and why the sense of familiarity with a total stranger? - similar to how I'd felt about Mr Manolides when I first met him, but with much stronger emotions and a far deeper sense of familiarity.

While I was still wrestling to regain my composure and trying to work out what to say, Mr Manolides was anxious to hear about the Brazilian visitors.

"Oh, very interesting," said the Teacher, while pulling up a chair for himself and beckoning us to join him.

I was practically ignored for a while as he became involved in relating the Brazilians' story.

He was a big man, the Teacher. Well over one metre eighty, with black curly hair, wide forehead and pronounced features that were not exactly classical - slightly bulbous nose and fleshy face - large imposing body with big bone structure and a belly that was beginning to be noticeable. He was about the same age as the other two men, but there was something magnetic, charismatic, about him.

"They're from Rio de Janeiro," he began. "And listen to this: his wife passed on in a car crash a few weeks ago. Selfish man. He did not appreciate her when she was still alive. She's a very spiritual person. He divorced his first wife because he thought she was unfaithful. They had a child together, a daughter, who he was convinced was not his.

"But his second wife, the one who died in the accident, thought otherwise. She was - is - quite psychic, you know. She became fully aware that she was on the other side seconds after the crash. She was on her way home with evidence to show that the girl was indeed his daughter, when the accident took place. The man is very wealthy but his daughter and her mother live in abject poverty in a shanty town.

"After the accident she began to haunt him both in his dreams and his waking state. She's been wanting to get through to him and tell him about his daughter and get him to help her. The girl has turned to prostitution in order to keep herself and her mother".

"Wow!" exclaimed Mr Leonidas.

"Wow, indeed," said the Teacher. "They've been to exorcists and voodoo practitioners and god knows who else but to no avail. She wouldn't give up. She went on haunting him, until they came here."

"Why was the boy in a trance?" I ventured to ask.

"Ah, that's even more interesting. You see, the boy doesn't speak much English, so I put myself into a trance for his mother to speak to him through me in their own tongue. But as soon as she started talking, off he went into a trance himself. And before you knew it, the mother was speaking through the son. The boy, like his mother, is very psychic."

He gave a little chuckle.

"They could've saved themselves a journey," he added. And then, as he quietened down from another chuckle, he turned to me.

"Now, young man. What do you see?"

"What?" I didn't understand the question.

"What do you see? You're looking at me. What do you see?"

The other two men looked on expectantly. It was obvious they knew what he was asking.

"What do you see, hear, or feel as you're looking at me?" insisted the Teacher.

"Bells," I said. "I hear bells. Not big, church bells. Little bells, tinkly ones."

"Good, good. What else?" he prodded.

"Ehm, I see you wearing a long curly beard and a funny-looking hat - almost like a cone. And something like a gown, similar to what the Greek archbishops wear."

He burst into laughter.

"Good," he said. "Not bad, not bad at all." Then he turned to the two men. "You know what he's picking up, don't you?"

The two men shook their heads.

"No. What?" asked Mr Manolides.

"Babylon. When I was a hierophant, a high priest, there. What he has just described were part and parcel of the priest's ceremonial apparel. He'll pick up more in a minute," he said, referring to me.

In fact, the moment he mentioned Babylon I had a clear image of him as a hierophant in his full regalia officiating a ceremony in a temple. The imagery wasn't full size, standing in front of me; it was in my head, in my minds's eye, but it was very vivid. I wasn't sure whether it had been suggested by his mentioning the high priest and my supplying the imagery from pictures I'd seen. So I kept quiet. He waited for a beat or two and then spoke to me again.

"It will come back to you. You were there. It will come back in its own time." Then he straightened himself and slapped his right thigh saying:

"Enough. Where's my coffee?"

Right on queue, his wife appeared at the door with a cup of Greek coffee.

"Oh, good. Thank you, dear." Then he turned to Mr Manolides. "We'll go in as soon as I've had my coffee."

"No hurry," said Mr Manolides, appearing to be happy by simply being in the company of the Teacher who began to drink his coffee making sucking slurping noises and drawing reprimanding looks from his wife.

"What? It's too hot. It cools it down," said the Teacher, responding to his wife's looks. Then he turned to the rest of us who were looking on and smiling at his rather entertaining behaviour and weak justification. "No, really. It does." And he continued with the slurping of his coffee unperturbed.

He hardly had time to take a few more noisy sips when a car pulled up in front of the house. A middle-aged couple and a young woman emerged and headed straight for the veranda. The couple looked sad and concerned, the young woman was downcast and lethargic - she was practically dragging her feet and looked as if she were drugged.

"Uh-oh!" exclaimed the Teacher. "I'm afraid your case will have to be put back a bit," he said addressing Mr Manolides. "Something much more serious has just come up."

The couple and the young woman climbed the few steps to the veranda, greeted us, and asked if they could see the Teacher. It was obvious they'd never met the man before. The Teacher introduced himself and ushered them into the house. I and the other two men stayed on the veranda wondering what the story with the new arrivals might be.

When I casually remarked to Mr Manolides that he'd lost his turn in the queue, he explained that this was quite normal - it was like an accident and emergency department at a hospital where urgent or important cases took priority. He didn't know what the case was with the recent visitors but he was certain it ought to be more important than his for the Teacher to take that action.

Seeing how people just dropped in to consult the Teacher, I wondered whether the concept of an appointment system had bypassed everybody.

"Oh, no, people do make appointments. Well, some do. But, as I said, it's like a hospital - there are routine as well as emergency cases." He smiled. "You should see the queues sometimes."

We moved on to discussing the Brazilians' case, and Mr Manolides pointed out that getting into a trance was not normal practice for the Teacher. The only time he entered into anything remotely resembling a trance was when he was being overshadowed during a lecture.

"What do you mean? What happens then?" I asked with obvious interest.

"Sometimes, when he is giving a talk in the Stoa," he explained, "one of the Masters overshadows him and speaks through him. But the Teacher doesn't fall into a trance, he simply coordinates himself with the Master, and then steps aside, so to speak, and lets the Master deliver the speech."

"But isn't this trance?" I asked, not ignoring the amazing statement about "coordination".

"No, no. The Teacher is fully aware of what's happening. This is coordination, alignment with another, more advanced being of a greater consciousness."

His explanation was not altogether to my satisfaction, but I decided not to pursue the subject at that point, and asked him instead to throw some light on the Teacher's remark concerning Babylon and my 'remembering' him.

"What he meant was that you had an incarnation in ancient Babylon at a time when he was a high priest there and that you began to have glimpses of him in that life."

He went on to expound the belief system propagated by the Teacher which, although Christian in essence, included aspects similar, if not identical, to Hindu and Buddhist beliefs that spoke of such things as chakras or "psychic centres", reincarnation, and karma, among others.

There was a hierarchical structure to the system. Absolute Be-ness is placed at the top. This is beyond explanation, beyond conceptualisation in any detail. You may call it God if you like. It is populated by countless monads who are units of the same essence as Absolute Be-ness. Then you have Absolute Beingness which is the same as Absolute Be-ness except that now in it there is the decision/desire to manifest itself in itself. From that position, two aspects of it, the Logos and the Holy Spirit take on the part of creators, co-creators. The result is the world of Existence, an emanation of Beingness, a creation within itself.

The monads project parts of themselves into the world of Existence, which they now populate, and participate in its unfoldment and development. Through a series of unfoldments we reach a level which, in this system, is called the higher noetic and which contains laws, causes, forms or ideas. The lower noetic level is the world of ordinary concrete thought. Then there is the psychic, otherwise known as astral or the world of emotion. All these worlds have numerous subdivisions. The physical world sits at the bottom, so to speak, being the lowest and most concrete.

All the worlds, including the physical, are traversed and maintained by a type of energy which is also so disposed as to make communication amongst the various levels possible - this is called etheric energy. The incarnated personalities are projections of a more permanent aspect of that part of the monad that came into Existence. The controlling consciousness, or soul, is truly eternal and indestructible.

Experience takes place in the worlds of Existence and may involve aspects of the physical, emotional and noetic or mental levels. An incarnated person inhabits, besides a physical body, also a psychic and a noetic body through which he feels and thinks, and by virtue of which he can exist in a discarnate form in the emotional or mental worlds where other, non-human, forms are also to be found.

Healing, for which the Teacher was renowned and which is the most spiritual of all activities, is effected through the manipulation and direction of etheric energy, and so-called miracles are also the result of such action.

Mr Manolides further explained that the lower noetic and emotional worlds are inundated by thought and desire forms which he called "elementals". These are thoughts and desires that we human beings, and other entities, create continuously and thus give shape and outlook to the psychological worlds we live in; and often become slaves to our own creations.

He began to give me examples to demonstrate and elucidate the various aspects of the system when we heard conversation in the hall and the voice of the Teacher advising the visitors on something or other.

As they emerged onto the veranda accompanied by the Teacher, the visitors looked very different. Gone were the sadness and pain hanging on their faces when they had arrived. The young woman even looked cheerful, shaking the Teacher's hand and thanking him profusely, with moist eyes and intermittent sniffle.

"Thank you, thank you ever so much, sir," she kept saying over and over again and kissing his hand.

"Don't thank *me*, my love. I'm only a channel. A catalyst, if you like," responded the Teacher casually, withdrawing his hand gently from the woman's lips.

"Who should we thank, then?" asked the older woman anxiously.

"Keep asking that question and the answer will come," said the Teacher cryptically, and placed his hand gently and comfortingly on the younger woman's shoulder.

The couple conferred whisperingly very briefly and then the man dipped his hand in his pocket and turned to the Teacher.

"Ehm....Hm...How much do we owe you, sir?" he said, clearing his throat.

"Nothing."

"Nothing?" asked the man, with uncertainty in his voice.

"Yes. Nothing. We can't accept payment for this kind of work."

The man looked rather puzzled, a bit lost, not knowing how to react.

"It's a labour of love," added the Teacher.

"But...ehm...we'd like to," mumbled the man, "we'd like to show our appreciation at least for--"

"Alright," interrupted the Teacher. "Do you know anyone who needs help - financial or otherwise?

"Ehm....Well, yes. There's always someone...."

"Good. Go help them. But not as payment for our work. Do it with your heart. Because you want to help," concluded the Teacher firmly.

Suddenly, the young woman grabbed the Teacher's hand and, in a burst of emotion, began to cover it with kisses, and wouldn't let go.

"Okay, okay. Enough already," said the Teacher. "Let me have my knuckles back, young lady," and, in a determined movement, pulled his hand away. He, then, examined his hand and, in mock horror, added: "Look. You've worn my knuckles down."

There was a gentle laughter all round that dissipated the obviously emotional atmosphere. When the couple offered their hands for a handshake, the Teacher accepted them with the humorous proviso: "No hand-kissing, please. Enough for one day," which drew some more laughter and sent the visitors away with a clearly restored outlook on life. It also drew a pretend disapproval from Mrs

Katina who stood at the doorway shaking her head.

"This hand-kissing must be stopped, you know. What do they think you are, a priest?"

"No, not in *this* life, my love," responded the Teacher, apparently alluding to a past incarnation.

He pulled up a chair and rejoined us. As he sat down he turned his head and gave his wife a brief glance.

"I know," she responded. "Coffee. Anybody else while I'm in the kitchen?" she asked the rest of us.

The two men nodded and said "yes please" and I followed suit, feeling embarrassed that we were putting her to so much trouble. I offered to help. She told me to stay where I was; she was used to it, she said.

"It's amazing the problems people create for themselves," the Teacher exclaimed. He leant back and shook his head.

"What? Was the girl in serious trouble?" inquired Mr Leonidas.

"Serious? You've no idea how serious."

He, then, went on to tell us how the girl attempted to kill herself a number of times, each time as a reaction to her boyfriend's infidelity. But every time she tried to top herself she would have visions of wonderful buildings and plans for buildings, and these visions caused her to bungle her attempts. The Teacher smiled to himself as he reflected.

"The girl has no idea that these visions were flashbacks to a previous incarnation when she was a famous architect. And a man. And that her present lover was also her lover in that incarnation - only the roles were reversed: he was the woman, she was the man, and she, as the man, was the unfaithful one in that incarnation! God help them! They have a lot to sort out in this life." He stopped for a second and then added. "But that's not the worst of it."

"What? Did the boyfriend try to kill himself, too?" asked Mr Manolides.

"Oh, no. Far from it. But the girl had been internalising and continuously building on her frustrations with terrible elementals that in the end she created a cancer in her body."

"A cancer?!" all three of us exclaimed.

"Yes, a cancer."

He explained how the girl had been to the hospital with chest complaints and that the doctors could not tell whether it was cancer or tuberculosis. They took a number of Xrays and carried out other investigations to satisfy themselves that it was indeed cancer. She was due back to the hospital the following week when the doctors would tell her for certain that she had cancer.

"But she doesn't have cancer any longer. That will throw a spanner in the works for the poor doctors when they Xray her again!" he said and threw his head back laughing.

"What do you mean?" I querried. "I thought you said the doctors found out that she has cancer."

"True. But that was before she came here. Now, with the work she did with me in the lounge, the cancer is gone, dissolved, disappeared. And if she follows my instructions it will never come back."

He glanced at his watch and, all of a sudden, stood up.

"We'd better go in," he said, addressing Mr Manolides. "We'll have our coffee in the lounge while we speak with your wife."

He made for the door followed by Mr Manolides. I heard Mrs Katina talking to them in the hall, and presumably giving them their coffee, before coming out to the veranda with the tray. We asked her to join us and take the weight off her feet for a while but she declined saying they were expecting relatives next day and she had a lot of work to do. She suggested that if we got bored we could go to the Stoa grounds and water the plants, the Teacher would appreciate that; and went back into the house.

Although enormously intrigued and fascinated by all the goings on, I had felt rather disconcerted by the fact that the Teacher had been freely dishing out personal information regarding his patients. I had thought that divulging personal details to outsiders was not the sort of thing healers or doctors were supposed to do. I voiced my concerns to Mr Leonidas.

"Oh, I shouldn't let it worry you," he responded casually. "For a start, the Brazilians are already on their way home, and the couple with their daughter will probably come back and join one of our groups. Besides, when the Teacher does anything like this, it is always for a purpose: teaching us a lesson, drawing our attention to certain spiritual truths, giving us food for meditation. It's up to us to pick it up."

We decided to take Mrs Katina's advice and walk down to the Stoa. A couple of cars were parked nearby and a dozen or so people were standing around talking to one another in an area that I could not make out whether it was an empty field or the courtyard of a house - there were no fences or walls to indicate any boundaries between the dirt road and this plot of land; there were many plants, especially cacti some of which were very unusual, and a clump of lemon and other citrus trees. Farther in, and parallel to the dirt road, stood the Stoa.

Mr Leonidas introduced the small crowd to me using their first name with the prefix "brother" or "sister", and there followed warm embraces, kisses, handshakes and wide welcoming smiles. Two of them had already been busy watering the plants. All of them were engaged in discussing the teachings and their relevant personal experiences that had taken place during the past week. One of them related how the Teacher had cured a cousin of hers of breast cancer by dipping his etheric hand inside her chest and dissolving and 'dematerialising' the offending growth.

Some cases involved physical healing, others were more obviously psychological. In one case, a man who was about to throw himself into the sea with the intention of drowning himself had been stopped by the 'apparition' of the Teacher who shocked him into changing his mind and staying alive to support his needy family - the man later had another shock when he met the Teacher face to face in the flesh and recognised in him the apparition.

Gradually, more people began to arrive. They were of all walks of life, and mostly older than myself. Amongst them were teachers, doctors, architects, lawyers, manual workers, craftsmen, business people, and other professionals. The sexes were equally represented, too.

There were a number who had come to receive healing, but were told to wait until after the meeting - had they come earlier, they would have been seen by the Teacher before the lecture - as in the case of Mr Manolides and the other two lots of visitors I'd already met.

Apparently, it was his custom to receive people with physical or psychological problems before every meeting and help them with the 'laying on of hands' or with advice. Sometimes, he did the same after a meeting, if he considered the case to be urgent enough. On other days of the week, including weekends, people dropped in with their problems. If he happened to be in, he would always receive them. Not infrequently, 'patients' came to see him from abroad.

After a while, someone arrived from the house to say that the Teacher would be with us shortly and would we now go in and take our seats for the "lesson". Inside the Stoa, on the left, were rows of chairs to seat about forty to fifty people. On the right, there was a thinly veiled partition with an entrance leading to what must be a very small room. Right in front and towards the opposite wall was a small table and a couple of chairs. Incense was gently wafting up to the low ceiling.

As we found our seats, more people arrived. Two assistants busied themselves around the room. Mr Leonidas appeared to know nearly everybody. He turned left, right and back greeting all and sundry.

Soon, the Teacher arrived accompanied by Mr Manolides who came and sat next to me. The Teacher went into the small room escorted by the two assistants. A few minutes later they re-emerged wearing white robes. The two assistants took their seats while the Teacher stood at the front. He looked across the room as if taking in everybody's presence, then welcomed everybody, said a short prayer, and announced the subject of his talk: healing. I'd been told that the themes of his lectures were never announced beforehand, nobody knew what he was going to speak about.

He began by addressing everyone as "brothers" and "sisters". It smacked of church, and so did the incense. But the subject-matter of his talk was very exciting. He spoke with authority. I was, of course, no expert on this but he appeared to me to know the ins and outs of his subject. He mentioned various methods which he employed to suit each individual case. The manner in which he delivered his talk was an enthusiastic mixture of abstract academic lecturing and the hands-on approach of a craftsman imparting his knowledge to his apprentices. And yet, in all this, he was deferring to a higher authority which he variously called the Logos, the Holy Spirit, and Absolute Beingness.

He talked of the employment of etheric energy in healing and further explained the subdivision of this energy into four types or aspects. I was somewhat familiar with the term 'etheric', having come across the word 'ether' in Pythagoras' *Golden Sayings* where it meant 'fine air' or the world of the soul which is "undying" and eternal.

The Teacher was using the word 'etheric' to mean the essential energy/structure of the world. The way he spoke, I was given the impression that the physical world was a form of 'solidified' etheric energy, and that the latter was the creative and sustaining substance, the *sine qua non* of everything in existence. In this view, it made good sense to propose the use of etheric energy in healing. I was very excited by this idea. Was etheric energy the same stuff I often found myself floating in in dreams and, sometimes, in wakefulness? The Teacher said that etheric energy was to be found at all levels, physical and mental, the way Mr Manolides had already explained it to me.

The little knowledge I had concerning healing - and it was extremely limited, confined to what I had heard or read - allowed me to assume that healing took place between two people, the healer and the patient. Faith healing I took to be something totally different, more of a miracle. But, according to the Teacher, they were both the same. Technical knowledge, such as anatomy and physiology, as well as experience in the manipulation of etheric energy through visualisation and projection of this energy and the use of reliable clairvoyance were useful aids in effecting healing, he said - as if such things were not feats in themselves! And, yes, healing does take place between two people, or so it seems.

In actual fact, nobody heals anybody. Etheric energy passes from the healer to the patient in the sense that the healer acts as a conduit for the energy to be transferred. The actual healer, if we must point to one, is the patient himself, his inner or spiritual self, or, to put it another way, God or Absolute Beingness. The physical person who plays the part of the healer in this equation is merely an agent, a spiritual agent, sometimes just a trigger. Nonetheless, a healer to be really effective must learn to efface himself/herself so that he or she acts as a pure conduit allowing the energy to flow uninterrupted and uncontaminated.

The ability to heal is the highest of psychic abilities, the most spiritual. Healing, however, is not always successful, and this is not always or necessarily due to the lack of ability on the part of the healer: it is often due to karma, the fact that the patient is not "ready" to be healed. Despite my excitement and admiration for the wonderful ideas expressed, this latter admission sounded like a cop-out - any unsuccessful attempt at healing could always easily be ascribed to the patient's non-readiness to be healed.

More interestingly, though, underlying the Teacher's approach to healing was not so much the personal achievement of the healer as much as the healer's spiritual development. Every "brother" and "sister" in that room he designated "Researcher of the Truth". And every person searching for the Truth had one main task in life: to cleanse themselves of egotism or self-centredness, to make oneself available at all times and in all circumstances to serve the needs of other human beings. A very obviously Christian ideal in which personal success or failure in healing should be treated with equanimity.

I was not particularly interested in Christianity itself, that is, the 'sentimental' aspects of Christianity and the attitude of the Church to subduing individuality. I was, however, attracted to approaches to personal psychic development. So, I more than welcomed the Teacher's exercise at the end of his talk.

The exercise entailed physical relaxation and visualisation of the heart centre or chakra and concentration on its size and colour. We were asked to raise our consciousness to the higher emotion of selfless love.

After the talk, and when everyone else had left, my two companions and I, coming from another town as we did, we were kindly invited to stay for a while and have refreshments on the Teacher's veranda before driving back home. Mrs Katina was pleased to join us this time, and so were their two daughters - the one I'd already met and another one, two years older. It was a normal family gathering, and it became more so when another relative, in his late twenties, dropped by for a coffee and a chat. The conversation drifted hither and thither in the usual casual family manner.

But pretty soon the Teacher began to 'talk shop'. I was told later that that was his customary way of doing things - he would always find a way to guide the conversation into a "lesson". On this occasion, the trigger was the relative who expressed his anger at his fiancée, their disagreement on a number of issues. It soon became obvious that he hadn't just dropped in for a coffee; he'd come to seek advice.

At a certain point, when Mrs Katina and the children had gone into the house, he came straight out with the main issue: his fiancée would not let him have sex with her until they got married. They would kiss and cuddle and so on but she would stop him short of completing the act.

The Teacher laughed his head off, which didn't help the poor chap in the least.

"You should see what she gets up to when she gets home after your romantic rendezvous," said the Teacher still chuckling along.

"What, what?" asked the relative, not exactly pleased with the Teacher's response. "Are you laughing at the afflicted now?"

"Yes," said the Teacher. "And you're both afflicted - with each other." Then he turned to the rest of us. "You see this character here?" he said pointing at the relative. "This silly man here had a previous incarnation with this beautiful girl, his present fiancée. He was not nice to her then. She was like a trophy to him. He liked to show her off to boost his ego. She loved him but he had a string of mistresses, and humiliated her with his silly behaviour. Now he's crazy about her, and she's tormenting him. How's that for a payback?" he said, laughing again.

"She's mad. She probably doesn't love me, anyway," said the relative, peevishly.

"Ah, but that's where you're wrong," retorted the Teacher, looking more serious now. "She loves you to bits. She's passionate about you. That's why she's suffering as much as you do."

"What do you mean?"

"Listen," said the Teacher and leant a little towards him. "Every time she leaves you, after your amorous rendezvous, she goes home and vents her passion and frustration by masturbating like crazy. She'll injure herself one of these days if she's not careful." And then he went on to give a graphic description of what the young woman did in the privacy of her bedroom and how she tried to muffle her noises to prevent her parents from hearing her.

"What?!" exploded the young man.

"She wants you as much as you want her. Even more," said the Teacher, adding oil to the fire.

"Why doesn't she have sex with me, then?" asked the man quite reasonably.

"Easier said than done."

"Why?"

"Because you're both mad," said the Teacher, and turned to us again. "They love each other and yet they don't know what love is.

Their personalities get in the way."

Then he addressed all of us.

"Love is unconditional but our personalities get in the way and restrict its expression - they even choke it sometimes," he said, looking at the young man as he emphasised the last sentence. "We build up elementals with our thoughts, emotions and desires like a wild forest and we cut out the light of love," he continued, addressing all of us. "Our personalities end up being no more than a bundle of elementals which are carried from one incarnation to the next.

"Is it any wonder that love gets so distorted?" he said, looking at the young man again.

"What am I going to do? You're the Teacher, teach me," pleaded the young man.

"Be less selfish. Dissolve those elementals."

"How?" asked the man eagerly.

"By ignoring them. And by being gentle. Work on your gentleness. Make no sexual demands on her; for a while."

The young man bent his head and mumbled "Easy for you to say."

"I know, it's not easy. But try it," said the Teacher lowering his voice to the tone of the young man.

"She'll probably walk all over me, if I do," said the man plaintively.

"No she won't," said the Teacher, gently but firmly. "At first, she'll be surprised, then intrigued, then she'll drag you to bed."

The young man lifted his head up, excited.

"Now, now. Let's not get carried away," continued the Teacher. "Remember, you're not doing this just to get her to bed. You must work on your personality. Develop your loving nature, and in doing so you'll help her develop hers." He waited a few seconds for his words to sink in.

"Promise me you'll do as I said and I'll guarantee you it will work," demanded the Teacher firmly.

The young man considered the 'offer' for a bit, smiled and promised. Then stood up and got a hug from the Teacher who sent him home with his blessings. He left looking quite satisfied with the result of his visit.

"Will he follow your advice?" asked Mr Manolides.

"He'll have to," answered the Teacher, and returned to his chair.

"He has no alternatives. *They* have no alternatives. The ties are too strong. Those two have a long and happy life ahead of them together - once they're over these silly problems."

"How are you going to keep your side of this agreement, your guarantee?" I asked, intrigued by such a promise.

"I'm not," he said flatly, and stared at the look of surprise on my face. "I tricked him," he added.

I turned to the two men who wore the same look of surprise on their faces. The Teacher continued:

"Every time he comes to me complaining that this plan of developing the gentle side of his nature isn't working, I will send him away saying that he's not putting enough into it, not doing it properly. And then give him more advice and encouragement. It will work. Don't forget there are two people in this tango of love. She's not going to hold out long. She loves him too much - if there is such a thing as loving too much."

Mrs Katina's appearance at the doorway seemed like a signal telling us that we were dangerously slipping into overstaying our welcome. Mr Manolides glanced at his friend and then at me, and we were on our feet. The Teacher followed suit. We thanked Mrs Katina for the hospitality, and the Teacher embraced each of us and wished us goodnight and a safe journey. The embrace seemed casual but, in fact, was, as on the previous occasion, most powerful; once again, I felt flooded with love. As we began to walk out of the veranda, the Teacher called out to Mr Manolides.

"Bring him with you on Wednesday."

He was referring to me, and it pleased me no end to hear that.

On the way back, the two men congratulated me on my being admitted to the Inner Circle, an unusual decision on the part of the Teacher, they said, who normally accepted "brothers" to that group only after a number of attendances at the Saturday outer or public meetings, and after a vetting procedure involving the "invisible Masters" who advised on the running of the Circles. I was thrilled.

Mr Manolides filled me in on the ceremony of admission to the Inner Circle which would take place in the small room, the sanctum, in the Stoa. I would kneel in the presence of the Teacher and some other brothers and/or sisters of the Inner and Innermost Circles and recite the seven promises of the Society.

These were basically promises to love and serve wholeheartedly

Absolute Beingness, to love and serve my fellow human beings, to endure without complaining any pains and problems I might encounter in life, and to meditate daily with the purpose of aligning myself with the Divine Will.

I was quite excited to find out that one of the promises was actually a Pythagorean one literally plucked out of the *Golden Sayings* which instructed that, before going to sleep at night, a committed disciple should examine his/her actions of the day three times checking to see which were the bad things he/she had done, which were the good ones, and which good things he/she was supposed to have done but hadn't, and adjust his/her daily activities in the future accordingly in order to eliminate the bad and increase the good actions. On this, the promises of the Society further elucitated that one should aim at developing mental and emotional control to the extent of becoming able to check one's bad thoughts and actions at their inception.

Having made these promises - which were not oaths but simply sincere declarations of intent - the Teacher, standing in front of me in his white robe, would touch my shoulders with the unpointed sword - a small sword with a broken tip - and declare me accepted in the Inner Circle. I would then stand up, he would drape over my shoulders a white ribbon and everybody present would embrace me, kiss me and congratulate me.....

At the ceremony itself I felt greatly uplifted, and happy to enter into the society of like-minded people. I experienced---

– 6 –

Yianna the Twin
(On Being a Hue)

....The sounds of a braying donkey began to pull me rudely back to the present. I had my eyes shut in order to cut out visual distractions and make it easier to recall possible connections with the past. I tried to ignore the assinine noises and stay with my recollections. I pondered briefly on the years that followed my entry to the Inner Circle, the twice weekly - sometimes more frequent - journeys to the capital to participate in the activities of the Society, the exercises - in groups and at home - which increased in scope, depth and complexity, the.... The braying became too loud, it sounded very close. I couldn't maintain my concentration.

I opened my eyes to be faced by a donkey standing barely two metres away from me. He stopped braying and now began to defecate and urinate, the urine splashing on the ground and almost reaching me. I thought of the Teacher's words: "Ah, you're back"! although a different kind of welcoming this time. Was it a coincidence that a donkey had decided to bray and empty his bowels right in front of me while I myself was so absorbed in reliving a ceremony of such spiritual significance? I looked around me: the fields were empty, save for the fruit trees; he could've brayed and done his other business somewhere aïse.

Standing next to the donkey was a billy goat, chewing some fodder. Oh, no! Beside him, on the ground, lay the hat Bob had given me, half-chewed. He kept looking at me, as if studying me. When I tried to retrieve the half-eaten hat, he bent his head and looked as if he were readying himself to head-butt me. The intensity of his stare was almost human. I was about to pick up a stone to throw at him when a screeching bevy of crows suddenly descended on the field a few metres away. I was surprised they didn't go for the fig tree; maybe there was something more interesting on the ground. The billy goat turned and moved slowly towards them, bleating loudly.

I took this to be my cue; I got up, picked up the remains of my hat, dusted myself, stroked the friendly donkey's neck, thanked him for his luminous comment on my spiritual aspirations and his ever so explicit visiting card, and took my leave. Having put some safe distance between me and the animals, I turned to see what they were up to. They were looking in my direction. One of them brayed and the other bleated. Was it a goodbye or a good riddance? or an expression of frustration at my having deprived them of a further opportunity to abuse me? I was clearly no Dr Dolittle.

I had no time to stop elsewhere to continue with my reflections and evaluations. My immediate concern now was to get back to the hotel, shower and change, and set off to Yianna's house hoping to catch Yiannis there. The small boats ferrying people to and from the mainland and the island were out now; but they were not stopping anywhere along my way. I had to stick to my original plan and walk all the way to the village. From there I would be able to get across.

Back at the hotel, I left a note for my two friends to meet me at Zeno's, a local taverna, for our last evening meal together, then walked back to the seafront, got into one of the small ferries, and returned to the mainland. I tried to follow the directions Bob had given me but I soon realised I was going in circles. When Bob told me to turn left at the church he'd forgotten to tell me which church - to my chagrin, I learnt that there were no fewer than four churches in the small village! I went up a hill to the edge of the village and came down again exhausted. I sat on a low wall to get my breath back and asked a passer-by for directions. The old man stopped, leant on his walking stick, and looked me up and down.

"You can get a room at the seafront. Why go that far out?" he said, almost dismissively.

"I'm not looking for a room," I said, wondering as to how he got that idea. "I'm just asking for Mrs Yianna's place."

He shrugged his shoulders, turned his back on me, and as he began to walk away he lifted his arm above his head and waved it pointing in a vague, nondescript direction. "It's way over there. Good luck."

I looked all around trying to decide which way he had actually pointed. A dog appeared out of nowhere, stood a short distance from me and studied me for a while - or, he seemed to. It was a strange kind of dog: a mongrel with pointed ears and a rather bushy tail like a fox or a jackal. He gave a little growl and wagged his tail, a weird combination of anger and friendliness, then turned to walk away, stopped, turned round again and looked at me one more time, and then walked off. A passing child had no idea what I was talking about.

In the end I decided to work it out by a process of elimination. There were four sides to the village, the way there are four points to the compass. The way I first came to the village from the beach after I'd met Bob, the seafront, the hill opposite the seafront which I had climbed unsuccessfully, and the west side which I hadn't explored yet.

I went west and away from the coast. This area was more shaded by the backdrop of the mountain than the other parts of the village, and sparsely inhabited. I sighed with anticipation when I came across the last church in that part of the village. As I turned left to walk up the narrow cobblestoned street, I ran into the mongrel again.

He was standing there in the middle of the road as if waiting for me, and, as before, he growled and wagged his tail. I didn't know what to make of this animal, but I certainly didn't want to get into a scrap with him. Then he backed off as if to allow me to carry on with my search. He walked ahead, seemingly away from me, and I followed from a safe distance to nearly the end of the street. Beyond that there were only fields and orchards. He sat at the edge of the dead end road as if guarding an exit. He reminded me of Anubis, the Egyptian jackal god I'd seen in pictures.

I was getting fed up with this adventure and I was about to backtrack when my attention was drawn to a house on my right. It was surrounded by a whitewashed wall, nearly two metres high; a bright blue door was ajar, allowing a partial view of the sizeable courtyard at the end of which a few steps led up to the house whose walls were, again, whitewashed, with a bright blue door that was hugged tightly and profusely by a brilliant bougainvillea; bright blue window shutters and garish curtains completed the picture.

I peered in to see a clean, well-kept courtyard: bushes, climbers and flower pots everywhere, tastefully arranged, without a plant out of place, a veritable little paradise. And the smell! Delicious. Shame about the curtains and the doors and the window shutters, I thought. I glanced back towards the dog to see what he was up to but he'd gone. I returned my attention to the garden in front of me only to notice another discord: the figure of a woman clad in black, bending over and watering a large hibiscus which was literally covered in unusual creamy colour flowers. She had her back to me and didn't notice me, so I called out to her.

"Excuse me."

There was no response.

I called out again. "Hello. Excuse me."

She half-turned towards me but remained bent, with the watering can in her left hand. I noticed that she was supporting herself on a walking stick in her right hand.

"Why should I excuse you, young man," she said. "You haven't done anything wrong. Have you?"

I had the shock of my life! It was Yiannis! Except that the voice was pitched a little higher than his normal register. What was he up to now, I wondered. But I was so pleased I had found him - alive - that I was prepared to overlook the prank. I began to laugh and walk towards him.

"You, you old codger, you! You gave me the fright of my life," I shouted as I approached him.

He turned to face me fully with a frightening scowl, dropping the watering can, and raising the stick ready to strike me.

"Who are you calling an old buffer!"

I froze in my tracks. This person looked exactly like Yiannis, sounded almost like Yiannis but.... I couldn't really tell for sure. It could have been Yiannis dressed up as a woman. The headscarf concealed the top of the head but I could see black hair over the nape. And he/she had a small hump. I didn't know whether to apologise or call his bluff by pulling the headscarf off - and the wig! I decided to play it safe. I apologised and explained that from a distance they looked so alike.

"I know," she said, lowering the stick and her voice. "It's the bane of my life." She picked up the watering can and added: "What can I do for you, young man?"

I couldn't get over it. The likeness was unbelievable.

"Stop staring at me. We're identical twins."

Ah, that would certainly explain it. I sighed with relief. But why didn't Bob say anything about this? I would undoubtedly take it up with him when I saw him next.

I apologised again, introduced myself, and offered my hand for a handshake. She relinquished the walking stick to shake my hand. As with Yiannis, she gripped my hand in a strong and yet warm handshake and squeezed the centre of my palm in precisely the same manner. For a moment, I was in Yiannis' presence - rather unsettling. I pulled away gently and explained that I'd left Yiannis swimming round the promontory and that I was to meet him at the restaurant over the other side but that he'd never showed up. I was very concerned about his safety.

"Up to his old tricks again, eh? Typical. No consideration for other people's feelings," she said, shaking her head in disapproval and resuming her watering of the hibiscus but ignoring her cane which was left lying on the ground. "Did he actually say he was going to meet you at the restaurant?"

"Well, not exactly. Ehm, I'm not sure."

"What did he actually say?"

"To go back. 'Go back' he said."

"What did he mean by that? Go back where?"

"I don't know. I assumed he meant the restaurant. But it could have been something else."

"Oh? What?"

She continued with her watering. The tone of her questions was pretty casual, making conversation almost. She didn't seem to be particularly disturbed by the possibility of Yiannis' drowning. I pointed that out to her.

"Oh, I shouldn't worry about it, my boy. He'll turn up. You know what they say, don't you?"

"What?"

"'Evil dogs never die'."

I couldn't believe my hearing her saying that. Her own brother! First I had Yiannis himself confusing me with his contradictory behaviour, then the kids and Bob putting him on a pedestal and praising him for his wonderful qualities, and now his own sister dragging him down and calling him an 'evil dog'! I felt I should defend him.

"Surely, he's not that bad," I said calmly, not wanting to enter into an argument.

"Ah, that's because you don't know him as well as I do," she said, placing the empty watering can on the ground.

She straightened up as much as she could, which wasn't much because of her hump, ran her eye over the garden tenderly, and gave a sigh of half-satisfaction and resignation.

"Well, at least they won't die in this heat. I'll give them a proper soaking later."

I followed her horticultural inspection with some interest, and complimented her on her beautiful garden, while I was searching for the right words to respond to her comment on her brother.

"And it would've been an even better one if he'd spent more time here instead of roaming around, at his age," she said, and then pointed to the stick on the ground.

"Bring it up to the veranda, will you? And let us have some fruit juice." She turned her back to me and started for the veranda.

I bent down to pick up her cane but the second I touched it I felt a shiver coursing down my spine. The stick was straight, not bent at the handle end, and it felt almost alive to the touch, like a short pole of wood dressed with flesh. The top end was decorated with the head of an Egyptian pharaoh bearing the emblems of the lord of upper and lower Egypt and the raised head of a cobra. Below it, carved into the stick, were the symbols of a staff and a crook - all exquisitely crafted. I was holding it in my left hand but, instinct-ively, I placed my right hand on it too and grasped it firmly with both hands.

The most weird feeling came over me: warmth, power, joy, and a sense of recognition. Strange as it may seem, I fell in love with it! I wanted to bring it close to my chest and embrace it like a baby, and I did. The moment it touched my breastbone I had a sense of it melting into my body and entering and assimilating my spine.

Suddenly, I felt a powerful jolt, as if the stick in my spine had become a lightning conductor and was receiving a bolt of lightning. It caused me to straighten and stretch, and I was filled with un-believable energy and clarity of thought. I was, also, practically blinded by the flash. The surge of energy was such that I found myself shaking. I was inundated with joy. Tears began to pour down my cheeks.

Momentarily, I was back at the rock again. And then, I found myself dressed like a pharaoh, holding the ceremonial crook and staff and surveying the ancient land of Upper and Lower Egypt and its temples... I entered the gloriously wonderful temple at Karnak – which was intact, as it must have looked in its heyday. I walked along the rows of rams and went in through the enormous gate, the huge columns towering all around me--

"Stop hugging my walking stick as if it were a woman. Bring it up and let's have some juice," the old woman called from the veranda.

She shook me out of my vision. Still empowered by the experience, and somewhat still living in two worlds at the same time, I held the stick in front of me like a sceptre and walked up the three steps to the veranda.

"What are you doing?" she said rather abruptly. "It's only a stick. Give it to me."

I handed over the cane to her which she took, wrapped her right hand, unceremoniously, over its pharaonic top, planted it on the tiled floor, and walked indoors using it to support herself. I stood there still shivering from the experience and refusing to come back to the present.

"Pull up a chair," she called from inside the house.

I concentrated hard to comply. There was a small table and some chairs on the veranda. I sat on a chair half-facing the garden and the inside of the house. I could see her placing the walking stick on a table just inside the front room. There was a jug of orange juice and a few empty glasses on the table. She poured juice in two of the glasses and walked back to the veranda with them.

"Here, young man," she said, offering me one of the glasses. "Pure juice from the oranges in my orchard."

She sat down near me and raised her glass. "To life, on this side and beyond, and may the devil never catch up with you."

I raised my glass feeling that this wasn't so much a peculiar toast she was making as a strange and cryptic benediction. The juice was refreshingly cold, as if it had just come out of the fridge - I supposed she had taken it out not long before I'd arrived. I thanked her for the drink and expressed my admiration for the craftsmanship on her walking stick.

"A veritable piece of art."

"Oh, yes," she said casually. "It's one of Yiannis' bits. He collects all kinds of rubbish."

My god, I thought, how could she say such a thing? This belonged in an art museum.

As if reading my thought, she continued.

"Yiannis says it came from a royal tomb. Robbers, you know. It wasn't really a walking stick originally. It was something they used in pagan rituals, like.. ehm...Ooh, I don't know. Yiannis knows all about these things. For me it's just a useful cane. I mean, what's the point of keeping it hidden somewhere in a collection when I can make practical use of it? Eh? What do you think?"

I knew exactly what to say but I wasn't sure whether I might not cause offence. Out of the corner of my eye I saw her rubbing the palm of her right hand gently on her knee.

"Mind you, I may have to round off the top with a saw and sand-paper. It's cutting into my hand," she added.

I was horrified! I begged her not to damage it in any way and promised to buy her a new cane, a more comfortable one. She shrugged her shoulders.

"You like my cane, don't you?" she said, sounding a little in-trigued by my interest.

"Yes, I do," I said, holding myself back from opening up and talking about the experience I'd had a few minutes earlier - and which was still with me and buzzing throughout my body. I kept quiet about it in case the old woman thought I was a sandwich short of a picnic!

"I'll do an exchange with you," she proposed. "I'll let you have this cane, since you like it so much, if you get me a really good one, one with a proper handle. As you've just promised."

"But this is not yours to give," I objected, pointing to the stick on the table. "It belongs to Yiannis, doesn't it?"

"Oh, well, technically, I suppose," she said wearily. "But he won't mind, he won't even notice. I've been using it for ever, it's practically mine."

I agreed on the exchange - and was secretly thrilled with it - with the proviso that she talked to Yiannis first. She had no objections. She simply shrugged her shoulders again and said "okay".

We sat there quietly for a while enjoying the colourful garden. The sun was going down behind us and the neighbouring trees were beginning to cast their lengthening shadows. The almost horizontal rays of the sun were bathing the garden in soft, warm hues. In the sky, a couple of small white clouds were dressed in shades of pink and red.

"Shall we go round the other side and catch the sunset?" the old woman said, breaking the silence.

"Oh, yes, let's," I responded, more than pleased with the suggestion.

The house, being detached and facing southeast, had an L-shaped veranda which wrapped round its front and southwest side so that by simply moving to the other end we would be looking west. I picked up two chairs and took them round the side and placed them facing the sunset. I helped the old lady into one of the chairs and sat next to her.

We sat in quiet again. The sun was now about to dip behind a small mountain which rose up five hundred metres away from us. I knew that the other side of it was a sharp precipice, a sheer drop to the sea below. I'd been up there once on a donkey ride and, although it was only a passing visit, I remembered clearly the cliff and the panoramic view it afforded - a breathtaking bird's eye view of an expanse of land and water that went on and on.

The sky was ablaze. The two small clouds were hanging up there motionless, glued to the firmament, dyed red and orange. There was a spread of yellow around the sun, and pink farther out. The blue of the sky was deepening, turning from the light Mediterranean to navy blue. And there was that wonderful, almost liquid, turquoise, and subtler colours that kept changing imperceptibly. All this colourful tapestry was like a raised, open, ceremonial cloak radiating from the sun. No wonder the Greeks called a sunset "the reigning of the sun". The Evening Star was already visible. Soon the whole sky would be full of trillions of brilliant, shimmering stars.

All of a sudden, the atmosphere was filled with the strong scent of the night flowers - they stay obscure all day but as night begins to descend they pour their hearts out and inundate the neighbourhood with the most delicious smell.

I heard the old lady taking a deep breath.

"Ah, this is so wonderful," she exclaimed. "Don't you just love it?"

"Oh, yes. Magical," I concurred.

"Ah, my boy, you've just hit the nail on the head: *magical* is the right word. Yiannis, the old scoundrel who thinks he knows everything, says that this is the time of day when magicians do their best work. Now and at sunrise." She took another deep breath. "Who knows? This may not be one of his hair-brained ideas - and, god knows, he's got plenty of those! It feels right. It *feels* magical."

She fell quiet again, contemplative.

I didn't like her comments about Yiannis and wanted to defend him, but she looked so calm and frail and the atmosphere was so filled with tenderness that I felt reluctant to spoil it. My memory of wincing at her occasional curt response towards me and her un-cultured attitude towards obvious works of art was, somehow, erased. Her love of, and care for, flowers, and the fondness she was now displaying for sunsets, together with the peacefulness of the dusk, dissolved any desire I might have had to comment adversely on anything she had said that I did not agree with. I sank into the soothing atmosphere.

Some time went by, time that seemed 'timeless', when everything went quiet; even the barkings of the dogs and the noisy chirping of the sparrows gathering in their trees and the flying of the bats that had begun to come out for their nightly foraging, receded and slow-ly disappeared. Yianna turned to me and spoke gently, as if she were letting me into a secret.

"When we were children, Yiannis and I used to play a little game of imagination. You know, the sort of thing kids do, picking out figures in the clouds. But a little different. Our parents taught it to us. They guided us through the basics and told us to allow our imagination to be inspired, to let it take us where our hearts and minds needed to go." She took another deep breath. "And, d'you know something? I'm in the mood for it right now. Fancy having a go?"

She surprised me with her tender invitation.

"Well, okay. What do I have to do?"

"Take a deep breath, relax and close your eyes."

"Okay. I can do that."

I followed her instructions and waited. She began to speak again. Her voice was gentle but firm, and the register dropped a little.

"In your mind's eye, see and feel both of us standing up there on the clifftop facing the sea."

She stopped and waited for me to follow her instructions before continuing.

"The clifftop is flat," she continued, "like a plateau. We are standing close to the edge looking ahead. We are barefoot, and the flat stone surface is warm from the sun: we feel it. We are wearing only a thin white gown, like a tunic. We feel a gentle sea breeze rising up the face of the cliff and reaching us. We feel its welcoming coolness running through our gowns and causing them to flutter; we feel it in our face and in our hair; we smell its saltiness. There are seabirds coming to roost in the cliff."

She stopped talking again, presumably to allow me to build up the picture. This was, obviously, a guided visualisation, and I was enjoying every bit of it. I loved heights, and the sea, and empty spaces. It was easy. Then she continued, at a much slower pace.

"Now, as we stand on the clifftop enjoying all these welcoming sensations, we bring our arms up and cross them over our chest. We see and feel a golden-yellow light rising from below, from between our feet, and entering our bodies like a column of energy, encasing our spine and travelling upwards, towards our heads. We see it and feel it. As it reaches our heads it begins to revolve, like a vortex, turning clockwise - from the left to the front, to the right, to the back, to the left, and so on. It shoots up through and above our head like a small volcano. We raise our arms into this vortex and open them out into a V-shape, the shape of the vortex itself."

She stopped and waited. I followed her instructions and continued to spin the vortex. After a short while I began to experience a giggly sensation that rose from my lower abdomen and went up to my stomach, my chest, my throat, my mouth, and into my head. I felt light-headed, a little dizzy.

And then something fascinating happened. I felt myself rising, lifting off. My feet were not touching the ground any longer. As I lifted, I also moved into a more horizontal position. I looked down and saw the dark blue sea. I bent my head a little more and caught sight of my feet, and the gown fluttering around them. Below and beyond them I could see the water lapping gently at the foot of the cliff.

But what was more amazing, I was not following Yianna's instructions - it was the other way round: her voice followed my experiences, like the voice of a narrator in a documentary film describing the action that had just taken place. I raised my head and looked ahead at the sunset. I was now flying. I was weightless, as if I'd caught a thermal and was riding on it. And just as on a thermal, I bobbed up and down gently occasionally. But then I straightened and the 'thermal' variations had no effect on my flight.

I turned to my left to see Yianna. Imagine my surprise when, instead of the old woman I'd been enjoying the sunset with a few minutes earlier, I was now looking at the most gorgeous young woman I'd ever imagined! Her smile radiated unbelievable charm. She was not so much a beautiful woman as an angel. I was filled with such wonderful joy!

We flew together towards the sunset which was now incomparably more beautiful than the one I'd been enjoying from the veranda. Yianna's voice faded away and was gradually replaced by music reminiscent of Sibelius' *Swan of Tuonella*. We passed over what looked like a very small island, an outcropping of rocks in the middle of the sea with a couple of trees growing on them. In the semi-darkness I could see the water lapping on the massive rocks and a few seagulls flying around and landing on them. I could hear their crying in the distance.

The sun was now practically below the horizon and in the far distance I could just about make out the outline of land. As we drew closer I saw that it was a cliff, similar to the one we had flown away from. It was gigantic. We flew close to its face and saw the seabirds flying in to nest in its nooks and crevices. We rose up to its lip and, like eagles on the wing, we lowered ourselves and landed on it. The stone surface was smooth and warm.

In the fast fading light of dusk, and reflecting the light of the rising moon, I could see the shining shape of a very large white building about a hundred metres away. It looked like a classical Greek temple, save that it was circular instead of oblong. There were columns all round it and steps leading up to its floor. The way to it was paved with smooth slabs, easy to walk on with bare feet. As we approached it, I realised that there was no doorway. The only way you could tell that you were inside was simply by walking past the first row of columns, which we did.

The interior felt vast, despite the fact that it was dark and we could not actually see its size. Some distance farther in, a row of columns formed an enormous circle, presumably round the centre of the building. We walked towards this centre on a floor that was continuous and smooth to perfection. I could see light but could not decide where it was coming from. I assumed it came from somewhere in the ceiling.

As we got closer the light became brighter, but the increased brightness didn't seem to be due to our increased 'physical' proximity, as you would normally expect when you approach a source of light. It appeared to possess a different component, a different characteristic from ordinary light: the more I noticed it, the more my attention was focussed on it, the brighter it became. We drew close to what felt to be the centre of the building, where the light was the brightest. I could now hear music in the background, soft and distant.

Out of the surrounding darkness, human figures began to appear, 'taking shape' as if they were being conjured up. Or, maybe they were there all along but I hadn't noticed them before. They came forward, towards the light - scores, hundreds, thousands. All kinds of races, wearing all kinds of clothes. The colour of their skin was of an unbelievable variety: golden, green, blue, brown, purple... But as they approached the light, all their clothes changed to white gowns, like ours, and their faces radiated with goodness and joy. Some of them stepped into the light itself, and, as they did that, they became weightless and began to waft upwards.

I looked up to see where they were floating to and I saw this enormous dome - I *felt* it was a dome for I could not see the end of it because of the brilliance of the light which was pouring down from it. More people stepped into the light and floated upwards, smiling and happy. They were like children on a trampoline. All the while, the volume of the music was increasing almost imperceptibly. I looked around for Yianna and realised I'd lost her. I couldn't see her anywhere. But, somehow, I 'knew' she was not lost, she was somewhere amongst the crowds. Or, maybe she had already stepped into the light and had been lifted up into it. I myself felt the need to do just that.

I moved forward and was immediately flooded by the light. I began to float upwards. The higher I floated the brighter the light I went into and the more 'penetrating' the music: it travelled through me and vibrated throughout my body. And I began to rotate and spin, the way the vortex had spun inside me as I stood on the cliff. And I went higher and higher. All around me were innumerable humans, and other beings, rotating and spinning like me, and I could 'see' the music vibrating and playing 'through' them.

And then, instead of human forms, all those around me began to dissolve into mere shades of colour, hues, that swirled around with the music. Gradually, I realised that the music I was hearing was not external but rather internal to the hues themselves: the sounds/music were emanating from the colours, or, perhaps, it was the other way round, the sounds were giving rise to colours - maybe both; I couldn't tell and it didn't matter. The moment I became aware of this fact, I also realised that I myself was a mere hue swirling around and contributing to this wondrous symphony of colour and sound.

I continued to swirl and 'sing' my part, and, on and off, I would change hue and musical line, like playing different instruments in an orchestra or singing different voices in a choir. And I had the clear realisation that all the hues were intrinsically connected to the source of the brilliant white light that flooded the temple. This was not an intellectual understanding but experiential: I *felt* the connectedness. As I took on different hues, as I *changed* into different hues, I experienced the difference in 'texture', in 'timbre', but I remained always aware of an underlying 'sameness'.

I don't know how long this experience lasted - time seemed to have evaporated. And when it came to an end, it was not the end. What I mean is that the experience in the light did not appear to have a beginning and an end in my consciousness. I had the certainty that it had always been there, and perhaps always will be. But that it had become obscured and pushed to the background by my attention being focussed on issues that Yiannis might have called 'irrelevant'. It possessed the character of a recurring *déjà vu*: I had the feeling that I had experienced it before, forgotten about it, and then experienced it again and forgotten it, and so on....

At some point I found myself back on the veranda. It was dark. The sky was deep blue and thick with stars. The night flowers were still spreading their delicious scent and the heat of the day had given way to the balmy softness of the night. Yianna was not in her chair. I turned around but I couldn't see her anywhere. I stood up and walked over to the front of the house.

By the light of the full moon I could see someone in a chair by the table, near the door. As I approached I realised it was not Yianna. It was a much older woman with very thin white hair. She looked weak, very weak. I greeted her with a "good evening" but got no response. Instead, her whole frail body was shaken by a racking cough. I waited for her cough to subside. I thought of going inside and getting her a glass of water. Was she choking on something? Then I saw Yianna appearing out of the darkness and coming up from the garden, carrying her watering can and supporting herself on her walking stick. She left the can by the steps and greeted me as she climbed up to the veranda.

"Ah, you're back. How was the sunset on the cliff?"

She was casual. As if nothing had happened. She spoke as if she were making polite conversation, as before. I was dying to talk to her about my experience but the older woman's cough sounded very urgent. Yianna approached her and patted her on the back.

"I'll get you something to drink, dear." Then she half-turned to me on her way in. "Come in. I'll get you something, too."

I followed her inside. I wanted to know how much of my experience she shared, what happened with her in the Temple of Light. With experiences of this nature one needs confirmation: was it mere fantasy, shared hallucination, or 'real'? I also wanted to talk about my experience with the walking stick - but then I decided to leave this one out, until I saw Yiannis.

She opened a cupboard and took out a bottle and poured some of its clear content into a cup. The moment I smelt it I knew it was raki, a very powerful alcoholic drink. I was definitely not going to drink that! While searching for something else in the cupboard she asked me where I was staying. I told her, and also told her that my friends were leaving the following day. She wanted to know if I were planning to stay at the hotel by myself. I said that I would for the next few days before moving on.

"Why stay in an expensive hotel by yourself? Why not move in here? Free of charge."

It was a totally unexpected offer, and I wasn't sure how to respond.

"This way you're bound to catch that elusive guttersnipe you've been looking for when he comes here to roost." The way she spoke it wasn't clear whether she was abusing Yiannis again or using insulting words as terms of endearment.

I dithered, but the offer was definitely very attractive, although the house was so small. Where would I sleep? I asked her. She finished pouring a sweet rose-and-almond smelling drink in a glass.

"That's for you," she said. "Come with me."

She led the way to another room. It was small but tidy, with a window overlooking the back yard. There was a small wardrobe, an old sofa and an unmade bed. A black dress lay draped over a chair.

"Here," she said.

"But somebody else sleeps in here already," I said. "Whose room is it?"

"The old woman's," she said casually.

I looked at the bed, then at the sofa, trying to work out what she was actually suggesting. As if reading my thought, she added.

"You can take her bed. She'll sleep on the sofa. She's very small."

I stood there thinking that if this was a joke - and it had to be a joke! - it was in very poor taste.

"Unless you'd like to share the bed with her," she continued. "She doesn't take much space; and she's usually very quiet. She doesn't normally cough this much." She looked at my puzzled face and added. "Don't worry; she won't be with us long. Another day maybe."

Now, surely, she must have meant that the white-haired lady was moving to another house, or a hospice perhaps. But I needed to know for certain that that was what she meant.

"Where is she going?" I asked.

"What do you mean 'where'? She's dying, can't you tell?"

I was glued in my tracks, dumbfounded. She was actually suggesting that I should sleep in the bed of a person who was close to dying, having got her out of her own bed and on to the sofa, or, if I preferred, get into bed with her, all the while expecting to have her bedroom to myself when she had died! - her death probably occurring while I was lying in bed next to her! I was getting dizzy just thinking about it.

"Unless you prefer to sleep in here," she said, and led me to an adjacent room.

This was a more spacious room, airy, not as tidy as the other one but plush, with a dressing table and a double bed. There was a big wardrobe standing next to a window which was draped with heavy curtains and frilly netcurtains. Unusually, there were no outside shutters to this window.

"Whose room is this?" I asked, still not comfortable with the tour and the suggestions.

"It's mine," she said, and waited for me to respond.

"And where are you going to sleep?" I asked.

"Well," she said, and went over to the bed and patted the covers gently. "It's a double bed. Plenty of room." She spoke in a soft, seductive voice.

I knew that if I opened my mouth to say anything I would be mumbling and fumbling for words, so I kept quiet, trying to compose myself, waiting to see how this minor nightmare would develop. At the back of my mind I continued to hold that all this was nothing more than a very, very bad joke.

The weird thing was that the whole room exuded a sense of gentle femininity, affection, and sensuality. The plushness of its interior and the absence of external shutters gave it an air of abandon and inner security. The scene of flying with young and beautiful Yianna flashed before me and I was filled with joy, affection and yearning.

I looked at her and almost believed that she was young and desirable. In other circumstances she would have looked utterly ridiculous. But there was something of a veneer of youth about her that did not look artificial, superficial perhaps but not artificial. Still, something held me back, I couldn't go to bed with her. Was it, perhaps, because her offer came hard on the heels of her other suggestion to sleep with the dying white-haired old woman? I couldn't tell. Besides, every time I looked at her I was reminded of Yiannis. Ooh, no way!

I said that I would think about her generous offer, looked at my watch and explained that my friends would already be waiting for me at the taverna, and began to backtrack towards the door. Strangely enough, she did not make any attempts to dissuade me from leaving, although she did express her regret that I had chosen to leave so early.

She held the walking stick up in front of her in the same manner that I myself had done earlier, like a sceptre, and reminded me of my promise to get her a better cane to exchange with her present one. She held it up with the carvings and decorations facing me. I was certain she was doing that deliberately. I could see it in her eyes. I wanted to grab it out of her frail bony hand and claim it as mine. I glanced from her eyes to the cane and back to her eyes again. I could go to bed with her for the ownership of that cane! And she knew it. She was daring me. It was a battle of wills. No, not of wills. Just my will, my intellectual will, against a glamour, an illogical fascination I felt for the cane and Yianna.

I stood my ground. And then I heard her voice saying "it's only a cane". That bolstered my resistance. I shook myself out of the semi-hypnotic state I had allowed myself to slip into and renewed my promise to her. She insisted I drank the soft drink she had prepared for me, which I did and found refreshing and invigorating, and asked me to carry the other drink to her friend on the veranda.

She walked behind me, and the slow shuffling of her feet felt like an affectionate caress all over me, a sad, sad goodbye. Would I ever see her again? I wanted to turn round and take her in my arms. And tell her that I was sorry. Sorry for what? Sorry for the fact that, although she was amazingly beautiful inside, on the outside she was old and wrinkly and therefore I could not make love to her.

I put the glass of raki on the table in front of the old woman with the white hair, and stood there momentarily to take a last look at her. She was quiet, very quiet. She was not coughing any longer. In fact, she was not breathing. I looked at Yianna who nodded to me almost imperceptibly and shrugged her shoulders in quiet resignation.

She moved closer to me and patted me on the back affectionately, and I couldn't resist bending down and giving her a tender kiss on the cheek. It felt cold, deadly cold. And then a tear trickled out of her eye, warming her cheek and touching my lips. To my surprise, it was not salty as tears normally are: it was sweet. Instinctively, I licked my lips. She smiled. And then, at a totally unguarded moment, I took her bony hands into mine and kissed them very very lovingly and affectionately. She looked happy.

As I moved away she called out to me to "Come back soon." I promised. After all, we had an agreement to exchange canes; and her place seemed as good as any to find Yiannis on one of his occasional visits.

I walked quickly, I practically ran, down the road to the church and sat outside on a step and let go. I wept; I had to; I had to let my emotions out, I was bursting. The church was dark and there was nobody going in or coming out, and there were no street lights. The moon, however, shone brightly, and anyone passing by would see me, but I didn't care, it did not matter - I was bowled over.

It took me a long while to compose myself and attempt to take stock. The brightness of the moonlight created great contrasts between light and dark, and the shadows appeared more imposing than normal; they felt alive. The whole area had acquired a secret, mysterious, glow, reminiscent of the time when, as a child, I used to play hide-and-seek with my friends in the old cemetery. But thanks to the general calmness of the surroundings and the continuous exudation of the night flowers' balmy scent, eventually I pulled myself together.

I took a few deep breaths and reflected. There were certain similarities between the two siblings, the twins Yiannis and Yianna. Not only in their physical appearance, which was naturally striking, but also in their behaviour and the effect it had on me. They both presented me with contradictions, enormous contradictions.

But, whereas Yiannis' contradictions - besides his behaviour - were mostly intellectual, those of Yianna's were purely emotional. In her behaviour - as with that of Yiannis - one minute she was terse, dry, and even curt, the next minute she was very affectionate and caring. Granted, there was an overlap and similarity in some of the emotions that both elicited from me, but Yianna aroused a whole spectrum of them, a number of which were on the same line as those engendered by Yiannis but more delicate - if, at times, intense - and personal.

How could I possibly have that range of feelings towards an old woman I had just met for the first time in my life? How could I feel so much for her? And, most puzzling, how could I possibly be sexually aroused by her?! This latter not only puzzled but definitely worried me!

Strong emotional reactions towards strangers and brand new acquaintances as well as places and buildings, I had come to recognise as indications of past intimate connections, of past incarnations, which I would confirm to myself with further investigation. In earlier days, I would carry out the investigation and then seek confirmation from external sources, including, in some cases, the person(s) involved in these relationships. But later I began to rely entirely on my own, 'internal', investigations - even so, I would, on advice, only delve into such situations if I deemed it utterly necessary.

In the case of Yianna, as with Yiannis, I felt the connections strongly but, for whatever reasons, I was being denied access to their source - and I needed to get to their source in order to make sense of them. I was not prepared to give in. I would investigate in other ways - later, when my heart and mind were more settled.

The pharaonic incident had to be deciphered. Because it was so short, I had no time to get into it to ascertain its status. My 'obsession' with the sceptre was almost unbelievable! To get into it further I felt I needed to touch it again, to hold it. I should get back to Yianna at some stage to do just that if nothing else, even if she changed her mind and reneged on our agreement to exchange canes, after she had spoken to Yiannis - which reminded me that first thing in the morning I should go and find the best cane I could lay my hands on, just in case.

The guided visualisation worked, again, on an emotional level, even the final part of it where I had turned into a mere shade of colour and a musical note - an experience almost identical to another one I had had in my teenage years, except that the earlier one was the result of intellectual insight. I felt that many of my earlier experiences were repeating themselves but that they were coming from a different perspective. They had an emotional/devotional aspect to them....

A low growl brought me out of my reflecting mood. When I turned my head I was faced once again with the mongrel. He was hanging about at the other side of the road. I couldn't see if he was wagging his tail this time, and his growl wasn't particularly threatening - in fact, it sounded more like a friendly growl, the sort of growl dogs make when you play with them. When he noticed me looking at him, he simply sat down and formed a perfect representation of Anubis. I wasn't apprehensive of his presence any longer, just curious. I resisted a strange, unwarranted, urge to go over and stroke him; and he wouldn't come any closer.

I glanced at my watch and realised how late it was. My friends would be wondering what happened to me. I stood up and looked around. Apart from the dog and me, the place was all but deserted. It was, after all, at the edge of the village. I saw a water tap by the door to the church's sanctum and walked over to it. I washed my face and dried it with the corner of my shirt and let the water run to create a pool on the ground; I then looked at the dog to let him know it was for him, took a deep breath and set off for the seafront.

Returning was easy: all I had to do was follow the distant lights of the island and my nose - the evening breeze from the sea helped me find my bearings and work out the direction to the seafront by simply breathing in its saltiness. It was a game I and the other kids used to play, called "find the water".

– 7 –

At Zeno's Taverna
(Athespodos - and something about Life after Death)

At the seafront, the place was bustling with tourists coming and going in the little ferries. Life was carrying on as normal. Getting into a boat to travel across to the island, I wasn't sure whether I was waking from a dream or stepping into one. Which was more real - the events at Yianna's house, including the wonderfully liberating experience in the Temple of Light, or sitting among the tourists whose only concern was to gravitate towards the nearest taverna?

I looked around me and saw happiness and excitement in their faces; they were alive and three-dimensional, but that was all. There was something missing. They were puppets, following the movements dictated to them by invisible, 'instinctive', controls.

And then, through them, right through them, I could now also see the hues and hear the harmonious music resounding from the Temple. They were superficial, clueless, shortsighted in their 'earthly' personalities, and yet glorious at another level. Oh, my god! I could actually see them as, for want of another term, 'angelic beings'! Wearing human flesh, limited in time and space, and yet gloriously beautiful. Oh, the human condition! And suddenly sadness descended on me: why would human beings not live in that wondrous state all the time? WHY?!

As I stepped out of the boat I could hear the voice of the Teacher merging with that of Yiannis: "It's all a matter of degree, and a matter of 'seeing'. Beauty is everywhere, in everybody and in everything." And above that, the words of Yiannis at the rock: "Stay with happiness... Stay with happiness..." I shook off the sadness and the negativity and walked on along the island's seafront.

The taverna I was going to was farther down, at the seafront. There were a number of shops and a bank on the way, and then a row of tavernas. After that, a patch of rocky land and at the very end a disco. Then the land curved to shape off a promontory and continue over the other side with a small rocky cove before stretching out into a coast littered with hotels. On my right, were a number of yachts moored on the quay, with some tourists already sitting on the decks enjoying their drinks and the lights and watching other tourists sauntering up and down the narrow seafront in their usual relaxed holiday manner and going in and out of shops in search of souvenirs.

I could hear the music from the tavernas in the distance and felt myself merging back into the holiday spirit when I bumped into, of all people, Bob the 'Australian' restaurateur! Was I pleased to see him again! After the initial but genuine pleasantries he told me that he'd come over to the island to visit a cousin, answering an emergency call which, thank god, turned out to be a false alarm, and was now hurrying back before a real disaster struck his restaurant, as the place had been left in the hands of amateurs. We had a laugh, he told me how much he'd like to see me drop by again soon and, as he was leaving, he asked me if I'd managed to pay Yianna a visit. I told him that I was just coming from there, and gently rebuked him for not telling me that Yianna was Yiannis' twin.

"What are you talking about?" he querried with genuine surprise.

"Yianna. You know, the twin. I had the shock of my life, I tell you."

He looked at me in disbelief.

"Wait a minute. Have you been drinking?"

"No. Why?"

"Because Yianna isn't Yiannis' twin. For a start, she's much older than him."

It was my turn now to look at him in disbelief. I couldn't understand this. I was there, I saw her. We talked about Yiannis. I held his cane in my hands. We were to do an exchange... Unless... A totally illogical thought crossed my mind.

"Did you say she is much older than him?"

"Yes."

"Is she dying?"

"God forbid, no! She's the picture of health and strong as an oak. What's the matter with you, boy? Are you sure you haven't been drinking?"

I felt dizzy. I pressed my foot against a bollard next to me for support, and took a deep breath.

"No, no. It's just that..."

I didn't know what to say. I didn't know what to think. Bob started laughing. Very inappropriate, I thought. Was he taking the mickey? Was this a practical joke?

"You went to the wrong house, didn't you?" he said.

No, no. I didn't go to the wrong house. I gave him the description of the location and the house. His response was another bout of laughter.

"You did go to the wrong house. In fact, I think you probably went to the wrong village!"

He couldn't stop laughing. Fine for him to laugh but I was totally disorientated. I seemed to be jumping from one nightmare into another - granted, with bits of paradise in between. I wanted to talk to him about my adventure in detail, hoping that he might help me make some sense, but he had to get back to his restaurant. He asked me to visit him the following day, anytime, he said, shook my hand warmly and jumped into a departing boat, still chuckling and shaking his head in disbelief.

And then, as if it were an afterthought, or as if he'd just remembered, he shouted that he'd seen Yiannis on the island, and pointed somewhere in the direction of Zeno's taverna - or, maybe he was simply waving goodbye to me, it looked that way. Was he doing this deliberately, leaving me hanging in the air like that with bits of uncertain information? Confusion descended upon me once more with a vengeance. He'd thrown a spanner in the works as far as Yianna's identity was concerned and then he threw a bone of hope to me in regards to Yiannis' 'survival'.

I sank to the ground and rested my back against the bollard. My day's adventures began to look like those popular but thoroughly inane English mystery novels which are replete with red herrings and wild goose chases. Whatever next?

Out of the corner of my eye I caught sight of a young tourist couple who stopped three or so metres away from me and were now looking straight in my direction. They whispered to each other and one of them put his hand in his pocket. Oh, no! That was all I needed right then, to be taken for a beggar. They'd be throwing coins at my feet in a minute. I quickly stood up, in the nick of time. They hesitated, I waved my hand to them and turned my back. They got the message. They looked embarrassed and walked away.

I sat on the bollard and gazed at the water lapping on the side of a yacht. Looking at the water always helped me calm down and organise my thoughts. But it was difficult right now, too much going on around me. And I couldn't go back the way I'd come - it was worse in that direction. But if I walked fast past the tavernas, hugging the edge of the seafront, I might just escape the notice of my friends who would definitely be at Zeno's by now, and get to the rocky area where I knew it would be more quiet - the disco wouldn't have started yet - and the sea would be open and clear in front of me. All I needed was a few minutes staring at the sea and listening to the lapping of the water.

I walked quickly and as close to the edge of the sea as possible. But there were so many lights and I was so very visible. The tavernas were already packed full. Everybody was sitting outside, of course, under the vine pergolas and in the wide courtyards of the tavernas that stretched all the way out to the small street which separated them from the narrow promenade - on which I was rushing along.

I was fast approaching Zeno's when I noticed a sizeable commotion outside the adjacent taverna, the one beyond Zeno's. Some customers from Zeno's were going over to the other taverna and standing around watching some kind of show. I thought this would be my chance to pass by unnoticed. I hurried.

But as I arrived at Zeno's, Mike, one of my friends, called out to me. He was sitting alone at a table near the street. That was it, I couldn't get away. I had to shelve my personal, psychological, concerns and join my friend. The best laid plans of mice and men..., as the saying goes. You see, I couldn't open up to Mike and Harry because neither of them was prepared to entertain a belief in "metaphysical nonsense", inspite of the fact that they were both well educated with university degrees, or perhaps because of it.

I walked over to Mike and apologised for being late. It was okay, he said, they'd only just arrived themselves, hence the position of their table at the edge of the courtyard, practically in the street.

"Where's Harry?" I inquired.

We spoke in Greek, and switched to English only when Harry was around. Mike and I came from the same island but had never met prior to this summer. He was studying in the States, where he spent most of his time doing his doctorate in musicology. Harry was American and studying at the same university doing a science degree, having already completed one in English.

"Over there," he replied, pointing to the small crowd at the adjacent taverna. I couldn't help noticing a lack of cheerfulness in his normally lively voice. He looked preoccupied.

"Is everything alright, Mike," I asked, and sat on a chair next to him.

"No," he said, and half-turned away to hide his emotion. "Everything is not alright." He sighed and turned back to me. "Uncle Costas, my favourite uncle, died yesterday. I've just heard."

"Oh, I'm sorry. I really am. But... he was fit and healthy, wasn't he? How...?"

"Heart attack."

"Oh, god."

That was all I could say. What else? The man was about seventy but fit as a fiddle. I'd seen pictures of him that Mike carried in his wallet. He owned a watersport facility back home and he himself was a windsurfing instructor. He looked healthier than any one of us boys.

"What are you going to do now?"

"I don't know. I should cancel the flight to the States and go back home for a few days, but I can't afford to. I don't know. Harry said he'll help."

"Why don't you, then? He has the money. What are friends for?" I encouraged him.

Just then, Harry walked over from the crowd next door.

"Hi, Andrew. We thought you abandoned us."

"Sorry. I got held up."

"By a chick, I bet."

"I should be so lucky," I said, and quickly changed the subject; there was no point in talking about my day. "I've heard the bad news."

"Yeah. Terrible, isn't it? We were with the guy only a couple of weeks ago."

He turned to Mike, patted him on the back and sat next to him.

"Take it easy, pal. We're all sorry. Forget the flight, I'll take care of it. Let's have something to eat and wash it down with a little wine; it will help. Tomorrow, when we go up to Athens, I'll sort it out for you. I wish I could come with you, but you know I have to be back."

The waiter arrived and the conversation glided naturally into food and wine. As he was about to leave with our order, there was a loud cheer and clapping from the neighbouring taverna.

"What's going on over there?" I asked.

"Oh, it's just an old man doing a dance. He pops round the tavernas every now and then and does a dance for a meal. He was here two nights ago, you missed him," explained the waiter.

"Ah, you should see this," added Harry enthusiastically. "It's a little old guy dancing by himself. He's fantastic. Come and have a look-see."

He got up and told the waiter to keep our table, we'd be back. We followed him to the adjacent taverna - you could hardly tell they were two tavernas as there was no boundary wall and the two courtyards merged into each other.

Some tables had been pushed outwards from the middle of the courtyard, creating a small clearing in the centre of which a man was dancing a Zeimbekiko, a dance involving a great deal of leaning forwards and touching the floor and jumping and turning and twisting to the upbeat of the music; a tricky dance which, when executed properly, tends to give the false impression that the dancer may be drunk and about to fall over. And whoever was dancing at that moment was doing an excellent job of it - drunk or not.

When we arrived on the scene, the dancer had his head bent and was turning like a top with his arms outstretched and his hands pointing to the ground in big sweeping movements. Then he jumped a couple of times like an acrobat landing on one foot and then shifting his weight onto the other. Very athletic, I thought. At some point, he turned and faced in our direction and straightened himself into a new position which was followed by another vigorous twist. I caught my breath! I thought I recognised Yiannis! Surely not. Oh, no, not another red herring! Not another identical twin! Harry noticed my reaction.

"I told you he was good, didn't I?" he said, taking my intake of air to be a sign of appreciation of the dancer's performance. "And I bet he's at least a hundred, if a day. How about that?"

When the dancer turned to face us again and straightened to full height, my sharp intake of air must have sounded more like the effect of a shock - which, indeed, was - than a sign of enthusiasm.

"You okay, buddy?" asked Harry, with genuine concern in his

voice, and placed an arm over my shoulder.

I found it extremely hard to conceal my reactions now. There was no doubt. It was Yiannis. Either that or I was hallucinating or dreaming. But, no, it *was* Yiannis. Just before the very last twirl of his dance, he raised his right arm and waved to me. There was no doubt about it - that movement of his arm wasn't part of the dance, it was clearly aimed at me. I responded automatically by returning the greeting.

"Hey, you know this guy?" shouted Harry in the midst of the clapping and cheering of the appreciative crowd.

I only had time to say "Yes" before Yiannis made a beeline for us. Customers offered their hands for congratulatory handshakes and invited him to join them at their tables as he passed by. He was courteous in declining and thanking them for their offer.

This was a new side of Yiannis' character I hadn't suspected. He was displaying a different personality from the one I'd seen before, a bit of a parochial old hippie popstar. He wore a shirt that was open all the way down to his stomach, with a long gold chain hanging round his neck and a gold medallion at the end of it - a blank disk of gold.

I made the introductions and he accepted my offer to join us at our table next door. This was my chance; there was no way I was going to let him get away this time. Only, I'd have to wait till after the meal to raise any questions with him, in order to avoid confrontations and, possibly, bad feelings because of my friends' views on "metaphysics".

The waiter was more than pleased to grab an extra chair from next door to accommodate our guest - it turned out that the two adjacent tavernas were owned by two brothers, which made me wonder whose mother was doing the cooking for which taverna! Yiannis asked the waiter for whatever mezedes - small dishes - they had, and sat at one end of the table, between my friends who were very complimentary about his dancing and his amazing energy.

"Clean living, boys. Clean living," said Yiannis, and looked them up and down.

"You don't drink, then?" said Harry, making a statement more than asking a question.

"I could drink you under the table, young man," Yiannis responded laughing, "but I wouldn't want you to end up in hospital."

We all laughed at Yiannis' mock challenge. But I noticed that Harry wasn't very happy with that.

"What do you mean 'end up in hospital'?" he asked.

"Nothing. Just that drinking as a challenge is simply daft and can ruin your health," said Yiannis smiling.

His answer was reasonable enough but I could tell from Harry's reaction that Yiannis had touched a sore spot, and the old man seemed to be aware of it. But, happily, the conversation changed direction when Mike asked him if he made his living by dancing.

"No," said Yiannis, "but I'd do anything to earn a crust."

A middle-aged woman at a nearby table smiled at Yiannis and greeted him with a wave of her hand.

"I'd sell my body, if I had to," he added, and beamed a smile at the woman.

The rest of us couldn't control our laughter at the thought. Then Mike pointed at the medallion Yiannis was wearing and asked him if it meant anything. He had spoken to Yiannis in Greek and used a word for 'anything' which, in the shorthand manner of everyday speech, could be turned into 'nothing' by simply omitting the negative particle 'not' in the answer, which was what Yiannis did.

"Nothing," he said, and then proceeded to explain to Harry the play on words.

I was quite impressed with Yiannis' mastery of English. He spoke fluently with only the trace of an accent, which I could not place - it was definitely not the accent of an Athenian Greek speaking English.

"So, the medallion you're wearing is *nothing*", Harry concluded, getting into the spirit of the wordgame.

"No. Not the medallion, the *meaning* of the medallion, not the medallion itself," Yiannis corrected him, and gave me a wink as if to say 'watch this'.

"So, the medallion has no meaning, then," Harry persisted.

Yiannis laughed and addressed his next remark to me.

"Listen to him," he said. "Listen to the English language making something out of nothing."

"What do you mean," reacted Harry.

"Look: for example, in English you say 'there is nothing in this room', in Greek we say 'there isn't anything or something in this room'. In Greek we refuse to make a statement about what does not exist; in English you do not only make a positive statement about it, positing that *nothing* does actually exists, but you also often stress the verb that accompanies that statement. You bring *nothing* into existence, you turn it into a *thing*."

While Harry began to mumble various sentences to himself trying to work out the logic of Yiannis' statement on the conceptual structure of existence in the English language, Yiannis turned to Mike.

"What do you think, Mike?"

"I don't know," came the answer. "English is not my first language."

"Maybe it's just an Anglo-Saxon thing. Concentrating on what your senses can tell you, being scientific," Yiannis concluded, being deliberately provocative.

And Harry took the bait. "What's wrong with that? Where would we be without science?"

"Oh, I'm all for science, Harry. Don't get me wrong," Yiannis came back. "So long as by science we don't mean concentrating all our attention exclusively on the caterpillar, forgetting the chrysalis and the butterfly."

The conversation was suddenly diverted by the arrival of the food. No argument there! Whatever the merits or demerits of a discussion on the scientific approach, the body needed sustenance.

"Okay, guys, let's forget the chrysalis and the butterfly for now," said Harry, with an obvious appetite to satisfy, "and let's get stuck in!" And then, with a side-look at Yiannis: "Wow, this is some caterpillar, pal!"

We all laughed and agreed. The food was good, and so was the wine. Mike, however, was merely nibbling, and becoming distant again. Harry, who was sitting opposite him, tried to get him to eat some of his appetizing mezedes, offering him beans and making jokes about them, but Mike didn't seem to be interested.

"Lost your appetite, have you?" Yiannis asked, and turned towards Mike on his right.

"Well...," was the half-response from Mike.

"His favourite uncle died yesterday, and he's very upset," Harry explained.

"Oh, I see," came Yiannis' casual response. "And not eating is going to help your uncle, is it?"

The comment sounded insensitive and even cruel but, remarkably, Mike did not react in the way one might have expected him to - by showing that he was offended, that is. He simply said "No, but...," and let his mind wander.

Yiannis took a mouthful of some meze and continued in the same casual manner. "Or are you feeling guilty for having had so much sex last night?"

He dropped it like a bomb. Now, that was the Yiannis I remembered from the rock - shocking! Harry and I stopped eating and looked up to see Mike's reaction. Mike appeared numb; then, with his head bent and still, his eyes darted in all directions. He didn't say anything for a few seconds. Then he turned to Yiannis and spoke in a subdued tone.

"What do you...how did you....What are you talking about?"

Yiannis took another mouthful and mumbled "Mmm, this is really good," before responding to Mike's question.

"I shouldn't let it worry you, Mike. It's natural. When someone very close to you passes on, they bequeath all their energy to you - well, nearly all of it." He patted Mike gently on the back and added: "Eat your meatballs. And I'll show you how to help your uncle."

Mike stared at the plate in front of him, then raised his head and stared at me and Harry. We were already staring at him, waiting for his reaction. Strangely enough, Harry kept quiet, not his usual behaviour. Normally he would have reacted at the sort of remarks Yiannis had been making and the assumptions implied by his advice to Mike. Maybe he was stunned by Yiannis' audacity, or perhaps intrigued by his apparently inexplicable possession of information regarding Mike's sexual activities the night before.

I was on the edge of my seat, waiting. I nodded my encouragement to Mike who glanced furtively at Yiannis and decided to join us in the land of the living by beginning to eat, grudgingly at first, and then with more gusto.

"That's my boy," shouted Yiannis approvingly, and raised his glass. "To life, on this side and beyond, and may the devil never catch up with us."

His toast sent shivers down my spine: although delivered in English, it was Yianna's toast on the veranda! - except that he included himself in the toast. Yiannis gave me a knowing glance that made my heart jump - he knew, and he would explain! (?).

Harry scooped a mouthful of beans from the small plate in front of him, and added to Yiannis' toast:

"And to the beans, the glorious Greek beans!"

"And may they fill our sails with favourable wind!" old Yiannis completed the toast.

With a natural bonhomie re-established, we showed our appreciation of the Greek cuisine by clearing most of the mezedes as well as polishing off a couple of bottles of the local wine and working on a third one.

Harry kept glancing at Mike every now and then, keeping an eye on him, making sure he did not slip back into a state of sadness, becoming morose. Harry's gregariousness seemed somewhat sullied by Mike's undercurrent of sorrow - you could just feel Mike's sadness simmering under a forced veneer of cheerfulness.

In the end, having got a little tipsy and forgotten his sensibilities - or, maybe, he was too intrigued by the old man's intimations of afterlife - Harry broke the silence:

"Well then, when are we going to see you restore old Costas to life?" he asked, addressing Yiannis teasingly.

"It is not a case of restoring him to life, as you put it, my young friend," responded Yiannis. "Life is never lost, restoring is not necessary."

"Life is never lost?! But the man is dead, finished, kaput."

Yiannis gave a little chuckle. I was watching Mike to see his reaction to Harry's rather insensitive comments. He kept quiet, listening, not participating.

"Funny you should use the word *kaput*," said Yiannis smiling.

"Funny? What's funny about it?"

"No, I don't mean funny ha-ha. Strange. It's interesting you used a Latin word - okay, German of Latin derivation. You used the word *kaput* which means broken, not functioning properly, which is precisely the state Costas is in right now.

"There was an expression used in the Middle Ages, *caput mortuum* which means 'dead head'. It was used by alchemists to mean 'worthless residue' when they referred to whatever was left after distillation, or, more importantly, sublimation."

Harry scratched his head and pulled a face to show puzzlement as a comment to Yiannis' tour of the Middle Ages. But I could see what Yiannis was driving at, and waited with anticipation. I'd been careful not to drink too much. I had suspected that Yiannis might come up with something interesting, and I didn't want my mind clouded or my senses dulled.

"So?" said Harry.

"D'you remember my mentioning the caterpillar, the chrysalis and the butterfly?"

"Yes?" answered Harry with a tinge of sarcasm.

"Well," said Yiannis, shaking his head gently from side to side, "Mike's uncle has sort of left part of the caterpillar stage behind, that part which is *kaput*, but he's not in the chrysalis stage yet. Like most of us, really."

"What do you mean?" asked Mike whose interest was suddenly aroused. "He's in some kind of limbo?"

"There will be zombies walking about, in a minute, " said Harry, bursting out laughing.

"Oh, please be quiet, Harry!" came Mike's reaction. "I want to hear this."

"But you don't believe in this stuff, Mike, do you?"

"All the same, I want to hear, if you don't mind."

Harry had begun to look a bit more tipsy - well, drunk - than his consumption of wine to that point would have warranted. Yiannis turned his attention to him.

"Ehm, I don't want to sound personal, Harry, but don't you think you should go easy with the wine?"

"Why? It's great, I like it, man," said Harry raising a full glass.

"I know you do, Harry," said Yiannis, and gave Harry a long penetrating look, "but your kidneys don't."

Harry's hand froze in midair. "Who told you about my kidneys?" He looked at Mike and then at me as he began to lower his glass. "Did you?"

"No, of course not," I said, very surprised at the accusation. "I didn't even know you had kidney problems."

"Well, I don't!" said Harry very defiant. Then he placed his glass on the table, lowered his head and stared at it, sighed quietly, and mumbled: "Well, I do." My heart went out to him. He looked up at Yiannis and spoke in a more subdued voice.

"How did you know?"

"Ooh, I don't know. Someone must have mentioned it. I forget. But why worry? You're young, with an otherwise healthy constitu-

tion. If you're careful and you don't indulge too much you should
be okay," said Yiannis, clumsily brushing the issue aside.

Harry didn't look as if he were buying all that, and I could feel
he was formulating some response. But then something else
happened. I saw Mike shuddering a little, as if a mild draught of air
had caught his neck. As I concentrated on him, I felt the presence of
his uncle about him, enclosing him, talking to him, desperately
trying to draw his attention. I looked at Yiannis who gave me a
knowing smile.

"My uncle," said Mike, all of a sudden.

"What about your uncle?" asked Yiannis casually.

"Exactly. What about him? You started saying something about
being in a limbo."

"No, I didn't say that. You said it."

"Well, alright, I said it. What were you saying, then?"

Yiannis reflected for a second or two before speaking.

"Look, let me tell you two things for a start. Your uncle, like you
and Harry, doesn't believe in anything beyond the grave. Second-"

"Doesn't? You mean *didn't*," interrupted Mike.

"No. I mean *doesn't*. Just bear with me," Yiannis insisted, and
continued. "Second, he went suddenly, right?"

"Yes. But how did you--?"

"Listen. I'm not going to argue with you to convince you about
anything. That's not my place." Yiannis then turned to Harry. "And
I'm not going to enter into a series of experiments to try and prove
anything to either of you. You take it or leave it. Do we agree?"

He sounded a bit impatient but authoritative. Mike said "okay"
and Harry simply shrugged his shoulders. Yiannis then turned to
Mike again.

"Now, your uncle passed on suddenly. He came out of the water,
felt a severe pain in the chest, felt breathless and weak, and slumped
down to the ground. The attack was sudden and death was quick.
This is all in the past now, the physical frame you identified as your
uncle is dead, finished - kaput, as Harry would say. Are you with
me so far?"

Mike nodded and added a "yes?" with some anticipation, but
slouched in discomfort. Being constantly reminded that his uncle
had died didn't exactly fill him with a zest for life. Yiannis leant a
little towards him and lowered his voice. Fortunately, sitting at the

edge of the courtyard now proved to be an advantage, as we happened to be a good distance away from the loudspeakers of the taverna and did not have to shout to be heard.

"But as far as your uncle himself is concerned," Yiannis continued, "he's not dead: he lay down to rest because he was in pain and felt weak and exhausted. And then he fell asleep - that's what he thinks has happened. Next thing, he's back in his village as a child. He thinks he's dreaming, and he's happy. He also runs into some old pals of his from his adult life whom he knows have passed on many years ago. They are happy to see him and vice versa.

"Then he shoots down to the beach where he meets up with his friends, who are still alive, only they don't respond when he talks to them. He gets angry and frustrated and thinks they are ignoring him. He gets confused. Those who are dead talk to him and tell him how happy they are that he's now with them but those who are still alive appear to ignore him, except that some of them, especially some relatives, are crying and feeling sad at having lost him, and they make him feel pretty miserable: if only they would keep quiet and listen to him and stop being so fucking - his word not mine - deaf!"

Yiannis stopped talking for a beat or two. I had my eyes half-closed while he was talking, concenrating on what he was saying. And the same thing happened as with Yianna's guided visualisation: I saw what he was saying before he said it.

Moreover, I saw much more, which Yiannis left out. He had been 'editing' the material, leaving out a great deal that would have upset Mike. I was surprised by the fact that I was able to see so much more, and also by Yiannis' editing, but I understood why he did it. And this understanding came visually and intuitively: it was packed solid with information that would have taken a thick book to explain or a very long film, and even then it would have had to be an edited version.

I was pulled out of my musings by Harry's voice.

"Wake up, pal! The story's not that boring!" Then he turned to Yiannis. "See what you did? You put him to sleep."

"Yes, I know. I'm afraid I have that effect on people," responded Yiannis, jocularly.

I opened my eyes wide to catch Yiannis' knowing smile. He looked at Harry and then went back to Mike who was still absorbed in Yiannis' report on his uncle's fate.

"Where is he now?" asked Mike, with genuine concern.

"Where do you think?" was the return. Yiannis stared at him with intensity and repeated the question: "Where do you think?"

All of us went quiet for a while, even Harry who was now watching his friend with interest to see what he would say or do. I saw Mike shuddering again, and then he started crying like a baby. His uncle was practically overshadowing him. Yiannis patted Mike on the back, comforting him. Harry looked on bewildered at his friend's behaviour; then he straightened up and seemed angry, and was about to cut in. Yiannis raised his hand and shook his head at him, stopping him from interfering. He kept his other hand on Mike's back comforting him for a while longer before he spoke again.

"Now, where is he now, Mike?" he said in a low voice, stroking Mike's back gently.

Mike couldn't speak right away, he was still sobbing. But he made an effort, he took a deep breath and managed to subdue the sobbing, then took another deep breath and raised his head a little. And there, cutting through the intermittent sniffling, quivered a timid smile. Harry stared in disbelief - what was happening to his friend?

Yiannis repeated the question. "Well, where is he now?"

"Here, with me," flowed the answer, and Mike's smile widened and the sniffling stopped.

Harry continued to stare at Mike. Then he looked at me and Yiannis, trying to work out what kind of trick we were playing on his friend.

"Good," said Yiannis. "Now that he knows you're responding to his desperate efforts to get through to you, he'll be more amenable to guidance. He loves you, and he knows you love him. That's important. You send him loving thoughts - not thoughts of sadness at losing him but purely loving thoughts. And, as you're doing that, you tell him - you can voice your thoughts or just do it mentally - that you know he's passed on and that's alright. The others will take over from there."

"What others?"

"Those whose job it is to take care of people like your uncle and help them adjust to their new environment. Don't worry, he's in good hands. Soon, he'll be with his brothers and sisters and other relatives, and he'll be settling in to a new life."

"New life? What new life?" murmured Mike.

"A new life without a physical body."

"What, as a soul?"

"Well, not exactly," answered Yiannis, and showed no inclination to elaborate, but continued with instructions. "Listen: for your uncle's sake, when you go back home try to keep those relatives from crying and wailing too much. It doesn't help him. Tell them.... tell them that he's in a better place now, and that they shouldn't disturb his soul... Anything to stop them wailing."

Yiannis was clearly skirting the issue, he didn't want to go into it any further. Why? I'd seen part of the reason when he was talking to Mike about old Costas' activities immediately after his death. But that was personal. This was general, about the fate of the personality after death, and I expected him to expound on it.

His attitude towards Mike hadn't been entirely that of the 'normal' Yiannis; it was more that of the Teacher. Indeed, from the moment he'd begun to describe Costas coming out of the water, just prior to the fatal heart attack, I sensed a personality change: he was becoming more and more the Teacher - and I could feel the presence of the Teacher very powerfully.

I was wondering what Yiannis would do next, when Mr Zeno, the owner of the taverna, a genial and polite middle-aged gentleman, turned up. He greeted us cheerfully, inquired as to whether we were enjoying our food, offered us some extra wine on the house, and asked if he could have a private word with Yiannis about something urgent.

I became concerned when I saw Yiannis getting up to follow Mr Zeno back inside the taverna - I didn't want Yiannis getting away from me again, not before answering my mountain of questions. Yiannis sensed my concern and promised to return to our table as soon as he had finished his meeting with Mr Zeno. I must have looked unconvinced because Mr Zeno laughed and added his own assurance by saying that he would bring him back himself. I had to settle for that.

Truth to tell, there was another reason: I didn't want Yiannis to walk away at that moment, leaving me alone with Mike and Harry - I didn't want to have to answer their questions on what had taken place. But, as it happened, I was thrown in at the deep end, and as I tried to convey my understanding of what had transpired, I could see Yiannis laughing his head off, and I began to suspect a deliberate plan on his part to leave me to my own devices.

Both Harry and Mike wanted to know how Yiannis got hold of the information about them and the late Costas. I could only tell them that the man was clairvoyant. Harry laughed the idea off, although he admitted he had no explanation himself short of insisting that there had to be a 'natural' explanation.

I argued with him that 'natural' needn't necessarily mean only what we perceive through our five senses, which he conceded, but insisted that clairvoyance was a ridiculous concept, and he disagreed with my distinguishing between 'physical' and 'natural' on the grounds that the distinction introduced 'metaphysics' into the argument. I decided that it would have been fruitless, and a waste of energy, to point out to him that even ordinary seeing and hearing involved 'metaphysics', not to mention the practice of science which cannot function without it - I'd gone down that road so many times before, and I simply refused to be drawn.

Mike, even though sceptical to a degree, was interested in the subject, but in a different way: he wanted to understand what lay behind Yiannis' descriptions, and what he had meant by Costas starting a new life. Yiannis had given me only pointers, and so I had to fall back partly on my own experiences and partly on the 'theoretical' structures provided by the Teacher - although the Teacher himself would have disagreed with my calling them 'theoretical' in the commonly used sense of the word, since, to him, they were totally experiential.

It had been pointed out to me some while back that the original meaning of the term 'theory' had more to do with factual experience than with a mere abstract hypothetical reality. The term derived from an old Greek root which stood for viewing, inspecting, having in one's sights. And that the stem itself had the same etymology as that of *theós* (θεός), the Greek word for god ('the seer'?). In this respect, the Teacher's *theory* on afterlife and other 'metaphysical' themes were to be taken as factual reports - and my own limited experience in the area bore out this interpretation of 'theory'.

So, I explained to Mike that, after physical death, a personality continues an existence in a body of similar form to the physical but obeying different laws, that it, eventually, undergoes another death in which it 'sheds' another body, that it ends up in a condition that could be called 'paradise' before it reverses the procedure and begins to take on body forms on its way to a further incarnation.

I couldn't have made the explanations less sketchy! Naturally, these explanations raised more questions than gave answers, but I did not feel particularly keen to delve into the subject too deeply. I knew I was not being thorough, and I was also aware of not being fair to my friends. I was selfish: my main concern was to make certain that Yiannis did not slip away again. I referred them to various groups and societies that dealt with the subject and to bookshops and publishers where they could read up on it. I felt rotten for being so sloppy. Unintentionally, I seemed to be doing what Yiannis had done to an extent: telling them, not explaining to them. It felt downright condescending coming from me.

Mike had turned out to be a very sensitive guy, with natural abilities in this area and a genuine interest; he also had an immediate need to establish an ongoing contact with his uncle - something that I was not certain it was a healthy thing to do. Mike wore his heart on his sleeve, Harry concealed his sensitivity under a veneer of intellect and wit. But I knew he had a deeper sensitivity than what he allowed to be seen on the surface...

About ten days earlier, while Mike was visiting a relative in the Peloponnese, I had taken a trip with Harry to Delphi. It was late afternoon, close to sunset, when we arrived, and we sat on a low wall, not far from the museum, to enjoy the view of the valley and the sea in the far distance. It was fairly quiet, with a few tourists still milling around and the occasional car passing by behind us. We talked for a short while about the beauty of the scene stretching out before us and how it must have felt to those people who had lived there two and a half thousand years earlier.

Slowly, the talking petered out, and we fell silent. I began to sink into the atmosphere of the place. I was drawn away from where I was sitting and moved all the way up the winding path to the temple of Apollo, the theatre, the stadium and down to the Tholos....

It was not the present day Delphi any longer, but the old Delphi in its full glory. The scenery kept changing, and I with it. Harry was with me, but he was much younger now. At some point, while in the theatre enjoying a performance, I had my arm round his shoulder, squeezing him affectionately. He was a budding athlete, and I was a proud father. As in a film, where I was the protagonist, a whole life unfolded before me, a happy life...

When I returned to present day Delphi, I was filled with joy but also with pangs of nostalgia. Tears were running down my cheeks, and when I turned to Harry, his eyes were moist. I saw him wiping surreptitiously a trickling tear, and then he justified his emotion by saying that he was moved by the beauty of the scenery. It was not a mere justification: he had contacted the past but not in full consciousness; he was moved but was not aware of the real cause of his emotion. I wanted to hug him - hug my 'son' - but I realised I shouldn't. Seeing that he was not aware of that past, it would definitely have been misunderstood. We were of the same age, and he was my friend now.

I was happy to have made the contact but disappointed with myself. I was not supposed to allow the past to affect the present with emotional outbursts. I had to learn control by dispelling indulgence and wallowing.

The past was to be contacted only to enable me to understand present situations and, whenever appropriate, resolve them. I should not go around hugging people just because I felt a connection with them from the past! - as the Teacher had put it when I mentioned my feelings towards Mr Manolides who had turned out to be my father in a past life. Likewise, dislike or hatred towards people shouldn't be allowed to surface from the past; it should be dissipated by placing it into perspective. Emotion from the past should only be allowed as an indication of connections and causes, and then checked and dispelled - it should only function as a marker.

This was not an edict for emotional suppression, but the tracing of a path to sublimation. I had gained some personal, but rudimentary, experience in this matter as I followed the Teacher who guided me to turn such feelings, with past connections with him, to universal love. And it was a tall order, in view of the fact that some of these connections involved a wide range of emotions, including great elation and unbearable pain that had led, on occasion, to desperate and suicidal action.

At the present, I found myself struggling to justify my attitude towards both of my friends in reference to past incarnations when I happened to be a father or an older brother to them. It was true they tended to look up to me, and even seek my advice in some respect, and I felt sort of protective towards them in spite of the fact that we were of the same age and similar build. All the same, it was condescension on my part, and had to be dealt with.

I decided to put my cards on the table, so to speak, and begin with Mike's ability - albeit subconscious - to pick up Costas' presence while Yiannis was talking to him. He was surprised to have to admit to the fact that he had felt Costas' presence very strongly. Even more surprising was Harry's admission that he too felt that way, and that his dismissive behaviour had been a fearful reaction, an attempt at 'exorcising' Costas' presence - what a psychologist might call suppression of reality by denial.

I hardly had the opportunity to make any inroads into the subject when the girls turned up: Mike's and Harry's lovers of the night before - two very attractive, and very keen, Swedish tourists. Unbeknown to me, the boys had invited them to join us for the evening. This was a complication I hadn't allowed for. My priorities had to be reassessed very quickly. It was the last evening I was to spend with my friends and, although in principle I had no objection to anybody else joining us, I couldn't help my mind drifting back to Yiannis.

Would he be coming back, and if he did, would we continue in the same vein? Would the boys still be interested in 'metaphysics'? Looking at the two scantily dressed beauties of the north, I was sure no hot-blooded young man would have any difficulty deciding how he would prefer to spend the rest of the evening! - given the right circumstances, I knew what my choice would have been. However, having spent most of my day and evening looking for Yiannis, I couldn't afford to lose him again. I knew I had to find him before the focus of the evening shifted too drastically.

I told the group that it was imperative to go and find Yiannis and bring him back. I didn't give them a chance to try and argue me out of it; I simply excused myself and made for the kitchen as quickly as possible. I just hoped they didn't think my departure too rude.

I found Yiannis, the old shaman, sitting at a table in the backyard of the taverna talking to a dog! The animal was sitting in front of him on the table with his ears pricked up and listening to him - the very picture of Anubis! Oh, it was the mongrel! True, there are many stray mongrels wandering the streets in Greece, but this one had a special atmosphere about him - and those pointed ears and bushy tail: unmistakeable. I also recognised that look on the dog's face: it was the same look I'd seen in the billy goat when he was staring at me in the field earlier that day.

I didn't catch exactly what Yiannis was saying to the animal, but he appeared to be giving him some advice. I could have sworn I saw the dog nodding his head in acceptance!? Yiannis ran his hand gently over the dog's throat and lower jaw ending at the dog's mouth; the animal licked his hand and then turned and gave me a mock threatening growl.

"You don't like animals much, do you?" said Yiannis.

"They're okay, I don't mind them." I answered. "So long as they don't bite me."

Mr Zeno was sitting on a chair a little away from the table. He acknowledged my presence with a nod and pointed to an empty chair. I decided to stand for a while. The dog turned his attention back to Yiannis. They stared at each other for a moment or two and then the animal opened his mouth and crawled closer to Yiannis. For a second I thought the dog was going to bite Yiannis on the face. But no, he simply opened his mouth and continued to look at him. Yiannis placed each of his hands on the dog's lower and upper jaw bones and stretched them a bit and examined the inside of the animal's mouth.

"You're okay now, my friend. You can go now," Yiannis concluded, addressing the dog.

The animal closed his mouth, licked Yiannis' hands, then turned and growled at me again before jumping off the table and walking away through a broken fence and off to where his fancy took him. I should have been surprised by what I'd witnessed but I wasn't. I merely inquired after the dog's health!

"What's wrong with him?"

"You mean Athespodos? Oh, nothing serious," said Yiannis in his usual casual manner. "He got into a fight with another dog over a couple of bones and lost. And then, in his rush to get away with a much smaller bone, he got a bit of it stuck in his throat. Nearly choked himself to death."

"Poor thing."

"Yes," said Yiannis and leant back in his chair. "There is a moral there somewhere, if only I could think of it." He was being sarcastic now.

"But that's not the half of it," added Mr Zeno. "He kept coughing like mad, trying to dislodge the bone, to spit it out. He looked dreadful. Some ignorant people, who don't like him anyway, saw him and thought he had rabies and began to beat him and throw stones at him."

"He was lucky he sought refuge here," Yiannis concluded and pointed to a bit of bone on the ground, presumably the one taken out of the dog's throat.

Then he introduced me to Mr Zeno by name, and I was sure he referred to Mr Zeno as his brother - or was it 'a' brother? I would have liked him to clarify this, as well as the other business with his sister, and I thought this was a good opportunity, but Mr Zeno was anxious to hear why I was there in the backyard instead of at my table. Was there something wrong with the food? No, I assured him that everything was perfect. I simply needed to talk to Yiannis.

"I am happy you're pleased with the food, young man, but why split away from your friends to spend time with an old man? Shouldn't you be out there having fun?" asked Mr Zeno.

I debated with myself for a moment whether I should tell him to mind his own business, but his question was put in such a polite, if condescending, voice, and he was so much older than me, that I decided it would be too rude. So I told him a half-truth.

"Mr Yiannis promised to be with us, as you know, and we are all anxious to have him back. My friends are leaving very early tomorrow morning. If you don't mind."

"No, not at all." Then he turned to Yiannis. "Shall I put on a Zeimbekiko?"

"No, no. I'm not going to dance. I'll just have a word with my young friends before they turn in. See you later."

On the way back I explained to Yiannis that the boys were fixed up for the night and that it wasn't they but just I who wanted to talk to him. I asked him if we could possibly make our excuses and leave them, I really needed to talk to him. He was very agreeable.

At the table, the two couples were into the swing of things. They'd finished another bottle of wine and were now talking about going to the disco. I made the introductions and we were both, Yiannis and myself, invited to join them. I dreaded the thought of

Yiannis saying yes to the disco invitation, but luckily he declined, saying that he didn't want to show up all the young men with his excellent dancing skills. The girls laughed not knowing how much truth lay in that statement.

"Hey, look at that dog," shouted one of the girls. "He's staring at us."

It was the mongrel again. He was sitting on the promenade, right at the edge of the street, facing us.

"Oh, it's Athespodos," I said, not so much surprised by the dog's presence as pleased.

"Who?" asked Harry.

Mike volunteered the explanation. "It's a Greek word which means that he has no owner, no master - he's a stray."

The dog gave a very audible growl. Yiannis chuckled.

"He heard you and I don't think he liked your description of himself as having no master; he didn't like your implication," said Yiannis, straight-faced.

"What?!" shouted Mike amongst the laughter that Yiannis' comment had generated. "He's only a dog."

A louder, angrier, growl from the mongrel stifled the laughter.

"You see, what did I tell you? He doesn't like your implication."

"What implication?" laughed Harry.

" 'Athespodos' doesn't just mean that he has no master: it's his name, like 'Mike' and 'Harry'. And to him it also means that he was born free, without a master; he eats and drinks and sleeps wherever and whenever he wants to; he lives by his wits, without anybody controlling him. He's free and has the right to be free and he gets upset when someone implies otherwise."

While Athespodos howled his appreciation of Yiannis' exposition of his true nature (!), the girls freaked out. And I wasn't sure whether it was the howling or Yiannis' talk that did it.

"He's also a loose cannon," added Yiannis, with glee in his eyes.

The girls jumped out of their chairs and moved to the other side of the table, away from the street, to a safer distance from the dog. They urged the boys to take them to the disco, as they kept glancing at the dog and then at Yiannis with apprehension. Yiannis scowled at the dog who stopped howling at once, and, with a slight nod of his head, sent the animal trotting off. Just in time, I thought, before the local authorities were alerted and a dog-catcher was sent out to deal with the disturbance.

A hasty arrangement was concluded whereby the two couples would go to the disco and I would meet up with them later, after I had my chat with Yiannis. I had a hard job suppressing a bubbling laughter as I watched the two girls glancing back at Yiannis on their hurried exit. I'm sure they thought he was a nutter - talking about a dog's beliefs in freedom and independence!

"Well, you did want them to go, didn't you?" said Yiannis with a smirk.

"Yes," I said, feeling a little guilty for what I had just done.

I looked around. I wasn't very comfortable with the loud music, the crowds, and all the noise. I wanted somewhere quiet where we could talk.

"I know just the place," he said. "Come with me."

– 8 –

The Mongrel and his Wife (?)
(On an Evolutionary Theme)

I followed him past the tavernas and into the rocky no-man's land, where I had wanted to be before I was spotted by Mike during my unsuccessful evading manoeuvre. The place looked bigger and darker than I knew it, despite the light of the full moon. We walked a short distance down this area and stopped. We were about half-way between the last taverna and the disco. I thought we were going to sit somewhere by the sea, to our right, but Yiannis turned left and began to climb among the boulders up the small hill. I followed him, keeping some distance to enable me to dodge the trail of loose bits of earth and stones he left behind him.

Where was he taking me? At some point I found myself in total darkness as I stood beside an enormous boulder that cut out the moonlight completely. I thought I'd lost him. I stopped to take a breath and heard him climbing at the other side of the boulder; stones came rolling down to my feet. I followed round the boulder carefully and came to a small whitish bluff. There, in the reflection of the moonlight, I saw him taking a path to the top.

It wasn't until I caught up with him at the hilltop that I realised how worth it this climb was. It took me a minute to recover from the head rush, and then I turned and looked around. The view was panoramic, the sort of thing tourists would pay to enjoy. Luckily, nobody had thought of exploiting it commercially yet, and the difficulty of negotiating the terrain also put off messy picnickers and couples seeking romantic locations - and kept the place clear of empty beer cans, bottles, takeaway containers and used condoms.

Looking towards the east was the headland. The disco was a good distance away in that direction, and beyond it, at the tip of the land, was the slaughterhouse, which, luckily, was not visible from where we were standing but was very unpleasant to see as you passed by it in a boat. On the right, was the narrow strait of water separating the island from the mainland, and in the far far distance I could just make out Bob's taverna. On the left, lay the small coves, and farther along the new hotels.

Behind us was the village, covering the rest of the hill, densely packed with small houses, and with the church at the apex. I turned round to face the village and the tavernas at the bottom of the hill, with the yachts rocking gently in the night breeze. All the noises were so distant now. I expressed my admiration for the panorama that unfolded before me.

"Oh yes?" Yiannis responded with a touch of cynicism. "What am I now - a tourist guide? I thought I brought you up here because you simply wanted somewhere quiet to talk. Well, then: talk."

I turned towards him: he looked so ridiculous in that get-up, in that open shirt and the chain hanging down on his bare chest - he was totally out of place up there away from the tavernas. I laughed. He smiled back and said nothing.

But he was right, we were not there to enjoy the view.

He sat on a rock and I followed suit a couple of metres away from him. Yes, I wanted to talk, or rather, I wanted *him* to talk, to explain. There were so many things that needed explaining but, suddenly, and shockingly, I didn't know where to start; my mind had become fogged with uncertainty. I decided to go for my notes, but the moment I put my hand in my pocket he stopped me.

"No, no notes. Otherwise you'll be defeating the whole point of the exercise."

"What exercise?"

He turned his whole body round to face me squarely, straightened himself perfectly, placed his hands on his knees, palms facing down, and looked at me, and kept looking, waiting for me to latch on. Automatically, I assumed a similar position and relaxed. I knew what he wanted me to do.

I felt thoughts and concepts rushing around in my mind, rearranging themselves. Emotions were jostling for position, as if competing amongst themselves. There was a sense of urgency, and expectancy, but nothing was surfacing as a priority. How odd! I'd been looking forward to and preparing for this moment and now that it had arrived I was incapable of even verbalising a question. I went to a list in my mind, trying to pick out the topmost item.

He cut in. "No, no lists."

I struggled: a fatal mistake - I slipped. Struggling to choose was exactly what I should not have been doing. I should have let go, but with intention – an act of delicate balancing.

"Remember the scream," he said quietly. "You never get answers to questions you've never been fired with."

It brought to mind something else I'd heard a long while back about prayer: you pray with abandon but with fire. I looked at him sitting there like an Egyptian statue; something from the distant past.

"On the rock, in the hole, you asked questions and went on to answer them yourself, didn't you?" he prodded.

"Well, not quite. I asked questions prompted by your behaviour and had some answers from you. But I also had answers to questions I'd never asked, and lots of puzzles thrown in that are still with me," I said, feeling a little impatient.

"Wrong," he said, with quiet certainty. "You always get answers to important questions. If you have answers but don't remember the questions, it's neither here nor there." He waited for a beat or two and then continued.

"Look for your reactions. You get excited, don't you? You call them revelations or inspirations or insights. They may come unexpected, and, at the time, you may think they were uninvited." He stopped again and looked straight at me before resuming.

"But you are wrong: they are not unexpected and certainly not uninvited. It is true that when we were in the hole you did not formulate them, not there and then, but you have been asking them all your life, or should I say lives. You have been screaming for answers." And then, in an almost dismissive manner, he added:

"As for the puzzles, they are there because your mind is inadequate; they'll dissipate when you are ready."

As usual, he was right, although I wasn't particularly enthused with his comment about my mind not being adequate. And I querried it.

"You make me think of university professors who try to demonstrate four dimensional space using the flat surface of a board," he said. "You can't do that. Anything above three dimensions involves a special contribution from consciousness. You must be out of your mind to be able to do that." He waited for me, to see if I took his point.

"Or, be *beside yourself*, as the English say. Or, be *ecstatic*, as the Greeks put it - which is the same. And this is why thinking in everyday concepts, in definitions derived from three-dimensional space, in lists of things prompted by the logic of the physical, three-dimensional model, is inappropriate, inadequate, misleading, distorting." He stopped, and remained motionless. Again, waiting for what he had said to sink in.

"It's like wanting to study the surface of the water while swimming and wearing a suit of armour made of lead: you'll never have the chance to see the surface, let alone study it. Or jumping off a cliff wearing the same suit and expecting to fly like an eagle."

I was listening to what he was saying but I was not entirely certain of the relevance. What was he driving at? In concentrating on his talking I became disinclined to ask questions, any questions. I reacted to that by making an extra effort to concentrate, to focus my attention, to stop drifting. I had the sense of losing my bearings, of becoming fragmented, so I exerted myself to hold onto a form of identity, any identity. I found myself in a situation similar to that of a pilot's spatial disorientation where, having lost his bearings, he panics and sticks doggedly to a mindset that might lead him to disaster. I had to let go.

The moon was high above behind me and its light was striking the medallion on Yiannis' chest and reflecting like a mirror. Yes, that blank disk of a medallion - what was its significance? As its reflection shone on my face it felt like a stage hypnotist's trinket.

I went into patterned breathing; I relaxed and let go. As the relaxation progressed, the distant sounds of the tavernas and all the other noises receded and faded into silence - a pregnant silence, full of something waiting to burst forth.

Gradually, I began to be aware of faint but persistent barking. It was a peculiar kind of barking: at times it sounded aggressive, and then it would turn into an almost painful yelping, full of yearning and anticipation. It made me shiver; and I couldn't get rid of it. The more I relaxed the closer it felt.

And then, there he was, right in front of me, between me and Yiannis, partially obscuring the old man. Anubis! sitting in his traditional posture as a jackal. It was not the image of Anubis chiselled in granite but a real living animal. It startled me. Instinctively, I jerked backwards. He was not threatening, he just sat there quietly staring at me. And then, slowly, he began to change, to grow in stature. It took me a while to realise that he was not simply growing in size. He was changing into another familiar shape of Anubis: the human body with the head of a jackal.

He now obscured Yiannis completely. He stood in front of me, still staring, with an almost human expression on his face, an expression that vacillated between friendly and stern, warm and chiding. In the middle of his chest a lively, vibrating, Ankh took shape which slowly settled into a rhythmic pulsing. As my whole attention was drawn to it, I felt my heartbeat and the pulsing blood in my arteries falling into its rhythm. It spread throughout my body - I felt it in my head, my chest and abdomen, my arms and legs. Then it 'streamlined' itself into a left-right pulsation.

I saw it also taking place in Anubis. It looked like two columns of energy starting at each foot, in the form of whirlpools that resembled the fluttering of small wings, and rising up to his full height. But when I looked closer I noticed that the two luminous columns crossed over four times: they rose from the feet, and moved along the thighs crossing over at the level of the genitals; they then crossed back at the solar plexus, and over again at a point just above the sternum before crossing once more at the throat level, weaving themselves across to their original side and shooting up from each shoulder and fanning out like enormous wings; and I felt the same process reflecting in my body.

The elation was indescribable! Everything was in its place, right, correct, perfect; my mind ceased to question, there was no need to question anything because everything was in perfect order; and I was carrying out a task - for which I was perfectly suited, my happiness and my task/function being one. This was a world in which nothing was out of place and everything fitted a design or plan of which I was an integral part.

And then, parts of these two brilliant columns began to undulate and seemed to duplicate themselves and move towards the middle of Anubis' body and 'tighten up' - they were not simply crossing over but entwining, slowly at first but increasingly furiously. As they came tightly together, I could see that they were entwining round a vortex whose lower tip touched the ground between his feet and rose through his genitals, abdomen, sternum where the Ankh shone and branched out at the level of the eyes and through his peaked ears.

I felt the same process coursing through me. As it reached the level of the genitals, I fell into an ecstatic orgasm the like of which I had never imagined. But it was not an orgasm localised in the genitals in particular: it felt as if it had started there but it spread all over me. I was spinning at the same time, and the spin became faster and more 'rapturous' the tighter the two 'duplicate' columns became. I thought I was going to 'pass out', and perhaps I did, but at the same time I felt the compulsion to stand up, which I did.

And it was wonderful! As I stood up, I saw the top ends of the 'duplicate' energy columns in Anubis turning inwards, facing each other from opposite sides of his head towards the middle, and they looked like the arching upper bodies of two cobras with wings. Oh, god, yes! It was the caduceus! The moment I realised that, I became conscious of the whole same process reflecting in my body. I felt I was being propelled forcefully upwards and out of my body, or that I was being lifted up bodily. But this tremendous surge of energy threw me into a state of ecstasis that proved unsustainable - I was knocked out!....

When I came to, I was sitting on the same rock I'd been sitting earlier - as if I'd never stood up - and Yiannis was sitting in the same place in the same posture as before, except that for a brief moment I thought I saw him sitting like a Buddha, even sporting a buddhic smile.

Judging by the distant sounds of the tavernas and the disco, I was back in my normal consciousness. The shadows cast by the moonlight were at different angles. I turned my head and saw the moon at a new position, it had moved a long way to my left. Obviously, some considerable time had elapsed. But I had no idea how long I'd been out, or what had taken place during that time - I had no memory of any events, it was a total blank. I went for my wrist watch to check the time, but I couldn't find it, it wasn't on my wrist, and I couldn't remember removing it. I began to panic.

"Forget the watch. You don't need it," Yiannis said, grinning at me.

"Where is it? Did you take it?"

"No, it's in your pocket."

I touched the outside of my trouser pocket to confirm that it was, indeed, there.

"But leave it, leave it. Forget about it," he practically ordered me.

"Who put it there? Did I take it off myself or did you?" I felt I needed an answer, I needed to know.

"It doesn't matter. It's not relevant," he replied.

But, when he saw that I wasn't satisfied with his answer, he gave in. "If you must know, it was you who did it."

"But why?"

"If you don't remember, I'm not going to tell you." And then in a different tone of voice: "What's all this obsession with watches and time? Is this another thing to add to your definitions?"

He threw me a little. All I wanted was to know what happened. There was a big gaping hole in my memory, as if I had ceased to exist for a length of time. I wanted that gap filled, preferably by remembering what had taken place, and if not, then by his telling me what had transpired, so as to trigger my memory. But he did not seem inclined to do anything of the sort. The least he could do would be to let me find out how much time had gone by since we had arrived at the hilltop.

"Okay," he said, as if relenting. "Tell me what time it is."

I went for my watch in my pocket.

"No, no," he interrupted. "No, forget the watch. Just tell me the time."

He confused me again. "What? How?"

"Just tell me the time," he repeated.

I turned and looked at the moon and tried to work out the passage of time by it's position. I had no idea what I was doing. I was guessing.

"It must be close to midnight," I said; and it could've been ten at night or four in the morning for all I knew.

"Good, fine," he concluded casually.

I got excited. "Really? Did I get it right?"

"How should I know?" he said and shrugged his shoulders. "I never carry a watch." He was clearly into one of his games.

"Why did you ask me to guess the time, then?"

"Oh, were you just guessing?" he asked, pretending surprise and incredulity.

Before I had a chance to respond to his tease, I heard a familiar low growl to my right. The mongrel was standing next to a small boulder, hardly visible, but with eyes shining bright in the dark. As the recognition dawned on me, his growl became louder.

"You should know better than to call him mongrel," he said.

"But I never have," I protested.

"You thought it, though."

"What should I call him, then - hybrid?" I thought it was my turn to be sarcastic, for a change.

But he chose not to pick up on that. "No, just Athespodos, his meaningful name."

The dog growled his approval.

"Or, if you prefer, you may call him by his spiritual name."

"His what?"

Surely he was pulling my leg - a dog's spiritual name?! But he looked as though he meant it - and so did the dog, judging by the tone of his growling.

"His inner, more permanent, name. Some people like to ascribe spirituality to it, whatever that might mean."

He sounded serious, so I decided to play along.

"What's his *spiritual* name, then?" I asked with unconcealed sarcasm.

"Hermanubis."

The dog sounded clearly content with it; but I'd never heard of such a name before.

"What?"

"Oh, it's the name of the ancient *mongrel* god who combined the features of the Egyptian Anubis and the Greek Hermes: *Herm-Anubis*," said he with a touch of teasing ambiguity.

But his tease washed over me like water off a duck's back because my attention was arrested by the vision of Anubis I had had earlier and the 'incidental' and loose associations I had formed between the dog and the image of Anubis when the mongrel seemed to follow me around - his behaviour and the likeness I picked up in the semi-darkness of the night, none of which I'd paid too much attention to. But now there was a feeling of these apparently unconnected bits of events and associations coming together. Was there some deeper connection between the dog and the image/symbol of Anubis?

Yiannis was grinning; the dog was giving out a continuous low growl like a purr, a virtual sound accompaniment to Yiannis' grin. I became fascinated by this 'orchestration': it was as if Yiannis were singing or playing the top line of a piece of music while the dog were providing the base line, but without undulations. It reminded me of the chanting in the Greek Orthodox Church where a singer gives out a continuous monotone which acts as the base line to the cantor's line above it.

Yiannis continued to grin and the dog continued to 'purr', and I was simply too fascinated by the pair of them to say or do anything. As I looked at the dog, the sense of an alternating friendliness and severity I had experienced earlier as being projected by the vision of Anubis, was now present and 'flowing' from the animal in front of me. I had never owned a dog in my life and had never felt the need to own one, but I was now beginning to understand what people meant when they spoke of a dog being a friend and a companion. I even felt a sense of protectiveness projecting from the dog.

He took a few steps towards me and stood there wagging his tail. It was more than protectiveness, it was love! I could sense it very clearly. And yet, in spite of all this display of affection there was still that edge of severity. He stood and stared at me and, gradually, I began to feel an enormous cloud of compassion embracing me - but it wasn't I feeling compassionate towards the dog, it was the other way round: the dog was being compassionate towards me! And then there was an added tinge to this compassion - it was mercy! Dog the merciful! Was I losing my mind?

"There you are," Yiannis broke the silence. "Your very own personal Anubis."

"My what?"

Yiannis did not respond to my question immediately; instead, the dog growled for attention and moved closer to me. He was now more of a jackal than a dog. He stared at me.

"Your personal Anubis," Yiannis repeated. "He'll be your guiding angel; he'll protect you and guide you but if you don't listen and learn he'll turn into your nemesis; he'll love you objectively and help you acquire consciousness."

I didn't quite understand the last bit.

"How can he love me objectively, and how am I to acquire consciousness when I'm already conscious?" I inquired.

"You think you're conscious? Are you kidding? You're not even conscious of what goes on in your physical body, which is built and maintained without your participation, without your *conscious* participation. Oh, yes, you get glimpses, alright, but that's all. Most of the time your consciousness is practically dull. As for objective love, I can't even begin to explain it to you. In any case, it cannot be explained in words and concepts."

While Yiannis was talking, I became aware of the dog stretching his neck as if straining to lift his head as high as possible. He made himself stand upright like a human, and then he turned himself into a man with a jackal's head - he turned into Anubis! Instinctively, I stood up. He walked over to me, beaming with benignancy, stood in front of me and embraced me. I was too stunned to react in any way. A dog, or some kind of canine, was turning himself into a sort of 'humanoid' and embracing me!

Momentarily, I was numbed of thought and emotion. And then, all of a sudden, I was flooded with love, a weird kind of love that I hadn't encountered before - I was an orphan under the wing of a foster parent, a parent I'd always had but had forgotten or ignored; oh, yes, it was a parent I'd abandoned a long time ago because I'd found him too strict. I wanted freedom, independence. But in engaging in what I'd thought to be an act of breaking the shackles I'd become reckless and totally missed the reasons for the parental guidance, the love and care showered on me, and mistook it for merely unfeeling strictness. The 'prodigal son'..... sitting under a carob tree..... eating food fit for pigs...

And then, I realised that the dog-turned-Anubis was not there any longer, he had disappeared as an external object, and instead, I found myself in a situation which I could only understand as internalising Anubis - I had not become Anubis but had entered into the Anubis consciousness, or it could have been the other way round: I had been inundated with his consciousness and perhaps absorbed into it. I entered into certain understandings that seemed to lie beyond conceptualisation - I could not understand them as concepts. I sat down and tried to make sense of them in the normal way of conceptualising but I found that process impossible, inapplicable. It felt as if I were attempting to externalise myself, turn myself inside out - but I couldn't.

Then it dawned on me that I was doing what I had been told not to do, that is, looking 'outwards', identifying 'objects'. And so I reversed the process, and I let go. And, lo and behold, I 'became', the very features of what seemed to characterise Hermanubis, the variety and depth of which features were utterly beyond my current knowledge - anyhow, that's how it felt at the time. And as the process unfolded, the experience also displayed sensory imagery - but I could not decide whether this was integral to the process or merely demonstrative, explanatory, or a side effect due to my incompetence.

The central feature was what I felt to be the Mercy of Justice, a merging of the somewhat contradictory feelings of affection and severity I'd experienced with both the dog and Anubis. I could see and feel Justice as a loving process: a strict father and a loving mother, all for the good of their offspring. There was Balance, severe yet loving, the weighing scales of Anubis; but the scales were not there to weigh and judge and condemn; they were there to balance, to adjust.

The Teacher's explanation of karmic redress sprang to my consciousness. There was no punishment, no eternal damnation, and no evil - only ignorance that needed guidance. The Socratic pronouncement that nobody does wrong knowingly was now fully meaningful. Even at the lowest level of ignorance, nobody was doing wrong, and everybody was right - an intellectually unattainable and inexplicable state of affairs and yet 'understandable' in the state of consciousness I was in. There was empathy with everything and everybody - there was Mercy! and self-sacrifice; buddhic compassion. The endless chain of hunter and hunted lay within this understanding.

But why Mercy? What is Mercy? In a flash of understanding I saw Mercy as the balancing act of Creation. My mind blanked out completely and the experience was now totally devoid of thinking. There was just light - was I that light? I had the utterly incomprehensible feeling of moving fast forward in time and simultaneously moving backwards. But there were no objects, there was no sequence of events.

And then there was no movement; there was stillness, and there was darkness, as if nothing existed - except Consciousness, Consciousness devoid of contents. Strange as it might seem - not to say 'logically' unobtainable - I had the sense of being conscious of Nothing! But, was I really conscious of Nothing? It was a glimpse of total darkness and void, a vast, limitless emptiness - *I* was that darkness and that void (?). A 'glimpse'? Could I say a 'glimpse' in the absence of Time? Whatever. Maybe it was a glimpse that stretched forever... I don't know...

And then there was light. Phanes, the first chink of light, the Appearance of Existence, Creation out of Nothing, out of Darkness. The explosion into Existence.... Lucifer, the bringer of light, and Prometheus, the seer, the provider of fire, the creator of Man.... Movement, 'shaking', vibration, life....

I understood Existence as an impulse, a creative impulse, a forceful creation, an explosion, a continuing process endowed with ceaseless creativity. Ah, the Cosmos, the positive world in which nothing is 'negative' (and Nothing *is* Negative!), in which nothing is wrong, and everything is right. Ah, but what of justice, of balance? In this continuing creation there is no ultimate balance, only periodic, apparent, homeostasis which is always ready to give way to incessant expansion. Mercy: the fight for balance, the correcting of the 'injustice' of creation, of imbalance. Love, Compassion, Mercy: the balancing act of creation.

Anubis, Hermanubis, the balancer, the equaliser, the messenger of Mercy, the connector of the Worlds, the facilitator who enables consciousness to move from realm to realm, from one state of consciousness to another, from one reality to another, who nourishes and expands consciousness. No wonder they called him *Psychopompos*, 'the guide of the soul'. Who would have thought the range of his activities, the range of his consciousness! Yes, Hermanubis the dispenser of objective love. Ah, the Teacher's 'etheric' connections between levels, between bodies, between states of consciousness, between innumerable spatio-temporal dimensions. Now I was beginning to understand....

"Well, then, my *mongrel* friend, how are you? You look as if you've been bitten by a rabid dog. Or was it a jackal?" Yiannis brought me back with his mildly sarcastic tease.

But I wasn't totally back. I was still in an afterglow, and continued to be in a daze. Part of me was still glowing in a weird, timeless, spaceless, zone. I was only at that moment beginning to register the experience I had just undergone. Weird, very weird: it was as if I were in a time-delay universe - I had had an experience which I was not conscious of having when it was taking place, but which was now registering as such! A bit like remembering a dream you were not aware you had had until you remembered it.

Only this experience was not a memory. True, I was aware that it had already taken place just a while ago, but it was also now unfolding in my consciousness as a present occurrence - it was happening now although it had already taken place, but it was not a replay! And to add to this, it suddenly registered with me that the whole experience was not new at all - it had taken place on numerous occasions in the past, with slight variations. But even though I would call these experiences 'past' experiences for the sake of narration, they did not feel as past events: they were very much in the present - and not as memories!! A constant *déjà vu*?!

"Well? Did the dog eat your tongue?" Yiannis continued to tease me out of my daze.

He was sitting on the same rock as before, but he had his arms crossed over his chest this time. Like my current experience, he was a figure in a weird time warp: I'd met him in the present but he'd come from the past and, most amazing, he was there in the future.

Regarding the past, he seemed to project a personality which was wonderfully familiar, stretching back to time immemorial, with connections with me that included all sorts of close relationships; but it was more than that: he was not an ordinary human being - there was a transcendent quality about him. I felt deeply privileged to be associated with him.

Despite the closeness I felt towards him, I was also aware of a great gap between us; and, momentarily, it was a reverential gap, awe inspiring. He was a great teacher, vast in consciousness, enormous in knowledge and wisdom and compassion who was also capable of donning the ordinary personality of a cynical joker in dealing with ordinary people like me. I realised how honoured I was that he was paying individual attention to me. I saw him again, as I had done in the hole, radiating brilliant colours that covered the whole hilltop.

There was a strong connection or similarity with the Teacher, or, more accurately, an assimilation of their consciousnesses. But, as in the rock, I fell short of unravelling the actual relationship.

The 'past' connectedness stretched all the way into the future, only the 'future' was not some temporal projection, something to happen at some future date: it was already there, it had already happened. I am not talking here about predicting future events. It was a future.... it was a future that did not differ from the past temporally! They both had occurred, and yet they both were with me in the present, as present events - except that there was a sense in which the 'future' seemed to have taken place before the past!!

This was not a matter of wordplay or logic-chopping or redefining the terms 'past', 'present' and 'future'. It was an experience that defied sequential logic. There was no problem in understanding it while it was taking place, while I was in it. The difficulty arose when I tried to verbalise it, to put it into words and locate it in terms of temporal sequence, to define it and make sense of it....

The sound of barking concentrated my attention on the three-dimensional world and brought me back to the physical reality more successfully than Yiannis' gentler teasing - brought me back reluctantly, that is; for I was certainly keener to stay where I was, in whatever spatio-temporal world I'd found myself in - if that could be described as a 'world' and if it existed in any comprehensible sense of space and time. I looked at Yiannis and then turned to see where the dog was, but he was nowhere to seen. The barking felt diffused and non-directional and then faded out altogether.

"Where's the dog?" I asked.

"Oh, around somewhere. He'll be back soon," Yiannis replied in a throw-away manner, and concentrated his gaze on me.

We remained silent for a while, I trying to pull myself together and he...well, he staring at me.

"Is that all? Is that all you have to say: 'where's the dog'?" he asked, with mock impatience.

I had asked that question automatically, without thinking. After all the consciousness-shaking experience I'd gone through, I ended up asking the whereabouts of the dog! It sounded bizarre. But, anyhow, wasn't it the way it had all begun - the dog Athespodos, Anubis, Hermanubis...? So I asked about the dog again.

"He'll be back soon. He went to get his wife," responded Yiannis in the same impatient tone.

Now I was definitely back, fully conscious in a three-dimensional world, and listening to an old man telling me of a stray mongrel who had gone to fetch his wife! Pinching myself would have been useless. And yet, as I shifted myself back, onto the border, away from the centre of three-dimensionality, a world in which a dog had a wife didn't seem totally out of place - simply intriguing.

"What do you mean 'his wife'? Is he married, really?"

"Oh, yes, he's married alright. To a beautiful bitch."

"Oh, really?" Yiannis' sarcasm was rubbing off on me, and I was almost seamlessly sliding from the sublime to the ridiculous.

"Was it a church ceremony? Did they recite vows to each other?"

"No, no church ceremony. But they did have vows. Very serious ones, too."

And, as if he'd been waiting for his cue, Athespodos made his appearance from behind a boulder. He came forward a few steps and sat on the ground, assuming an Anubis position. And, to cap it all, another, slightly smaller, dog popped out from behind the same boulder and sat next to him. In the dim moonlight I couldn't make out the gender of the second animal but I assumed, from what Yiannis had just said, that it was a female - Athespodos' wife! What next, I wondered - a repeat of their marital vows?! Will I be called upon to officiate at a canine conjugal ceremony? They both gave a gentle growl and then went quiet.

"You don't seem to appreciate the couple's presence," Yiannis said in a mildly chiding voice.

He was right. I had other concerns. I wanted to go with him through the various items in my recent experience and try and put them into some kind of perspective with his help: the connection between Athespodos, Anubis, Hermanubis and the other figures that had come up in the 'vision'; the time and space 'distortion'; the transformation of the dog into Anubis and his embracing me and then disappearing (into me?); 'objective' love, the Mercy of Justice, light out of darkness, the sense in which nothing seemed to be wrong....

And Yiannis himself: who was he? or, more interestingly, *what* was he? Why the tantalising closeness and familiarity and yet the incomprehensible 'barrier' that stopped me from knowing him fully despite the past connections?...Why did he call me his "mongrel" friend?.... And what about the countless other questions that had been gathering all day?... The list! Ah, I was going to put my foot down this time.

"Is Athespodos of no interest to you, then?" he prodded gently.

He stole a march on me by initiating the questions. I had to find a way to reverse the position.

"On the contrary, he is of great interest. I would like very much to know what or who he is exactly and what this business of having a wife is."

"Ah, good, straight to the point. But why ask? You know who and what he is, he's just shown you. Didn't you understand?"

"I understood the nature of Hermanubis, but not the connection with Athespodos."

"Oh, I see." He sounded genuine. He paused for a beat or two and looked up at the star-studded sky.

The night breeze brought up to the hilltop the freshness of iodine from the sea mixed with the scent of night flowers. The dogs were sitting motionless like statues, with their ears pricked - listening, waiting? The music from the disco could be heard faintly in the distance.

"The idea made flesh," he said in a low voice, almost whispering, still looking at the night sky as if divining the words from the spread of the stars.

"The what?"

He didn't answer right away. He looked at me first, studied me leisurely in the half-light, then asked me if I knew Prometheus and his brother Epimetheus. At first, I thought he was asking whether I was familiar with the myths surrounding these two brothers, and I was about to respond in that direction when I saw him shaking his head. He was not interested in the myths; he wanted to know if I knew them, if I was personally acquainted with the two brothers! I then realised, I felt, what he wanted me to do.

Prometheus had come up during my recent experience; I *knew* that he was the one great consciousness which created Man, that he made it possible for the Idea of Man to come into Existence, that he 'guided' and 'enabled' Man to unfold his capacity as a co-creator who carried within himself all the ingredients of preceding and subsequent Creations - Man, a self-sufficient procreator who possessed the ability to create new life from within himself according to his own image, a process of creation symbolised by the misinterpreted act of Prometheus 'sacrificing' his ever self-replenishing liver as 'punishment' for the 'gift of fire' he bestowed on Man. I also knew where he had come from.

His 'brother', Epimetheus, was another great consciousness, the one responsible for bringing into Existence the animal kingdom. He was also the one who, through an evolutionary process whereby higher fields of consciousness can inhabit lower forms of life, and an activity which might loosely be called 'natural selection', helped bring about a means of procreation, a 'sexual revolution', which contributed to Man's acquiring self-consciousness - an evolutionary leap in which Man feels cut off, thrown out of 'paradise', then re-creates 'paradise' to which he becomes attached and, in his struggle to disentangle himself, expands himself as consciousness.

But where was the connection with Athespodos?

I didn't want to ask Yiannis; I felt a great desire to investigate the issue myself, directly. Perhaps it was his prompting, his reluctance to explain, part of his teaching method of eliciting answers, not always offering them - how reminiscent of Socrates' midwifery!

I went back to the direct method. I deliberately slowed down my thinking processes and checked and dissolved emerging emotional reactions. The purely physical side was already relaxed.

I could now see lines of colour emanating from Athespodos, enlarging themselves as they spread outwards and then coalescing into a figure above him. It was a figure that resembled a human being but did not seem to be able to retain the human form: it kept oscillating and vacillating between a human form and an ever-changing, protean, amalgam of animal forms - it was Epimetheus! the visible form, *a* visible form, of an immeasurable consciousness. I felt mesmerised by its beauty and enormous scope.

As I watched, the sense of a plan, of a purpose, began to engulf me. There was an innate link between the human and the animal that travelled both ways, from the animal to the human and vice versa. The human contained everything that was animal and the animal possessed, in a latent state, the potential to acquire human qualities, to 'become' human! I'd always thought - believed - that species were distinct entities.

But what was now unfolding was an intriguing form of evolution. The Human Idea was distinct but at the same time contained everything else in the world, including the Animal Idea. And, in connection with the latter, it inhabited successively, and at the present concurrently, all animal forms but without being an animal at the core of its nature. The Animal Idea, on the other hand, 'aspired' to the Human Idea, it mimicked and tried to emulate the latter. It was not a matter of one evolving from the other but of participating in each other's nature.

And Athespodos? What was his... ? Oh, yes, he too was aspiring, he too... I could see Hermanubis overshadowing him, and Epimetheus overshadowing both of them... But why a dog, a jackal, of all animals? Why not a monkey or an elephant?

"No special reason," I heard Yiannis breaking the silence and bringing me back. "Except that Athespodos likes you."

Was he pulling my leg? I glanced at Athespodos, and in the semi-darkness he appeared to be smiling at me, or was he perhaps showing me his teeth? Was the low growl an indication of affection or a threat? In all honesty, however, I did not feel threatened by Athespodos any longer. If anything, it was the opposite. Ever since that act of embracing and 'merging' by Athespodos-turned-Anubis all apprehension I might have felt in connection with him had simply evaporated and its place taken by feelings of warmth and comradeship. And this latter was a really intriguing connection.

"Athespodos, like you, is under the guidance of Hermanubis; but for different reasons, although for similar aims - relatively speaking," Yiannis continued, with what purported to be an enlightening comment but which, in fact, obscured the issue further.

"What reasons, what aims?" I, justifiably, asked.

"Well, to begin with, the aspect that affects Athespodos most is one projected through Hermanubis by Epimetheus, because Athespodos is an animal, and aims at the acquisition of self-consciousness - a very long and complex process that involves an overlap with various features of human consciousness.

"In your case, on the other hand, because you are human, Hermanubis is transmitting a Promethean process - equally long and complex - whose aim is to guide you past self-consciousness, to a type of consciousness which is beyond definition but whose scope people attempt to convey by the use of terms like superconsciousness, god-consciousness, universal consciousness.

"But don't let it go to your head. Neither you nor Athespodos are unique. Numerous other individuals are undergoing the same process as you, and many other animals are in a similar position to that of Athespodos."

As usual, he stopped talking for a while to allow me to take in what he had said.

"Can you see now why Athespodos has a wife?" he continued by throwing in something apparently unrelated, almost ridiculous. This canine wife business again!

"No, not really," I said, still being unable to see the relevance.

"But you can see how an animal would aspire to self-consciousness, to human consciousness."

"Yes, I can see that, I *saw* that."

"Well then, there you are. You are human, you can take a wife. Athespodos aspires to achieving a status like yours, so why couldn't he take a wife?" said he, offering me a tongue-in-cheek logic-chopping argument. And I could make out the grin on his face. He laughed.

"Joking aside, though, they're not really married," he said, glancing at the 'couple' who sat there quiet and motionless. "They got there late - the registry office was shut. And the priest was not available - he was otherwise engaged, discharging his duties with the assistance of a local widow!" He burst out laughing, and the dogs made a noise that sounded like sneezing.

I began to understand now what Bob meant when he spoke about Yiannis and his comments regarding the Church and its ministers - these remarks were definitely too close to the bone.

"So they live in sin, then," I said, deciding to join in the irreligious banter.

"What do you expect? - they're profligate cynics," he quipped, nodding in the direction of the animals.

He was, of course, speaking to me in Greek, and was punning on the word cynic, an adjective derived from the noun *cyn* (Greek κύν) which means dog. Witty! The dogs were also amused, judging by their non-threatening low growl.

When they had settled down, Yiannis spoke again.

"Athespodos is a very misunderstood animal. Under the guidance of Anubis he is trying to unfold his potential. He's already a combination of many canine races; but this, for people, makes him a *mongrel* - they miss the fact that he combines all the canine features; so they kick him and stone him. The other dogs don't like him either because of his attitude, and so he becomes a sort of pariah."

"What attitude?" I interjected.

He waited for a beat or two, and looked as though he was collecting his thoughts.

"Look, when Anubis overshadows him his behaviour changes noticeably; he behaves almost like a human. But, unlike most ordinary humans who go around hurting one another unnecessarily because they have become slaves to the images they have created, Athespodos is guided to pick out and imitate the positive aspects of human behaviour."

"Ah, wait a minute. This is not what you told me earlier at the taverna. You said that he had picked a fight with another dog over a bone."

"Oh, well, you don't believe everything you hear."

"But you said that yourself. Were you lying?"

"No. Not exactly. I didn't feel like going into a lengthy explanation at the time. And it wasn't totally untrue, anyway. You see, this is another case of Athespodos being misunderstood. What he was actually doing at the time was advising another dog, trying to instill some sense of cooperation into him; and the whole thing got a bit out of hand. But he's learning; and so is his new recruit."

Athespodos' 'wife' growled her confirmation.

"It's an uphill struggle, since , not only does he have to work on himself, but also teach *her* to be less 'bitchy' and try and control her tendency to associate with other male dogs when she's on heat."

The growl from the 'wife' was not as pleasant this time, and it sounded rather dismissive.

"Listen to that: she's being *cynical*," added Yiannis and laughed at his pun. "Imagine: a dog being monogamous. It's like trying to teach an old dog new tricks."

He fell about laughing at his joke. I knew it was silly, but, what the hell, I joined him, and so did the good-natured 'couple' who 'sneezed' along.

But I wanted to get back on track, I wanted to bring this discourse on the development of canine consciousness to a close and move on to other pressing questions.

"What did you mean by *the idea made flesh*?" I asked.

"Ah, yes, the idea made flesh. But that's precisely what we've been talking about," he responded.

"Is it?"

"Of course. The unfolding, the unpacking, of potentialities residing within the species. Surely, you didn't miss that, did you?"

"No, not that. You were talking about Athespodos."

"And I still am. The new breed: human and animal, and everything else. The new impulse to the globe, to the solar system, to mention but those parts of the universe that we feel closest to. The seeds known as animal, and those known as human, are now ripe for a new stage in their development. The idea made flesh is a continuing unfoldment, a projection into a three-dimensional world of a seed structure conceived at a multi-dimensional level."

I could grasp what he was talking about but still couldn't see a direct connection with Athespodos.

"But how does Athespodos fit into this?" I decided to interject.

"Athespodos is an animal in a pack who, until recently, had no real sense of individuality - and is still a pack animal for the greatest part. But with the new impulse, which involves the participation of more advanced forms of consciousness, he is beginning to change, as is the case with many other animals. As I said to you earlier, it is a very slow and laborious process, but it's happening."

"How far will this process go?"

"If he continues, he'll be able to return, in the distant future, as an individual, an animal with distinct self-consciousness. But you saw all this, you know it: the idea of an individual animal, of a person, if you like, made flesh. And he is a mongrel because, as you know, he combines all the features of a canine."

I was about to ask him the obvious question regarding his use of the word 'mongrel' as he applied it to me, when he continued.

"And so are you; you are a mongrel, physically, intellectually, emotionally, racially. Over the millennia, you have touched on all those features that make one human, and now it is time to make yourself fully conscious of them, and go beyond self-consciousness. You, too, are the idea made flesh, but at a different level."

I liked his interpretation of the word 'mongrel', although it revived a dormant, if nagging, question concerning the belief in exclusivity, the sense of being special or unique that various human races felt about themselves; I raised the question with him.

"There are two topics here. The first has to do with the specific contributions that each race makes to humanity as a whole, and it is natural for them to feel special; the problem that arises, however, is that the people of that particular race, not possessing wide enough consciousness to see it for what it is, take their contributions to be utterly unique and thus feel justified to lay claim to a special relationship with what they perceive to be god, divine, supernatural, or what have you. Can you see that?"

"Yes. What's the other topic?"

"The second topic is more universal. As I said to you earlier, a new impulse into the world is taking place right now. This is something that happens periodically. Invariably, every time it happens, this impulse injects a new type of energy that brings along with it new forms of consciousness.

"In the human domain, it's a new race, that is, human beings who exhibit features which lay dormant, in seed form, and are now unfolding into full consciousness. These features are universal human characteristics, but also unique, in the sense that they are being made unambiguously obvious for the first time by this new race.

"In time, these new contributions become common place, they become the conscious property of all humanity - but until then, the people of the new race feel unique, and justified in laying claim to that special relationship with the cosmos."

He stopped, glanced at the dogs, then back at me, and added:

"Go back to Prometheus."

I understood. I just needed time to organise all this in my head.

"But you haven't asked me one other question you should have asked."

"What's that?"

"Do all humans and animals, and so on, make the grade, and, if not, what happens to those who don't make it?"

"Make the grade?"

"Yes." He stopped and reflected. "You seem to have forgotten. I'll have to re-introduce you to your old friends, to those wonderful Greeks who lived before, and all the way down to, Socrates. You've forgotten them. Tomorrow. You'll meet them again. For now, all I can say is that there are opening and closing stages, and at every closing stage there are those who don't make it."

He stared up at the sky, and looked as though his gaze was penetrating right through the milky way. I had no idea what he was talking about.

"Why do you think there have been so many wailers and woe-cryers and so many *saviours* of the world down the ages, so many of them threatening and beseeching and warning humanity about Armageddon and declaring that 'the end is nigh'?"

He looked at me before speaking again.

"Don't answer that. We'll deal with it tomorrow."

Then he turned and looked at the dogs who were still sitting in the same pose, motionless. He didn't say anything, just looked at them for a few seconds. And the animals let out a little low growl, straightened up, wagged their tails, turned round, and disappeared quietly into the darkness of the night.

"Where are they going?"

"How should I know? I'm not their keeper. Maybe they're going forth to multiply," he said laughing. And then he teased me. "Will you miss him if you don't see him again?"

I didn't know how to answer that. I had definitely become very fond of Athespodos. But why was he asking me such a question?

"You'll be catching mostly glimpses of him in the future - physically, that is. But he'll always be with you. I told you: he's your personal Hermanubis. His purring and his growling and his barking will become part of your consciousness. And when physically present, he'll still guide you, but also need your help at times."

"Why would he need my help?"

"Because as a canine who's developing, externalising, animal nature as a whole, on his way to self-consciousness, he's disadvantaged.

"A chimpanzee, for example, is better placed on the evolutionary ladder to achieve that - but, then, chimps are imitating everything human, including lots of bad habits which they pick up from the mental space floating around them.

"But most of the time you'll be aware of him inside you: you have internalised him, remember?"

He was, of course, referring to Athespodos-turned-Anubis embracing me and 'dissolving' himself into me.

"He seems always to be responsive to human thoughts and emotions. And I myself pick up his reactions so easily, as if he's talking to me. I've never had this before. Why is this happening now?" I asked. It was a question that had been nagging me ever since I'd come across Athespodos back on the mainland on my way to Yianna's house.

His response showed exasperation, some of which, I'm sure, was a put-on.

"How is it that you always ask me questions whose answers you already know?"

"Do I?" I retorted with a tone of wounded dignity.

"Yes," he said. "If only you would deal with your questions the direct way."

He cast a quick glance in the direction of the boulder where the animals had disappeared.

"Look, you know very well that whenever Athespodos is over-shadowed by Anubis he becomes extremely sensitive to human emotions and thoughts, among other things. You yourself can see that through your own sensitivity."

He stopped abruptly and walked over and stood in front of me. I stood up as well, not knowing why I did that. Then, without any warning, he put his arms round my waist and pulled me towards him. There was a tremendous shock in my solar plexus that made me feel electrified, sparks of energy flying all over me. I heard him speak but his voice was not reaching me from the outside: it was booming inside me: "Ah, yes. Your solar plexus. It's so open. You are so sympathetic now."

These were the words of the Teacher, and it was his voice, too! And Yiannis had used the same sentence, as well as that particular word - "sympathetic" - which in Greek carries the meanings of 'attractive' and 'empathic', that the Teacher had used on another crucial occasion (but only with the latter meaning). Like a shot, that other scene from the past superimposed itself on the present....

Some years earlier, I had left the island where I and the Teacher lived and went abroad where I drifted and, I believed, moved away from the teachings. I neglected my mental exercises and set about looking for ways to make money easily and enjoy a 'good' life. It occurred to me that an easy way to make money would be to become an actor (!?).

I looked in the mirror and saw a handsome young man looking back at me! Right, I'll become an actor then; that way I would certainly achieve my goal - and pick up a few birds on the way! So I went to drama school and came out with flying colours as a keen thespian, and embarked on an acting career. The weird thing about this situation was that, until that moment when I made the decision to become an actor, I had looked down on the profession and considered actors to be silly people who were simply incapable of doing anything else with their lives!

Anyway, not very long after, I decided to visit home to see my relatives, friends and, naturally, the Teacher. When I met him, he threw his arms around me, exactly like Yiannis did, and said the very same words, except that he had added: "It's worked. I'm glad it has." After we disentangled ourselves from the embrace, I asked him what he meant by those last words. He laughed raucously, like a person enjoying a practical joke.

"Why do you think we sent you to drama school?"

"What do you mean *you sent* me to drama school? You didn't send me, I went there myself. And I payed out of my own pocket."

He carried on laughing.

"Okay, okay you did it all by yourself. But just think how easy it was to find a suitable part-time job to fit the timetable of your drama school, the special terms the school arranged for you to pay your fees, etcetera, etcetera."

I reflected on those events, and he was right: there were too many coincidences.

"Why then? Why the drama school, why acting - something I'd never thought of doing before?" I was genuinely bemused.

"For two very good reasons: one, your natural vanity, two, acting is a very good way of developing psychically, and, for those who are ready, also spiritually."

"What do you mean my *natural vanity*?" I asked, feeling indignant at an unfounded (!) criticism.

He laughed again.

"You are like the tender leaves of a mint plant: your ego bruises too easily. And that's an attitude you must learn to dissipate: break, dissolve your egotism, your self-centredness.

"There's no point in arguing here. You were seen drifting, not practising your exercises. So, we went for your weakest point: your vanity. And it worked. While you thought you were training for an acting career, and possibly - probably - a life of debauchery, you were being guided into expanding the sensitivity of your solar plexus."

"What do you mean? How?"

"What do you do as an actor?" It was a rhetorical question, and he proceeded to answer it. "You learn to put yourself in somebody else's shoes; in other words, you expand the sensitivity of your solar plexus, you become *sympathetic*. Do you understand now? Exercises are a shortcut but not the only way to develop psychically and spiritually: there are lots and lots of other ways all according to needs and circumstances."

He went on to expand on the etheric, psychic and spiritual functions of the solar plexus, and turned our reunion into an esoteric lesson - as was always the case with him even with casual events.....

Yiannis was now standing before me, having disengaged himself from the embrace while I was still in the depths of reliving the previous encounter with the Teacher.

"Well, has your question been answered?" he said, with a tinge of teasing irony.

Oh, yes, it most certainly had. My ability to pick up Athespodos' 'thoughts' and intentions, albeit intermmitent, was clearly a function of the solar plexus - I was familiar with the theory, and, in practice, I felt the activity/connection in that region whenever I functioned in that manner - an expanded 'gut' feeling.

"Lucky for you, your solar plexus centre isn't that open," he continued, laughing. "Otherwise you would have picked up some not so flattering comments Athespodos made about you today."

"What comments?" I wanted to know.

"Never mind, it's not important. Suffice it to say that they were in the general area of your being an arsehole. But they were made in the good spirit of camaraderie, and they were funny."

And he laughed again, and I joined him. They say that being able to laugh at yourself is a sign of not taking yourself too seriously, in which case I might be on the right track - even if I were laughing at myself as a response to jokes I hadn't heard which had been made at my expense by a dog!

How seriously, I wondered, should I take all this talk about a dog and his wife? I had no problem with Athespodos himself - not so far as the Hermanubis connection went, that is; I'd felt it and understood it; and I liked the idea of the personal relationship. But dogs being monogamous!? I decided that, for now at least, I would take the canine monogamy suggestion with a pinch of salt - and put it down as one of Yiannis' 'cynical'(!) jokes. More interesting, and more to the point, was the proposition regarding the acquisition of self-consciousness - and there was nothing to contradict the notion of individual members of particular species heading for that evolutionary ideal. Exciting - and intriguing.

I sat back on my rock and Yiannis chose one for himself very close by. He continued to laugh. That was another similarity I'd begun to recognise between him and the Teacher: they both laughed a great deal, and often, at trivial, childish things. But, even when they were laughing at someone, they were never malicious.

There was a peculiar mixture here: sometimes I could detect a note of sadness, poignant almost, in a jokey situation or comment, especially in the case of Yiannis; and, in serious situations, they would always see a funny side, as if being serious were equivalent to being pompous - and, again, Yiannis' attitude was more obvious. He reminded me of people at funeral services who found it hard not to giggle.

9

At Yianna's Again
(What was all that about?)

And thinking of funerals, the white-haired lady sprang to mind, and I began to wonder... Oh, god, yes! Yianna! How could I have forgotten about her? In all the involvement with Athespodos and everything else around him, I'd forgotten a very important item on my list. Now, this was the time; I should grab the opportunity to have the whole confusing situation cleared up.

Had I actually visited Yiannis' sister, as I was certain I had, or had I visited a couple of old ladies who knew Yiannis intimately and decided to play a joke on me? No, no that couldn't be - there was the identical twin business that was clearly incontestable; and yet, hadn't Bob said that Yianna was much older than Yiannis?...

I took a deep breath and turned to him.

"I called on your sister earlier today."

"Oh, yes? Which one?" he asked casually.

"What? How many sisters do you have?"

"Loads."

"Your twin."

"My what?"

"Your twin sister. Your identical twin sister."

"My...." He started laughing again. "You're nuts, you know. You're nuts."

"Why? Why do you say that?"

"Because I don't have a sister, let alone an identical twin."

"What?! But you just said...! Are you sure?" A stupid thing to say but I was in shock.

"Am I sure? What do you mean am I sure? You *are* nuts, my boy."

"I'm sorry, but....but...but..."

"What - are you praying to Allah now?" he said in a relaxed, half-jesting, manner, playing on the sound of the word 'allah' which is very similar to the Greek word for 'but'.

He sounded callous to me at that moment. How could he possibly be making jokes at a time like that? Wasn't I confused enough having to deal with comments supposedly made about me by a dog?

"But I met her, I spoke to her, and we talked about you!" I practically shouted in my frustration.

"Whoa, whoa. Take it easy, calm down," he said in the same laid back way. "Let's take one thing at a time. Who told you I had a sister?"

"Bob."

"Who?"

"Bob. The Australian."

"Oh, yes. What did he actually say to you?"

"What do you mean?"

"Well, did he speak of my sister or of a sister?"

"He said you had a sister in the village."

"Ah, now we're getting somewhere?"

"What?"

"He didn't say that I had a twin sister in the village, did he?"

"No. But what's the difference? He said your sister lived in the village."

"No, no, that's not what you just said. You said he told you that I had *a* sister in the village, not that *my* sister lived in the village."

I was getting a bit exasperated with this conversation, and my exasperation worsened when I detected the outline of a smirk on his face. He was yanking my chain, he was pressing my button; he knew what he was doing - but why?

"What are you on about?" I said, trying hard not to raise my voice.

"Temper, temper," he continued in the same, almost indifferent, manner. "*You*'re the one with the definitions. Be precise."

"But I am," I retorted. "Whether you have one sister or ten we're still talking about your sister."

His smirk developed into a wide smile.

"Alright. I'll let you out of your misery. You see, a while back, some of the people I've been associating with began to call one another 'brother' and 'sister'. I did not instigate this but I did not discourage it either. If it makes them happy, where's the harm? So long as they don't turn it into an organised system, an organised religion, with compulsory collection plates and accountants. D'you understand?"

I understood part of it - such as referring to Mr Zeno as a 'brother' - but I also understood that he was fobbing me off with a story full of holes.

"I reckon Bob was referring to some woman in the village whom he knew as a 'sister'," he continued.

This was not mere tongue-in-cheek talk any longer; it was barefaced lying, and an insult to my intelligence. Why was he doing this?

"But, how do you account for the fact that I met a woman who looked very much like you, said she was your twin sister, and talked with me about you? And her name was Yianna?" I asked him, shifting myself into an interrogation type of tone.

"Yianna! Oh, even her name sounds like mine," he responded captiously. "Are you sure about this?"

Was I sure?! Of course I was sure! I'd gone to the house, met Yianna and the white-haired old lady, had the wonderful experience with Yianna at the Temple of Light,... and so on. I knew that Bob had dismissed my visit as a call at the wrong address, but we had had no time to discuss it in detail...

And then, all of a sudden, my concerns regarding the 'time warp' at the doughnut hole came flooding back.... My sitting in the field under a carob tree,... the incidents, thoughts, reflections, memories that had unfolded there... Visiting Yianna... All the events that had taken place in her house and beyond it... Was I losing it?... My querries about reality, dreaming, hallucinating, raised their heads like snakes from hell!...

I needed explanations desperately, and I voiced my confusion to Yiannis who asked me to relate my experience with Yianna. He let me recount the whole series of events without interruption.

"Were the scenes with Yianna real, physically real, or not? And if not, was the whole thing a hallucination, a dream perhaps as I lay under the carob tree? Or a past incarnation? Or what?" I asked at the end of my account.

"Ooh, you appear to have so many choices there," he said, in a tone of heartless teasing, and began to laugh again. "You make so much fuss about such things."

I couldn't believe this show of coolness, of indifference.

"Of course I do. I have to know. It's a matter of preserving my sanity," I practically whined.

He guffawed and couldn't stop laughing.

"You...you think you're sane, then?" he managed to say in between attacks of coughing caused by his uncontrollable laughter. "Oh, god, oh, god," he mumbled, as he wiped the tears of laughter off his face. Then addressed himself to some invisible presence.

"Thank you, thank you for sending him to me. My life had been so dry and boring before his arrival. Thank you for the medicine of laughter."

It was an act, and I could see through it. But he continued, now talking to me.

"I know: from now on I'll call you my *laugh-therapist* for the gift you have brought me." Then, he raised a hand and addressed me in mock seriousness: "I baptise thee and give thee the name of laugh-therapist and delegate to thee the enormously important office of *Fool of the Universe*." And continued to laugh.

As he was speaking in Greek, the word he used for laughter in the combined noun 'laugh-therapist' had the double meaning of laughter and ridicule; in other words, he was saying that I made him laugh because I was being ridiculous - which sounded better than the thought of being insane. But I decided not to take offence because I didn't want to be sidetracked.

"Okay, okay, you've had your laugh," I said, trying to bring him back on course. "And I'm pleased my presence provides such a relief to your boring life, as you put it. But, seriously now--"

"There you go again," he interrupted. "Seriously. Why seriously? Can't you see that nothing is to be taken seriously? Do you want to turn the whole world into a Greek tragedy?"

He took a deep breath to subdue his laughter and then continued in a dismissive tone.

"Greek tragedy, yes. Look at Oedipus: he beds his mother and then goes and gouches his eyes out in remorse. What a jerk! Is that how you want the world to behave?"

"What?! Are you saying you condone incest?"

"It is not a matter of condoning, it is a matter of not being stupid. Look: the man was happily married to a queen, to a reportedly beautiful woman, albeit older than himself, he was king of the land. And then, when he discovered he had killed his father and been sleeping with his mother, he went and blinded himself - believing he was the miasma that affected the country. What a waste! What a waste of evolution! What a waste of reason!"

He outstretched his arms for emphasis and added:

"And then, as if that behaviour weren't stupid enough, you get another clown coming on the scene years later who uses that family situation as a generalisation to represent and analyse *all* male behaviour! - and they call this the insight of a genius!!"

I couldn't see what exactly was the point he was making, and I didn't want to digress into another issue that appeared totally irrelevant.

"Would you mind if we left Oedipus and Freud out for now and concentrated on my problem? Please?"

"But this *is* your problem, my boy. You asked if your experience was real, physically real, or a dream or a hallucination or a past incarnation, didn't you?"

"Yes, I did."

"Well, there you are. What kind of reality do you think Oedipus lived in? Can't you see how we actually create our own realities, and live in them?"

"Are you saying I've made all this up?"

"No, but like Oedipus, you create according to rules - laws, I should say - which carry their own logic."

"Could you be more explicit?"

He pondered for a bit.

"Oedipus, like you, was after the truth. In his case, he was searching for the cause of the miasma. This was one part of his problem: if there was an effect there should be a cause - this is linear thinking. Then, there was another part: he believed that whatever the cause, the truth, that is, he would understand it and be able to deal with it. And, as we know, his understanding was so limited he couldn't cope with whatever he turned up."

He stopped and waited for me to make the connection. It didn't take me long to see that I, like Oedipus, was looking for a clear-cut answer. I had already implied that, whatever the answer, it should be in realms which were exclusive of one another: physical reality, dream, hallucination, past incarnation - notwithstanding the obvious implication that none of these areas were definitively defined. What if the answer lay in part in all of them? Or, perhaps, totally outside of them all?!

I saw the grin returning to his face. Was I, like Oedipus, incapable of dealing with whatever the answer might be? Would I be blinded by it because of my inability to comprehend it? Having approached it with persistent determination, and having glimpsed it, would I then prove myself incapable of facing it and, like Oedipus, hold desperately onto the rules of my reality for the sake of survival, for my sanity?

He had already made it abundantly clear by his reaction that being 'sane', abiding by the known laws of thought or linear logic, was an obvious sign of insanity. He was right: I was being stupid, behaving like a jerk. What a waste of reason, of evolution! I insisted on using the same limited type of thinking and understanding and analysing that other imbeciles were using: linear and exclusive. True, I didn't always do that, but my tendency had always been to return to it and consider it to be the base containing the rules. Why? Because physical existence was paramount, and everything else revolved around it. How idiotic!

His grin widened.

"Are you beginning to see now?" he said.

Yes, I was beginning to see - not the answer, but the fact that I was faced with a puzzle. I had just realised that if I looked for an answer in my normal way I would end up as Oedipus... And, then, oh my god! It was as if I'd come out of a dark cave into daylight! Of course, how could I have I missed it?! I'd been looking outside, to structures in the world outside of me, to provide me with the answer. Who was it that perceived, dreamed, hallucinated? *I* did. I as consciousness. *I* moved from one mode of 'perception' to another. *I* perceived/created the world I lived in - literally. Fine, fine. But where do I start to unravel this complex web of creating and perceiving?

"Start with dreaming," I heard him suggesting - or was it his voice in my head?

Okay. What was there in dreaming that would provide the clue? I meditated on it until I saw it opening up into modes of consciousness. Dreaming is such a vast and complex area, but I was now beginning to see relevant threads. I kept my attention on the question, and tried not to deviate into irrelevancies - something that dreaming is prone to.

There was the dreaming itself, a world with its own laws and multiple levels, then there was the consciousness of the dreaming -

the Fourth State as is sometimes called - and then there was the state in which our own creativity takes place in the dreaming and on the way out of it, into 'normal' wakefulness.

Ah, yes, there it was: the confusion arises when we apply our own creativity by using, or rather misusing, a logic that's inappropriate to that state. Confused? Naturally.

"And now the unravelling," he said.

Yes, yes, the unravelling. But I couldn't. I could see the multiple levels, and managed to shift in and out of some of them, but I could not stand out of them completely to understand them objectively. I was having glimpses, tantalising glimpses, but not a totality. Bits of my experience with Yianna were coming back, and I could tell they belonged to a variety of strands of consciousness, but I still had difficulties in separating them, in classifying them.

I heard him laugh again, enjoying my struggle - granted, without malice. And I heard him goad me: "Go on, define, classify." This time, however, he was not laughing at me for my predilection, for my attitude to organise and define - he was genuinely encouraging me to do just that. What a pleasant surprise!

I struggled, but my attention was being pulled hither and thither. I was catching bits which were obvious memories, and other bits which, although they felt like memories, I could not remember having experienced before. And there were others that I could not make out where they were coming from even though, again, they felt very familiar. Some were emotionally charged while others were cool observations.

Yiannis decided to intervene.

"Okay, okay. Let's take one thing at a time. The walking stick. What was all that about?"

"Ehm, I'm not sure. What do you think it was?"

"No, no. *You* tell me. It was *your* experience."

"Well, it felt very much like a past incarnation. But..."

"But what? Was it or wasn't it?" he prodded.

"It felt like it, but not altogether. I mean, there were parts of it that were very much so but others were not."

"You *are* confused, aren't you?"

"Yes," I had to admit for the zillionth time.

"Go back to it, then."

I inhaled deeply and slowly through my nose, filling the lower part of my chest first and directing the energy from the base of my spine to the centre of my head. I held myself there to a certain count and then exhaled through the mouth, emptying the lower part of my chest first. I repeated the procedure a few times.

Soon I was back, re-experiencing the sequence. But this time the understanding that accompanied the experience had different feelings within it. In terms of these feelings, it split itself into two parts: one feeling pertained to the experience in which the walking stick had become one with my spine, and the other to my being a Pharaoh. A degree of certainty and familiarity distinguished the two.

With the first one, the familiarity was overwhelming. In the case of the second, there was a slight touch of a sense of objectivity, of being certain and familiar and yet feeling as if I were acting - like an actor who immerses himself in the character he is portraying to such an extent that he identifies with him completely. This was a difference I hadn't noticed when I first had the experience. In fact, there was no such difference then: I *was* the Pharaoh. Now, I knew I was not. This realisation shocked me halfway back to my ordinary state of consciousness - halfway, because I remained with one foot, so to speak, in the more expanded state.

"Well then, who were you - Rameses the first, Tutankhamun, or perhaps Akhenaton judging by how ugly you look?" he teased.

"None of the above. No Pharaoh. But I came so close to identifying with one - it was almost impossible to separate myself from that personality."

He chuckled.

"Can you understand now how we come to have so many Napoleons in mental institutions?"

"And can you understand why I'm so concerned about my sanity?"

We both burst out laughing. Then, before returning to his 'Napoleons' comment, he made a small detour to point out how, in Greek, the word for brain/mind is the same as that for 'breaks', 'dampers', which means that using one's brain is another way of saying that one is slow or not moving at all or dumb! And to 'raise the dampers', for which there are some lovely Greek words (*frenéres, exofrenés*), is to run the risk of going crazy or becoming inspired.

To 'lift the dampers' is to allow for experiences which lie outside ordinary, linear logic, to enter one's awareness. And, if the person who is having these experiences is not solidly prepared, or if he/she is 'sensitised' in an inappropriate way, he/she will end up in a jumbled-up consciousness in which any particular type of logic could predominate irrespective of whether it is appropriate or not - most likely, not.

In such a case, an individual may 'adopt' a new personality for 'weird' reasons which to him/her are not weird at all - and the experience of being somebody else takes over. On other occasions, the person is 'taken by the fairies', ie, moves into a world which is legitimate and valid but abides by different laws and is inhabited by different entities - and this person is then lost to the world of three dimensions and its accompanying logic. Apparently, many artists fall into this 'trap'.

If, on the other hand, the person is prepared, the experience is one of moving from realm to realm, from logic to logic without being lost or confused - which, if my experience was anything to go by, is an extremely tall order to fill.

"It is also very dangerous," he added.

"Why?"

"Need you ask? Haven't your experiences taught you anything?"

"Well, stressful, painful, confusing, yes - but dangerous?"

He smiled, a knowing smile, a benign smile, the smile of a knowledgeable person dealing with an ignorant child. I'd come to recognise that smile, having gone through an initial reaction when I'd first taken it to be condescension. It was filled with affection and patience, limitless patience.

"You have no idea how dangerous it is," he said. "You have no idea how close you have come to losing it - more than once. But you're lucky: you have guardians."

"Guardians? Hermanubis, you mean?"

"Among others."

"How does luck come into this?"

"It doesn't. You're right. I was speaking loosely. What protects you is your attitude."

I was almost certain I knew what he was referring to but, still, I wanted him to spell it out for me.

"How?"

"You know how, I don't have to tell you."

I knew what he wanted me to do, so I took another deep slow

breath and tried to slip into his meaning. It opened up as a mixture of visual, emotional and intellectual perceptions. I became inundated consecutively by a variety of emotions, each emotion being accompanied by - expressed through - clouds of colours and shapes, mostly abstract shapes which every now and then took on recognisable human or animal forms, some pleasant and others extremely unpleasant.

Soon, I began to realise the implication of this display, and set out to experiment with it. It was fantastic! Every time I concentrated on a particular emotion or thought, I seemed to create a pool of colours and shapes which increased itself beyond my control - as other similar thoughts flocked in and the original emotion augmented itself and nearly choked me.

A childhood memory rushed in and unfolded in front of me. It was the scene of a bird catcher. The man would set up a small net just above the ground in a field. The net was slightly raised on a stick at one end creating an opening, an entrance, but touching the ground and sealing any other possible entrances or exits on all other sides. Attached to the stick was a long string which ran all the way to behind a bush. Inside the net was a little bird tethered to the ground, and on the ground itself, around the bird, were scattered seeds.

The man would wait behind the bush watching the little bird fluttering, pecking on seeds and calling, and calling. Before long, others birds would arrive, sometimes a whole flock of them, to join the little one, at which point the man pulled the string and the net fell and caught the birds.

I didn't see the relevance of the bird catcher himself, but the little bird calling and the other birds flocking to join it was crystal clear. I knew about elementals from the Teacher - thoughts, intentions, emotions created by us and floating around us, and I'd used them in meditation exercises and in healing - and now this experience was casting additional light. I could see how thoughts and emotions of love protected those who created them - by increasing their volume through attraction of like thoughts and emotions - and also how thoughts and emotions sent by loved ones had a similar effect.

And then something else happened. Besides colours, shapes, thoughts and emotions also powerful vortices of energy turned up which took on shapes: human, human-like and half-human. These were different from those other human and animal forms observed earlier. They were enormously powerful creative/protective or destructive entities. The protective ones came like gigantic birds to the assistance of the tethered little bird under the net, the others came to devour it. They all had an impersonal quality about them but, once they were in close proximity, they felt very personal. They came to rescue or to destroy, and the caller was the one with the choice.

Then I understood what Yiannis meant by "your attitude protects you". If my thoughts and emotions were those of love, I would attract more loving thoughts and emotions - and the powerful entities floating around - and be protected; if I projected hatred, then I would attract more hatred and destructive, devouring entities. I wasn't exactly going around spreading love at the time but I didn't hate anybody either. It suddenly occurred to me that there wasn't anybody I actually hated: I disliked a few, but hated nobody, and since I had begun to follow the Teacher's instructions - well, tried to, anyway - I had been more careful with my quality of thoughts, emotions and intentions. So, my attitude protected me, then?

"Yes. But there are areas in which you must be left unprotected. For your own development," Yiannis responded. "There are levels of understanding where you as consciousness have to function unaided, you're totally abandoned and have to cope alone - but these are levels where concepts like 'alone' do not exist as you understand them, if they exist at all; and there are also levels where there are no concepts whatsoever."

My experience at the doughnut hole regarding 'knowing' and 'understanding' was being put into perspective now, beginning to fall into place. But the idea of being totally alone - in whatever way that term might be interpretred - didn't exactly sit well with me. He sensed my discomfort.

"How else do you think you'd be able to function in total darkness if you yourself as consciousness do not learn to self-generate the light, to be the light?"

I knew he was talking about the Darkness 'before Existence' that I had had a glimpse of earlier. But he had also spoken of the conglomerate known as human individuality which had been 'created' in Existence and whose 'fate' was eventual total dissolution. And now he was saying that a human being, as consciousness, could reach a stage, acquire the ability, whereby he could 'exist', 'be' in...

...in... 'Non-existence'?! Was this possible, or even meaningful?

This puzzle had been with me for a while in one form or another: first he talked to me of total dissolution of the personality, and then he devoted, whatever time he spent with me, to instructing me on how to expand myself as consciousness - wonderful instructions, but to what purpose? This should be the perfect time to point out the contradiction and seek clarification---

"But this question is not relevant at this point. You're not there yet. You're at the *confused* stage, the intersection of logics. You have a different problem to tackle right now," he said, cutting into my thoughts. And then he continued, deliberately preventing me from interjecting with my query.

"Back to the walking stick, if you don't mind. Did you feel the same with the walking stick as you felt with the Pharaoh?"

It was obvious that he wouldn't let me deviate into my area of preference, despite his pretend politeness.

"No. That was different," I said. "With the stick I felt complete familiarity: it was mine - it *is* mine."

I didn't know what possessed me to put that emphasis on the present tense, but it felt right.

He chuckled gently. "Good, good. You're on track. But why the difference?"

"For a start, it's not a walking stick: it's a sceptre. And I used it as such."

I was absolutely certain about it now. I was having visions of me using it in Egypt, as an acolyte, in the temple... Oh, god, it was coming back to me, in full force: it was part of the training.... The 'sceptre'... the 'rod'... The experience of Athespodos-turned-Anubis embracing me... the rod... my spine... the rod in my spine...my spine: a long powerful stalk rising up into my head and culminating in a magnificent lotus flower... the power and the gentleness....

"I take it back. You're not so ugly after all," said Yiannis. "In fact, you're wonderfully beautiful," he added in a tone of ambiguous sarcasm. And then he dispelled the ambiguity with another observation.

"If only human beings could see how beautiful they really are at this level."

He was not sarcastic, he was genuine, and I could sense a touch of wistfulness in his voice. But not for long.

"So, the walking stick is yours, then? - oh, sorry, the sceptre," he baited me.

"Why, is it not a sceptre?"

"Yes, but what is a sceptre, if not a glorified walking stick, a prop?"

I reminded myself of the manner with which Yianna had treated it. The irony of it! Was it not sacred, sacrosanct? It felt so holy, and yet it was treated almost with contempt. I voiced my objection.

"Holy, sacred? Perhaps. Take care, though, not to turn the whole thing into idolatry."

"I am not. But I know that the rod is invested with so much energy, and I respect it."

"No, no. You don't respect the rod, you don't elevate it to something that it is not. The energy in the rod is neutral, neither good nor bad. It's what you bring along with you to unlock its energy that's important. If you, as consciousness, are not at the requisite level, nothing happens. If you are, but you bring along the wrong vibrations, the consequences are what you deserve. There is nothing morally intrinsic in the rod - the sceptre, the stick, whatever you would like to call it - save for the injected elementals and energy connections. Don't you remember?"

Yes I did. Now I did. He was bringing all this back to me now. And, for the first time, he was using words like 'elementals' and 'vibrations'. I remembered clearly how the Rod was used as a test and a 'qualification', telling us that we had achieved a certain level of consciousness, and gave us a boost to the next level. It was holy, alright, but so were we! - we were, or tried to be, for practical reasons: being 'holy' was a concept that stood for 'raising the consciousness'.

The Rod was like a multi-chambered vault full of treasures, and we were the hackers whose task it was to break the code that would enable us to enter it - chamber by chamber, test by test. But how? Using what tools? Consciousness was the means: *we as consciousness* were the means.

First, the realisation that we were not our thoughts, our emotions, our physical bodies; then, the control of thoughts, emotions, physical bodies, and, in the process, discovering that we have bodies which deal with thoughts, bodies which deal with emotions, bodies which deal with the three-dimensional world - but that *we* are not these bodies, *we* inhabit them. Then, the training and use of these bodies to break the code, to hack into the system. And the last code to be broken would have to be done by sheer consciousness, by us as consciousness devoid of thoughts, emotions, physicality! - this 'final' task lying far far into the distant future for most of us....

"Now, we can go back to the Pharaoh, if you like," he continued, guiding me away and into another direction.

"The Pharaoh? What about him?" I said, still involved in my memory/visions of the use and meaning of the Rod.

"Yes, what about him?"

"Well, I know it wasn't me."

"Yes; what else?"

"But it was *practically* me. I could hardly tell us apart."

"Good. What else?" he prodded gently.

I reflected. What was the difference between the Pharaoh and me? I couldn't see any... Save that I knew that I had never been that Pharaoh in an actual incarnation. Yes?... But I was capable of being that person in a *virtual* incarnation. I could read out his entire life, if I chose to. So, the difference... the difference lay in an emotional component, in an attachment. All my own incarnations were loaded with emotion, I felt strongly attached to them. With the Pharaoh, however, even though there was an element of emotion which lent it realism and presence, in the end I realised I could distance myself and observe it, something I found extremely hard to do with my own actual incarnations.

"Well?" He was smiling again as he watched my progress in unravelling the puzzle.

I explained to him my findings.

"Fine," he said, in a manner of concluding; and then, as if to recap: "We have two things here: emotional attachment to your own incarnations, and the ability to relive, virtually, other people's incarnations. Right?"

"Right."

"So, what would happen if you were to detach yourself from your own incarnations and, perhaps, allow the investment of a certain amount of controlled attachment when you enter other people's incarnations?"

I could see that the differences amongst incarnations would practically cancel themselves out.

"Would I go crazy? Become another Napoleon?"

"No, no. You missed the *controlled* bit - true, you could go crazy, but only if you lost your control and the distinction. And it is true that you would be viewed as 'crazy' from the position of three-dimensionality but only because the experience wouldn't fit that particular logic. But that's not your concern, anyway."

He waited for me to take it in before speaking again.

"You can see the breakthrough here, can't you?" he asked rhetorically. "The point is to manage to review your incarnations detachedly, and personalise other incarnations. In other words, you subjectify and objectify at will. The result: you put all incarnations, yours and all the others, into the proper perspective, on a par with one another, which is to deal with all of them with equanimity. They are only there for the sake of experience - my experience, your experience, everybody's experience. Nothing belongs exclusively to any one person, and everything belongs to everybody.

"Can you see now how such experiences, when picked up subconsciously by people, are turned into ideals such as brotherhood and equality? It's the realisation, at the subconscious level, that ownership is common - and a reflection, at the intellectual level, of an experiential actuality, of a fact. Can you also see its effect on the everyday physical life of those who come to 'understand' this consciously? Remember Pythagoras' admonition: 'Be *in* the world but not *of* the world', and Buddha's calling for detachment."

Once again, he stopped to allow me to take in what he was saying, not only intellectually but also by means of the direct method.

10

The Glory of Being Human
(We: the Storehouse of Everything)

Gradually, I began to pick up on *his* consciousness. I latched onto his solar plexus centre and found myself watching, from the inside, a fantastic array of scenes in which he was the central figure. They were all of an ancient past, stretching back to pre-pre-dinosaur eras. They had an earthly feel to them, and reminded me of an experience I'd had years earlier back home regarding myself - it seemed to be a reminder of our common ancestry, although richer and more 'ancient' than mine. It showed me the commonality not only of humans but of all other things, too - animal, vegetable and mineral. We, as humans, contained all of them in our experiences and in our make-up. We, as humans, could experience ourselves as animals, vegetables or minerals.

This was not a metaphor, it was actual experience - a spectacular display of 'creation' that would take volumes to detail. There were intelligent entities participating, conscious entities contributing each their own special essences in colour and sound. They were discharging their functions objectively and yet they emanated a sense of the personal in the 'love' which they wove into their work. Love was the only word that sprang to mind, and the only way I could comprehend the manner in which they expressed themselves. But I was aware that it was something above and beyond it; maybe, something entirely different that I as an individual or I as a human could not understand in any other way.

These entities were acting from within themselves, all their work was being carried out inside them. When I tried to identify them as 'bodies', as individuals occupying a specific space, suddenly they burst out into magnificent colours and sounds and multiplied themselves into zillions. They were everywhere, and they were partly human-like, outlines of human faces within floods of innumerable hues of pulsating colours. At first, I thought I had actually caused this multiplication myself by my thought but then I realised that it was they who were acting on my consciousness in response to my 'request' and attempting to make themselves comprehensible to me, that is, they tried to make themselves visible to me in human terms.

It took me a while to come to understand what was going on and even then I was left with a new puzzle: they were everywhere, like air or water, participating in the creation and maintenance of life, including mineral life - and they were conscious. Their multiplication seemed like a constant division and subdivision of themselves into smaller and smaller parts. I found myself looking into what, in terms of physics, would be subnuclear matter, but matter which was alive and conscious - they were the very substance of life, a conscious substance of life.

In human terms, there was a sense of 'sacrifice' about them in that they were giving themselves for the formation of life, their actual work being this activity of giving themselves - although they themselves would not have viewed it as sacrifice; they were far too happy and joyous in working-giving themselves....

I felt a pull to concentrate on Yiannis more exclusively, which resulted in another display of colours flowing out of his solar plexus and radiating like a sun, similar to the one I'd witnessed in the rock but more magnificent.

"Well? Are there any other insights to be gleaned from your pharaonic experience - to begin with?" I heard him ask.

Insights? The whole display was a series of insights, a series of 'understandings'. But which were the specific ones he was trying to draw my attention to now? I pondered. I knew the Pharaoh wasn't one of my actual incarnations, but it could have been. There had been other instances where I couldn't tell the difference, and now I'd learnt that it didn't matter. What mattered was the attachment, the attachment that kept me tied to my actual incarnations. And there were many...

As I was pondering on this issue, I saw and felt the display of energy radiating from Yiannis' solar plexus sliding slowly upwards to the area around his lower chest. I felt a jolt in the same area of my body and found myself transported to a past incarnation I was already familiar with.

Our country was being invaded. I was very young and attached to a temple, under the tutelage of the Teacher who was the Priest and whom I loved and respected enormously.

One of my duties was to pick fresh flowers for the altar every day. On this particular occasion, I had just placed the flowers on the altar and the Teacher was preparing for an invocation, when suddenly a number of invading soldiers burst in, swords at the ready, and began to pillage the place. One of them rushed towards the Teacher who was standing facing the rising sun, ready for the invocation, and ran him through with his sword.

I was stunned. I screamed with uncontrollable anger, picked up the knife from the altar and lunged for the soldier who had his back to me. The Teacher saw me, and shouted out: "Nooo! The knife's for cutting flowers! No killing, no shedding of blood! Don't!" Killing or shedding of human blood was against our beliefs. The soldier pulled his blooded sword out of the Teacher and plunged it into him again. But I couldn't stop him, I couldn't attack him with my knife. So, in my anger and frustration, I turned the knife on myself - something which, too, was against our beliefs.

The emotions of anger, frustration and the sense of utter loss were overwhelming. And they continued to be experienced with the same intensity every time I visited the same scene - including the current occasion.

And then, as I sat there shivering with emotion, it dawned on me, I understood. So, I went back and re-experienced the scene, again and again and again. And every time I went through it I managed to reduce the emotion, the attachment, that accompanied it, until I could experience it with detachment but still knowing that it was mine and that I could re-invest it with the original emotion, if I chose to.

Then I found myself in France during the French Revolution. I was in my twenties and married. The Teacher was again with me but this time he was my brother-in-law, my wife's brother; he was in his early teens and in my care. I hated the aristocracy of which I was a member - I hated them for their injustices and, at the same time, pitied them for their stupidity.

I joined the Revolution and took to the barricades to fight them, despite the heart-rending entreaties from my wife and my dear little brother-in-law who kept calling out trying to prevent me from getting involved in the spilling of blood. I was killed at the barricades.

But the hatred for the French aristocracy, and the pain and regret for having broken an oath not to spill human blood and for leaving behind a young wife and an even younger boy who depended entirely on me, haunted me ever since.

So, I repeated the process of revisiting that life again and again until I brought the hatred and the cancerous feelings of regret and guilt under control.

Similar problems with numerous incarnations had already been resolved by means of the more 'natural' slow and complex process of 'retribution'. I also knew that there were other incarnations, in other parts of the globe, which had to be treated in the same manner with which these particular two had been dealt with, in order for them to be 'neutralised'.

But why had these two incarnations been brought up at this juncture? What was their significance? There had been others, more spectacular, more painful, more horrific, and some - perhaps, too many - in which I'd been the villain. And why point to incarnations - and there had been a few - in which the Teacher too had been involved? why not an incarnation of mine during which Yiannis had also been around?

In response to my mental questioning, Yiannis' face shone with a broad smile on which the features of the Teacher were faintly superimposed. Why didn't that disturb me? It mildly surprised me but it did not disturb me. Perhaps I was getting used to Yiannis' games and the 'copying' of the Teacher's mannerisms.

But there was something deeper than that. There was a feeling of identification, of Yiannis taking over the Teacher's personality - or, was it the other way round? Was the Teacher taking over Yiannis' identity? There had been rumours of the Teacher appearing at different places, and in a variety of guises, simultaneously. Was I, at last, witnessing this phenomenon? The line between the two characters was blurred. Who was who?

Yiannis' face now beamed with a knowing smile mixed with irony. And the penny dropped: he was demonstrating how incarnations, and whole personalities, could overlap, be 'borrowed', or even appropriated by someone who knew how to - a human being was not only a mongrel but also a chameleon, among other things.

"You can be anybody. And anything," he said, daring me to

challenge him, "when you reach a certain breadth of consciousness in this landscape. And you don't even need to reach the mountaintop to be able to do this," he added.

"Are you at the mountaintop?" I asked.

"Oh, no. I'm only at the foothills."

"And where am I, then?"

"You? You're underground," he said, and burst into one of his laughs. "But there's hope for you yet," he continued, laughing.

Okay, fine, I'm taking all this on board, I said to myself, I too have a sense of humour; I knew there was a vast gap between us in terms of consciousness, but this whole experience, in spite of its being wonderfully insightful, was still very unsettling. I had no way of knowing with certainty, with absolute certainty, who was who.

And, adding to the uncertainty, was still the question of Yianna's identity, not to mention her existential status. Who was she? what was she? did she ever actually exist physically? - the initial questions that had instigated this recent inquiry in the first place. I wanted to return to them, but first I needed a clarification, as satisfactory as possible, to this issue of Yiannis and the Teacher: the 'who was who' question. I asked him.

As expected, he laughed.

"But is it relevant?" he responded to my question with another question.

"Very much so," I insisted.

"But does it matter, in view of our discussion and our understanding of expanding consciousness?"

"Yes, it does. It is one thing to expand yourself as consciousness to include and understand another consciousness, and another thing to *be* that other consciousness. Right now I don't know which of the two I'm dealing with - the Teacher or...or another Teacher?"

"I see," he said, making an obvious effort to control his laughter and subdue it to a smile.

He looked as if he were coming down to my level. The light and colours emanating from his chest were slightly reduced but continued to scintillate.

"You can't tell which of the two you're dealing with, the Teacher or another Teacher," he repeated my last statement. "What is it with you and this Teacher business? Another one of your obsessions?"

"No," I reacted. "I'm seeking clarification. Boundaries."

"You haven't been listening, have you? I said to you a few seconds ago that you can be anything and anybody, once you've expanded your 'normal' human boundaries - some might say *break* your human boundaries. Teachers come and go according to your needs. You call them and they arrive - as you did with me."

"I never called you. I never knew you ever existed until today," I raised a luke-warm protest, knowing full well that I'd had incarnations with him in spite of the fact that I had been repeatedly 'prevented' from gaining full access to them. I hoped to provoke him into some revelations.

"Oh, yes?" he said, and looked at me patiently.

A series of memory excerpts were paraded before me to remind me of numerous occasions when I had 'called' and been 'answered', and occasions when a 'lesson' was there to be learned: there was Mr Manolides who pointed to my "screaming" for help, the man from India who breezed in and out of my life one afternoon to deal a devastating blow to some of my beliefs and open new vistas for exploration, the child with Down's syndrome who loved me to bits and who died in my arms with half the skin of his little body burned when I pulled him out of the burning house, the neignbours' dog who was shot dead because he was rabid, my grandmother's gay cat... Hang on, hang on, wait a minute! This is drifting off the point.

Yiannis' smile returned to a full-blown teasing laughter.

"You see, my boy, teachers are everywhere. They pop up according to your needs. But it is always you who picks up the lesson. It is always you who can see and understand, according to your lights. Remember beloved Gautama? Everybody witnesses sickness and death but it takes a special type of readiness to pick up the lesson. After a certain stage of consciousness expansion, teachers are everywhere."

He stopped and looked down around his feet, searching for something. When he found what he was looking for, he bent down and picked up a stone and held it up in front of him.

The stone gave off dull, drab, colours. But then, as he held it pointing at me, it began to radiate an array of colours of ever increasing brilliance, turning into a virtual sun, obscuring Yiannis and the surroundings. And in this brilliance I saw again those wonderful entities who 'sacrifice' themselves in order to create and maintain everything in existence: the whole process of creation seemed to be

packed into this, from the first explosion into Existence, the appearance of what the Greeks called Phanes, to the ramifications and development of 'seeds', Principles, Ideas, Laws - and all this out of a
piece of stone?

"It could have just as easily been a grain of sand," I heard him
say.

The display of radiating colours began to reduce itself in brilliance until it, slowly, disappeared and Yiannis was left holding a
plain piece of stone which he then let fall to the ground.

"Beware of teachers who insist on imparting their teachings to
you," he said, as if concluding.

"Are you saying that the Teacher is imposing his doctrine on
me?"

"No, of course not," he said, and flashed an ironic smile at me.
"But, which teacher are you referring to now?" he added teasingly -
and challengingly.

He was turning the tables on me again. I was, of course, referring to *the* Teacher, but Yiannis was a Teacher too, and so were
others for that matter - and I'd been exposed to the views and belief
systems of many of them. Were they all trying to impart their systems to me, in the sense of Yiannis' words? Was Yiannis in the
same category as the others? Whatever his intentions, there was one
thing I was certain of at that moment: he had turned my logic
against me and put me into a predicament - like a hypnotist confusing his subject in order to produce an opening to slip in his suggestions.

"D'you see? *You* are the teacher. I, we, the rest of the world can
only provide hints. You teach yourself. We elicit responses by our
mere presence. Remember your friend Socrates? Midwifery. Are
you pregnant, ready to dilate yourself as consciousness for the birth
of a new understanding?"

He stopped and watched me for a while.

"You've always been fond of philosophical questions, so I'll give
you your next task: *omnipresence*. Try and understand it intellectually, and know it by the direct method. What is it to be *in* everything, and what is it to *be* everything? Is it a matter of losing your
identity or expanding it?"

It was obvious by now that he was not going to clarify the
identities of the Teacher and himself - not in the manner I was pro-

posing, anyway. The puzzle would have to be left unresolved until, as I intuited, the time came when I would see it in its proper light. Right now I seemed to be approaching it ill-equipped and in the wrong way.

And then I saw the emanations of colours moving up from the lower part of his chest to the centre of it. The colours themselves, too, changed gradually into softer and gentler hues but without losing their brilliance. The feelings that accompanied the colours were of the most delicate nature of love and compassion.

As I watched, the corresponding parts in me began to radiate in response, and the feelings were intensified. An enormous vortex opened up in the centre of my chest and spread outwards into a disk-like shape whose radius reached down to my feet, well above my head and the sides of my body. In this vortex, I could see and feel the beautiful 'sacrificial' entities I had observed earlier in Yiannis' solar plexus carrying on their work. But this time I felt that I too was participating in this work. And it was amazing: I watched and participated in the mechanics of love enacted in the vortex of my heart. I experienced the giving of these entities and found myself doing the same thing.

And, yes, I was right, my earlier experience was being confirmed in my own heart: the giving of oneself was not a sacrifice, it was the most wonderfully joyful activity. I was pouring out my heart, I was giving but the giving did not carry any sense of depriving myself, of diminishing myself. On the contrary, the more I gave of myself the more I 'received'.

It was a continuous process of acting as a vehicle, except that the vehicle itself was also functioning as the very material that was being given forth, poured into the creating and sustaining of the world. I had the understanding that I was raising love to a science, and to a practical activity, by observing and participating in the mechanics of its functioning. I was aware that at some other level this activity might be called sacrifice but such a term had no place here, it was totally inapplicable.

These were the mechanics of love, pure and natural. Giving, giving, giving in the most natural and joyous manner. In this vortex, in the midst of these creative entities, and to my happy surprise, I saw many humans participating: some of them were obscure or totally unknown to the physical world, others were well-known creators of world religions. And the puzzle of the often emotionally loaded so-called self-sacrifice was finally solved for me.

I felt myself being pulled up from my chest to the top of my head where another enormous vortex appeared and stretched outwards in a horizontal fashion, its centre being in the middle of my head. And here the activities of the heart centre were 'duplicated'. But here I also saw the activities of love-sacrifice being enacted in the physical world. It was a dog-eat-dog scenario. The stronger ate the weaker. There was no mercy.

Then I felt being pulled down to my chest, to the lower part of my chest, and my reaction was that of shock, of pain, of horrific pain. I thought I was going to pass out. But in the nick of time, it seems, I was back in the head centre where these physical activities did not have the same horrifying effect: indeed, it was the reverse - the violence and killing seemed most natural: it was the expression of love-sacrifice.

I was pulled up and down, from the lower chest to the head and back, a few times, undergoing the two different experiences. Until I realised what was actually taking place: it was basically the same activity but from a different perspective. In the lower chest, the experience was 'personal', that of a person, of an individual. It was limited, curtailed, as if blinkers were worn. In the vortex of the head, on the other hand, it was 'impersonal', it was universal.

Those great human beings who taught self-sacrifice, were acting with the experience of the head where the concept of 'self-sacrifice' does not exist: they acted from love in the most natural way of giving - they did not 'sacrifice' themselves. But for the vast majority of human beings who understand mostly through a lower centre, it was perceived from a personal perspective where self-preservation is paramount.

From the perspective of the head - the universal view - a gazelle being eaten by a lion is a mere exchange of energies, the whole world being energy 'solidifying' at different levels. From the point of view of the creative entities, this exchange of energies is totally natural: the gazelle's death could be viewed as self-sacrifice for the preservation of the lion's physical life, like the plankton is 'sacrificed' to the whale. Ultimately, however, it is the flowing, the giving of universal energy.

But what of humans - what is their exact position in this scheme of things? What of human consciousness? I was already aware of Yiannis' theory that the human personality was a psychological conglomerate, bits of various types of consciousness held together mainly by memory; and that they would, eventually, disintegrate. Earlier, I had wanted to broach this subject with him to see why he was 'helping' me with consciousness expansion when, at the end of the day, there would be nothing there to expand. But I had been discouraged. Now, I was ready to delve into it, once and for all, by myself, directly....

"Enough," I heard him say.

And, before I had time to react, I felt the brilliant displays of energies in my head and heart being supplanted by my physical sight. Yiannis, too, was now sitting on his rock without his glorious splendour. I was in an afterglow, still connected with my 'transcendent' sensibility, but somewhat reduced in my mental capacities - and so suddenly. Naturally, I wanted to know why.

"I told you why a while back. One step at a time. You try to run before you can walk. Now, take a deep breath."

I followed his instructions as he took me through a breathing practice that lasted a few minutes.

"We don't want you to be sick, and we certainly don't want you to get depressed," he said by way of explaining at the end of the breathing practice.

"Why should I get depressed?" I inquired.

"You went too far too suddenly, and without full preparation. There can be side effects."

I understood the feeling of 'reduction' in my capacities. Actually, it wasn't a reduction in real terms - it was simply the return to my 'normal' functions, but it felt like landing in a small, hollow, heavily shaded valley after soaring high above in a clear bright sky enjoying a brilliant unimpeded panorama.

But, that apart, I sensed there were other reasons for my being brought back besides the one given me by Yiannis. This was the second time that my inquiry into the contradiction concerning the fate of human consciousness had been brought to a sudden halt or diverted. So, I pressed the point.

"I take it you want to neither go crazy nor become more confused," he responded to my query.

I pondered, then shrugged my shoulders. Going mad did not

bother me. Getting more confused did.

"We're concerned here with an area which is much more tricky than the one we dealt with earlier regarding identification with past incarnations. Do you know why many religious doctrines do not include reincarnation?"

"No, why?"

"Because of the prevalent laziness in human nature."

"I don't follow."

"Look: if human beings were told that there was no such thing as moral law, and that reincarnation was a fact, the whole human race would be in an unbelievable mess. So, they are threatened with one, single, life and eternal hell for what they're made to believe are transgressions," he said, matter-of-factly.

"Are you saying there is no moral law?"

He shook his head in a show of disappointment.

"Why do you ask me such silly questions? You've had the experience."

Yes, I'd had the experience. And I'd always assumed there were moral laws. But, now he mentioned it, I had not come across any specific moral laws. The only morality I'd encountered, if it could be counted as such, were those feelings of love, compassion, tenderness towards everything and everybody, the joy in acting as a vehicle, the happiness in giving.... Oh, I see, I see...

"Yes, you do, don't you? It's your insistence on concepts and definitions that blocked it. What did you expect - to see it written on a wall: 'I am the moral law?' Consciousness is the moral law, as is the case with all other laws."

He stopped and stared at me for a beat or two.

"Remember dear old Socrates: 'Nobody does wrong knowingly'. Consciousness informs morality. You have the experience, and morality flows from it. One little step below that you'll find Kant's Categorical Imperative: 'Do unto others what you would have them do unto you'. At the present stage, however, none of this happens naturally, automatically. Hence the threats."

"But why should people be threatened, to what purpose?"

"To develop as consciousness."

"Ah, at last! We're getting there. 'To develop as consciousness'! But why bother if it's going to dissolve into nothing eventually?"

He smiled cheekily.

"Good. Excellent. You rumbled me, you caught me now. I can't escape," he said, throwing his arms up in the air in mock surrender.

"Well?"

"Well what?"

"Aren't you going to explain?"

"But I thought what you really wanted a few minutes ago was to find out why you were brought back so abruptly. Do I take it you are not interested in that any longer?"

"Oh, I am, I am. But the consciousness question, as well, if you don't mind." I had no intention of letting him digress this time.

He gave a little chuckle.

"Okay. But you do realise that both of these questions are actually the same, don't you?"

"Are they?"

"Oh, yes. From a different angle though. Just before you were brought back you were getting ready to investigate that yourself, weren't you?"

"Yes; and you stopped me."

"And for a very good reason: I would have lost you. Consciousness is a very complex and delicate structure. It's taken millions of years to bring it up to its present state. It can expand to include galaxies within it, but it can also get confused and mangled up. We are talking about you and me here as consciousness. Usually, there is a safety cut-off point to safeguard against what you might call accidents, but accidents do happen - many people experiment without adequate preparation: your Teacher surely told you about such things."

"Oh, yes. But that was to do with more practical applications."

"True. Imagine how much more dangerous this is. That's why at this stage, more than at any other, guidance is paramount. The cut-off point was removed - how else do you think you would have been able to glimpse what you did? - and we as your temporary guardians became responsible for your safety. And we stopped you when it was deemed unsafe to venture any further."

"I still don't understand why it was unsafe."

"Because you were reaching the point of abandoning all your bodies - too soon, you were not ready."

I did't agree with that. I'd felt as ready as I would ever be when I was in that state.

"What you felt and what was actually happening were two different things. Certainty and bliss are the ultimate traps."

He was losing me again. I was not able to follow.

"Do you remember how happy you felt at the hole-in-the-rock when you were told that eventually you'll disappear into nothing and therefore there was nothing to fear?"

"Yes."

"Well, happiness and certainty are like candy given, or promised, to children to entice them, to lure them. Can you see?"

"No. I'm sorry, but I'm not with you."

He didn't respond right away. He took a deep breath and looked up at the night sky. It was dead quiet, except for some crickets chirping in the distance. I caught sight of a couple of glowworms in a nearby patch of grass. The sky was packed full with twinkling stars. The vastness of it! A shooting star traced a line of light over our heads.

"Travelling light," he whispered, as if to himself.

"Yes. About 300,000 kilometres per second.

"Yes. On the physical plane. But how fast does it travel in your head centre? And how fast does it travel when there is nothing for it to travel through?"

"It must be instantaneous, if there is nothing to slow its path," I answered.

"No. You're thinking of 'empty space', an impossible hypothesis, since there is no such thing, cannot be such thing as empty space."

"What then?"

"Ah, use your mind, your thinking process. That's why you were brought back, it's safer this way, the safeguard is back in place. Think."

And I thought. He was asking me to think of a state of existence in which nothing impeded the path of light. That, by implication, meant that there was nothing for the light to travel through. There was nothing. But this was Darkness where light does not exist. Light, Phanes, exists. Light is Existence itself. No light equals no Existence. Light is everything, everything is produced, created, by light - it *is* light.

"And what is consciousness - you and I?" he asked.

"If everything that exists is light then we, too, if we exist, must be light."

"And what happens when Darkness claims us?"

"We cease to exist. We become Nothing."

"Right."

"Look. Forgive me for hammering on this, but what is the point of expanding ourselves as consciousness if it is our destiny to be devoured by Darkness, by Non-existence?"

"Ah, yes. Existence versus Non-existence. The very issue. Tell me: how does consciousness develop?"

"Hm... I'm not sure what you mean exactly?"

"Well, would you say, for example, that the worm is self-conscious?"

"Hm... I don't know. I wouldn't have thought so."

"But it acts and reacts for self-preservation. Surely, it must have some sort of sense of self, if only very rudimentary. Wouldn't you agree?"

"Well, it's all instinctive. I'm not sure if I could call it self-consciousness. Is a mechanical robot self-conscious?"

"Okay. How about a collective consciousness that, somehow, sets the rules of acting and reacting for all worms? Would you go along with that?"

"Instinctual rules, yes."

"Alright then. Would you further say that man has progressed to a degree where, while still obeying certain instincts, has acquired self-consciousness?"

"Okay...."

"And that he has reached where he is now through struggle?"

"Alright...."

I couldn't help laughing to myself inside. I was listening to Socrates! It was as if Socrates were standing in front of me leading me to some point he wanted to make. How delicious! I could almost see the sweet ugly face of Socrates with the snubbed nose overshadowing that of Yiannis'. Midwifery, that's what Yiannis had said earlier. And he was practising it now, and he was making it sound like one of Plato's dialogues.

11

'Surviving' the Darkness
(Egotism and Love)

I felt compelled to reverse this questioning procedure, just for the heck of it, to see how he would handle it.

"But why the struggle?" I asked.

"To develop self-consciousness, of course," was his response. "How else could human beings acquire self-consciousness? Struggling, at the physical level, on this planet. Earth is the perfect place for the birth of self-consciousness, of self-centredness, of egotism."

"But, surely, egotism is not a very nice trait to develop."

"Not from your present moral perspective perhaps, but absolutely necessary for the development of consciousness. It is a stage, which is still prevalent. And then...."

"And then what?"

"Then we come to your present question. We need a solid core of self-consciousness, even if selfish and self-centred, in order to fight the Darkness; and then ally ourselves with it. Do you follow me?"

"No." He'd lost me again.

I saw him dithering. For the first time since I'd met him he appeared ambivalent, indecisive.

"I'm of two minds about this," he said. "I'm certain we should have brought you back as we have done, but I'm now doubtful as to whether we should proceed with this theme, even at the intellectual level."

"Why not?" I was getting desperate not to let him slip away again.

"Because, first of all, this is not a subject to be treated lightly - which makes it difficult for me to deal with since I don't like too much seriousness; and it's not something that's widely revealed. It used to be part of an Initiation stage in the old days - occult, secret, a very important part of the Mysteries. You wouldn't know because you never reached that level."

He stopped and looked at the sky again, as if waiting for some assistance to arrive, an inspiration perhaps to egg him on. I decided to provide that nudge.

"First of all....?"

"What?"

"You said 'first of all'. What's 'second of all', 'third of all', and so on?"

He smiled at my silly attempt.

"You're right. I'm right: take nothing seriously. Right. Second: at the intellectual level you may or may not understand or accept this but at least you're safe - you're approaching it from within your bodies. Third, and just for the record: this, in a philosophical treatise, might be called *the cop-out clause*". And he burst out laughing. Back to his normal self.

"Okay. What is the purpose of the development of consciousness, in general?" he resumed.

"What, for the whole universe?"

"Yes. Consciousness, in general. No specific bits."

"Ehm... God knows. I don't know."

"Good. You hit the nail on the head: God knows. Only, for our discussion here we'll leave the concept of God out. We'll call it Darkness. The unknowable. All we know about it, all some of us know about it, is that it's uncreated. It simply *is*. Darkness. Light belongs in creation. Anything and everything that appears, that exists, is light. And light gets periodically sucked back into Darkness - and with it, consciousness. Are you with me so far?"

"Ehm...Yes." I resisted the temptation to remind him of the contradiction I'd pointed out earlier. I wanted to see where he was leading.

"Now. Individual consciousness. This is something that is split off, developed from, a collective one. It's almost an epiphenomenon. It has its beginnings in physical matter - the only place where it can form. It develops from a wider kind of consciousness, like ripples develop in a pond when bubbles of air rise gurgling to the surface. These ripples are human beings, us, eventual individualities."

I was suddenly reminded of the innumerable 'duplications' of the creative entities I had encountered earlier. Were all human beings duplications of some great entity?

"Our self-consciousness, our *intense* self-consciousness," he continued, "is part of our mechanism that would work eventually to prevent us from being devoured, if you like, by Darkness."

He stopped and smiled.

"You know the story of Pandora, don't you?"

"Yes. Pandora and the box."

"Pandora and the vase, actually. No matter. What was left in the vase after all the evils were let loose?"

"Hope."

"Right. A slip of a thing, a teeny-weeny weakling we call hope. This is ingrained into human beings, into human consciousness. It stirs them to a view of immortality, to a fight against dissolution, against final annihilation."

"Is that all we have - hope? We just hope that we will not dissolve into nothing?!"

"No, no. Well...yes. Basically. Yes."

I was aghast. Was this the great secret of the fate of humanity, a secret guarded by the ancient Mysteries?! And, again: why am I developing as consciousness? Just *hoping* that I'll survive the great Darkness?!

He was looking at me with a grin on his face.

"I told you it was a cop-out, didn't I? And I warned you that you might not understand. On the other hand, you might - would - have understood if you were left to investigate it in the state you were in before you were brought back. But then the price would have been incalculable, you would have been sucked into nothing, into oblivion."

"So, what is this - a joke, an experiment?"

"If it's a joke, nobody's laughing. If it's an experiment, well, I don't know."

"Is that it? You don't know?! What's with the expansion of consciousness, then?"

"Ah, yes. That's where hope comes in."

"Back to hope again?"

"Yes, back to hope. Do you remember the old admonition: 'Pray to the goddess Athena but, at the same time, do something about it?'"

"Yes...? But do something like what?"

"What you're already doing: expanding youself as consciousness."

"How's that going to help me?"

He exhaled as if losing patience.

"Have all the things you've learned, all the experiences you've had, been in vain? What have you learned about incarnations, for instance?"

"That, with practice, I should be able to identify with any and all incarnations, that no experience belongs exclusively to anybody, and that anyone with appropriate training can achieve such things."

"Anything else outside incarnations?"

"Again, with training, anyone can see and understand anything and anybody they direct their attention to - except you."

"What do you mean 'except me'?"

"Ever since I met you, you've been stopping me from finding out about you. Why?"

"That's not entirely true. You've seen aspects of me, you've seen past incarnations, you've... Never mind. Later. This is not relevant. What else?"

"I've had glimpses of Knowing and Understanding. I--"

"Enough. You see, what you're giving me here are the beginnings of an expanding consciousness which, if continuing to expand, should, in principle, encompass the whole universe, eventually. Do you follow me?"

"In principle, eventually, yes."

I couldn't help throwing that in as a tease. He responded with an appreciative smile, and continued.

"Can you see what I'm driving at now?"

"What - that I can be God?...."

"You disappoint me - you're proving me wrong again," he said, and his face dropped.

"What? What do you mean?" I said, feeling very concerned with his comment.

"I admit it, I'm wrong - you're not as stupid as I thought!" And fell into another one of his bouts of laughter.

I watched him and waited for his laughing to abate.

"Your face, oh, your face becomes so funny with worry."

Funny with worry? That was a new one.

"Look, let's put all the bits together, shall we?" he said, still chuckling. "On the one hand we have Darkness, on the other we have individual self-consciousness. Mixed with these two seeming opposites we have fear and hope and happiness - this last one encompassing pleasure and joy and bliss and the like.

"We have fear of losing our grip on physical life, of losing our bodies, of losing our individuality. And we have hope of retaining all this forever. The trick is to lose fear whilst retaining individuality. How? By expanding ourselves as consciousness to include the whole universe - and we are not speaking here of the physical universe alone. We create a boundless self-consciousness, a Superconsciousness. Okay so far?"

"Yes, I think so. Please continue."

"Now. Having achieved that, having become all the light, we are then ready to face the Darkness; hoping that our individuality, we as Superconsciousness, will survive the absorption into it by becoming one with it, by being assimilated - not obliterated by it."

As was his habit, he stopped and waited for me to catch up. My logical mind had a hard time trying to get round his exposition. But another part of me, the one that applied the direct method, had no problem with it and was impatient to move in and take control, supplanting the current logic. I resisted, and continued my efforts to comprehend it intellectually. He sensed my difficulty.

"It's the logic, isn't it?" he said, in a sympathetic tone. "Three-dimensional. You can see now what Plato was up against: trying to push the barriers of common logic, or surmount it with another. We need to allow for other types of logic to come into play, the kinds of logic you've been using in the direct method. But don't slide back into that yet - stay with me, on this side."

I was trying to, although very tempted not to.

"What did you mean when you said that happiness and certainty are like candy given or promised to children?" I asked.

"Again, this is something which is not always clearly understood," he responded. "Certainty and happiness are injected, so to speak, into our makeup to keep us wishing and hoping. In the lower realms it is simply soporific, it makes us feel comfortable, smug, makes us feel content to be there and, what's worse, causes us, through the creation of elementals, to crave to be there."

"Why soporific?"

"How else would a budding self-consciousness be *persuaded* - for want of another word - to remain in the worlds of struggle and pain if not by a hefty dose of numbness and forgetfulness coupled with the strong belief - certainty - that the pleasure experienced is indigenous to these worlds?"

He smiled almost ruefully.

"The irony of it all is that, deep down in our nature, the whole thing is propelled by something like a memory of utter and total certainty and happiness. We don't know how true that memory is, but it works."

"What do you mean? How does it work?"

"At one level it keeps us numb and happy and wanting to stay where we are, at another level it causes us to want to reach this, subconsciously felt, realm of utter certainty and happiness - the given and the promised. In the first, we become attached to the worlds and, through that attachment, we gain and strengthen self-consciousness; in the second, we are beckoned by Darkness with the promise of eternal bliss."

"But how can we be in eternal bliss if we return to Darkness, to Non-existence?"

"A good question. This is what the Mysteries had to deal with. And this is why the subject was not discussed openly, couldn't be discussed openly."

"Why not?"

"Because of two reasons: one, it cannot be discussed; it is a matter of experience, of particular types of experience in which other forms of logic, of reasoning, are applicable, such as, for instance, the logic of two or more bodies occupying the same space - you yourself have had experiences very close to what I'm referring to, in this life and in the past.

"Two, what use would this knowledge be to people who are not prepared for it, or even interested in it? They would either dismiss it or, if they experimented with exercises to gain an insight into it, out of curiosity, they'd become deranged. And you know precisely what I mean."

I nodded in agreement. He knew and I knew. He continued.

"It would be like trying to explain to four-year-olds complex geometry, or giving them a box of matches and teaching them how to start a fire. In some cases, there would be real physical danger, and in others there would be mental confusion. And do you know who would be the safest of all?"

"Who?"

"Those who would use linear, common-sense, logic and dismiss the whole thing as nonsense. And I'll tell you something else for nothing: common-sense logic is the safest tool in any circumstances; it derives from the three-dimensional world and it is solid. You can use it against all kinds of irrationalities, including phobias and nightmares: solid and dependable, but inflexible. That's why it had to be superseded in the Mysteries in favour of other types of under- standing which flowed from the experiences themselves."

He stopped and smiled at me.

"Now you can see how hard it is to understand this subject intel- lectually and what a cop-out it is philosophically. And how poor Plato wrestled with it and resorted to metaphors and parables, like the cave, in his efforts to put it across to the public, outside the Mystery groups and away from the hierophants."

"Yes, I can see. But let me backtrack a little and ask you why: why must we acquire self-consciousness and why should we want to retain it when we move back into Darkness?"

"Ah, you're asking questions like a child does: why, why. You should know the answers by now."

"No, I don't. What are they?"

"There are *no* answers."

"What do you mean? I don't understand."

"Of course you don't understand because you're asking ques- tions like a child. There are no answers to *why* questions here - only conjectures. Why are there no answers? Because our needs and our actions regarding self-consciousness are innate and inescapable, as I tried to explain."

Crestfallen might be an accurate way to describe how I felt at the time.

"You're right, it *is* a cop-out. But where does this leave us?"

"With the practical nitty-gritty: concentrating on the processes and procedures to get there," he answered.

"And when we get there, we would have the answers, I suppose."

"No, because the questions themselves would have evaporated by then: they would have become irrelevant, meaningless, in fact, and then disappeared altogether."

"So, it's back to work, then," I concluded, more or less resigned to the fact that, for the present at least, my intellectual capacity was not sufficient to grasp the logic of his propositions.

I comforted myself with an adaptation of his 'child metaphor', along the line of a very young child being incapable of comprehend-

ing, for instance, the general concept of volume and not being able,
therefore, to see that the exact same amount of fluid can fill up a
tall thin glass and a short bulky one of the same volume capacity -
he/she not being able to see it even after repeated demonstrations.

"Absolutely," he confirmed my conclusion. "Now, so far you've
been going up and down like a yo-yo and zig-zagging in all directions like a... like a... Come on, like a... like a what?"

"Like a crab?"

He'd brought back the image of the crab in the doughnut hole.
We began to laugh.

"Yes, precisely. So, you'll agree, you need more discipline in
your work. Right?"

"Right."

"Now,--"

"Wait. Before we get to the nitty-gritty, as you put it, would you
mind if we cleared some annoying questions first?"

"More questions?"

"Simple ones."

"But annoying."

"Yes."

"Go ahead."

"Yianna. The whole scene with her. Who is - was - she?"

"You found her annoying?"

"No, not her."

"Who then?"

"Not a *who*. The whole scene, the whole setup. First Bob sent me
to meet your sister, then, when I met her, she said she was your
twin, then you said you don't have a sister, let alone a twin...."

"And you're confused."

"What do you expect?"

"So, I take it you don't know who she is - or, was, then."

"Are you trying to be funny? - because I don't find this amusing
at all."

"No, no, I'm not trying to be funny. I just find it hard to accept
that you cannot see who she was. That's all."

"Who was she, then?"

"You tell *me*. You should know," he said, and looked me in the
eye and waited.

I knew that look, I'd come to recognise it over the hours we had spent together. I knew what he was inviting me to do.

I went into patterned breathing and slowly switched to the direct method. I found myself back at Yianna's house watching her watering the garden with her back to me as before. When she turned round to face me she radiated with beauty, goodness and wisdom, and her smile was the most benign and loving I could ever remember having seen. And there was this overpowering familiarity; she was someone I knew very well, intimately.

And then she began to change, undergoing various transformations: she turned into a young man, an older man, a young woman, a child....The settings against which the different figures appeared also changed together with the feelings that each evoked, ranging from paternal/maternal, to filial, to very close friendship, to sexual love.... I knew by then that I was experiencing past incarnations.

When the original setting returned, I was a child of six in the company of my beloved grandmother helping her with the watering of the garden, the most beautiful garden in the whole wide world, full of the most amazing butterflies and the loveliest flowers. Oh, the happiness!...

Back at the hilltop, I was weeping profusely with happiness and nostalgia, pining for 'my gran' and all the other wonderful things that were still pouring in. I was overwhelmed by a great desire to hug Yiannis and tell him how much I loved him - he was my grandmother and all the personalities that had popped up in this vision, including a 'companion guide' or 'teacher' who appeared a number of times and in different guises in terms of age, sex, racial characteristics and historical setting.

I couldn't contain myself. I stood up and walked over and threw my arms around him. He reciprocated and, all of a sudden, I was back at the Temple of Light, dissolving into a shade of colour and whirling round and round along with innumerable other hues, and participating in a wondrous symphony in which I myself was a note. I became aware then that I was reliving an old Initiation experience I had undergone more than once in the past under the guidance of a 'brother companion': the very person I was, at that moment, embracing with so much love and affection.

As we began to disengage from the embrace, I found myself going through - both, emotionally and intellectually - a series of aspects of love, practically the whole range of love situations, of love relationships - an experience similar to the one I had gone through just prior to my embracing Yiannis, but more generalised and not totally deriving directly from past incarnations. I was, somehow, reminded of the old saying 'birds of a feather flock together', feelings of love in one situation evoking other situations in which love was central, and altogether creating a pool of thoughts and emotions around this central core of love. And, surprisingly, most prominent in this hub of love was Friendship.

It was surprising because, prior to this experience, I would have picked out other forms of love as central, as prime examples of the generic concept of love - maternal love, for instance. But, as I coursed through the various types of love, I came to realise that Friendship represented both the purest form of all and a distillation of their best characteristics: it was not necessarily conditioned by blood connections, it was not necessarily sexual, it was not necessarily restricted by age. On the other hand, it could be passionately self-effacing and sacrificial. To love in the absence of genetic connections, sexual attraction, racial, tribal and national reference or association seemed to be the ultimate in love.

"Oh, I'm glad you've hit on that," he said, as he moved a step back and looked at me. "Although you do need a few more reminders of what love is in order to gain a more balanced view." He cut me short of asking him what kind of reminders he had in mind exactly. "But that's for later."

He took another step back and clapped his hands. "Can you now see why you've been killing yourself again and again, incarnation after incarnation?"

Like a selective review, like a film trailer, I saw myself committing suicide, getting killed by enemies, starving myself to death..... I could also see that, in spite of the fact that some of these acts had not been inspired entirely by 'brotherly' love, that they had been contaminated by a degree of misplaced passion or affection, they were, nonetheless, acts of selfless, unconditional, love.

And then, suddenly, I recognised this 'love' as being of the same kind as that I had experienced in the nature of those wonderful beings who created and maintained the world - selfless, unconditional, joyful. Except that, in my case, it lacked the detachment that these beings exhibited. Was this due to the fact that I was human or was it just because I, as consciousness, was not developed sufficiently to act purely and constantly at that level?

"Possibly both," he responded. "You're not there yet, for sure; but even when you are there, you would need to abandon your humanness, which may mean re-entering the Darkness and then re-emerging as one of these entities, in order to fully and totally be and act as one of them - and I'm entering the realm of conjecture here, you understand. The most likely scenario would be that you become superconscious, identify with them, and function as one of them while retaining your human individuality."

"Why is love so pervasive and so necessary?"

"Ah, you are back to the *whys* again. Well, the short answer lies, like memory, in the *glue*. It is in the essence of creation, as far as humans are concerned; it goes back to the feelings of happiness and certainty, to the *memory* of bliss in the absence of fear."

"But isn't fear the essence of creation, what keeps us alive?"

"No, no. Fear is an artifice, something injected into us to push us along the development of self-consciousness, of individuality. Take those great beings you became aware of earlier, for example - they have no fear, they don't even know the meaning of fear--"

"Does that mean they are not self-conscious, they have no individuality?" I interrupted.

"From a human point of view, from the view of three-dimensionality, that's right: they're simply happy and joyful. Whatever consciousness they possess is of a different order, of a different logic; and it's, therefore, inappropriate to define them in ordinary human terms. You need to enter into their particular state of existence to appreciate that. But, didn't your experience provide that insight?"

"Yes; but I'm still in awe of the fact that inspite of their grandeur, of their tremendous power, they are so totally selfless - literally."

"Only from a human angle. As humans we constantly define; it's part of our humanness, of the process of acquiring self-consciousness, of objectifying the world in which we exist. They don't do that, they don't need to, they don't need to acquire self-consciousness as we understand it. Right?"

I nodded in agreement. My earlier experience had confirmed it.

"But doesn't this type of consciousness also deny them the possibility of moral judgment - as we humans understand it?"

He smiled at my caveat.

"As we humans understand it, yes. And, if you remember our earlier discussion, moral sense is a function of consciousness. In their case, they're never placed in a position where they would have to make choices like we do: they are not required to develop *our* type of self-consciousness."

"Are humans, then, the only creatures that develop a moral sense?"

"That I don't know. But let us take a wider *human* view of what moral sense stands for. Would you agree with me that it is the sense of right and wrong?"

"Okay," I assented.

"Is the world, all universes, governed by laws?"

"Yes..."

"Is the moral sense a function of consciousness - developing and changing as consciousness develops and changes?"

"I'll go along with that, yes."

"Do we, as human beings, sometimes commit acts which later in our lives come to see as morally wrong acts?"

"Yes..."

"So, our first conclusion must be that the moral sense shifts within the individual - and this without any reference to expanded superconsciousness. Right?

"Right." It was Socrates all over again, leading me to inevitable conclusions.

"Would you, further, agree that the development of consciousness, like everything else, takes place under the laws that govern the world?"

"Yes."

"In which case, every physical act we commit and every judgment we make at any given moment takes place according to, and within the bounds of, the laws - be these physical or psychological laws. Right?"

"Okay..."

"Two conclusions then follow: one, if everything takes place under the laws that govern the world then nothing could be wrong; two, nothing we do could possibly be wrong because we always act according to the laws whether we are aware of them or not - and we act according to our lights, which are likely to change as our consciousness changes; we are always right in our understanding and acting and judging, even when we are thoroughly aware that we are committing the wrong act - because we can justify such acts and judgments according to our lights, which is all we have to go by: our lights, our current consciousness."

Once again, I was shocked by his 'revelations'. I couldn't, honestly, believe that he was putting forward an argument in support of all kinds of crime.

"But this is horrific. What you're saying is that any heinous act is right, that it can't be wrong, that everything that happens in the world is morally right, that there is no distinction between right and wrong."

"Ooh, too many conclusions," he responded provocatively. "All tautologies. Of which the last one is phrased the best. But look at what happens with this artificial polarisation between right and wrong: the world of our *normal* logic is inhabited by opposites, and all this does is to betray, to reveal, the underlying nature of Darkness which tends to pull us back to total equilibrium. We need the opposites to stay in Existence. Our *normal* logic tells us that we must have opposites - and we see opposites everywhere.

"What's more, it tells us that if one part of a pair of opposites collapses the other one also disappears. If nothing is wrong then nothing is right either. It makes no sense to talk of right in the total absence of wrong.

"And we have just seen, using the same type of logic, that there is neither right nor wrong in the world - only the laws, which, according to ancient Greek thought, even the gods could not escape, as you very well know," he said and looked at me, waiting for my response.

I looked back at him as I tried to adjust to his thinking. I knew of the ancient Greek view of the Law; I also knew that he was correct in his saying that there was no such thing as right and wrong - despite the shaky logic he'd employed to lead to that conclusion; but I had always taken it in an abstract sense, as an ultimate in philosophical explanation; I knew he was correct because I had already sensed it in an earlier consciousness expansion experience - and that experience was now returning to me in full strength.

"This is another thing - the function of the Law - that came out of the Mystery schools," he continued. "None of the details, however, were allowed to reach the general public - they would have been devastating for the development of consciousness. People in general were, and still are, made to believe in morality, overload it with emotion and sentimentality, until such time as they, as consciousness, develop and expand to the degree where they personally experience this truth about morality; at which point externally imposed moral laws would become irrelevant to them."

He stared at me for a few seconds and then raised his head and looked at the sky searchingly for a beat or two before clasping his hands in front of his chest vigorously in the concluding manner of the Teacher.

"Good. Now: your friends are about to give up on you, and I'm dying for a cup of coffee."

I felt as if I were being shaken out of a trance. And I panicked: if he was bringing this meeting to an end - enormously fruitful though it had been - what of my other questions? When would I get another opportunity to raise them and elicit answers from him? I was aware that it was late, that we had been up all night, that I should let him have his rest - even though he looked full of energy and as bright as a button - and that I was practically letting my friends down; but I should, at least, tidy up a few loose ends.

"Look, just a few short questions, alright?" I ventured.

"So long as you don't mind short answers. Go on."

"The white-haired old lady - who was she?"

"I have a good mind not to tell you. You should've picked that up. But since I don't want to stay up here much longer by entering into detailed explanations, here it is: she was from an old incarnation of yours, way back, not connected to the rest of the scene, which itself was made up of chronologically unrelated bits that your mind weaved into a continuous narrative - the sort of thing that happens in dreams where all kinds of disparate bits are brought together into a mishmash of a story by an undisciplined mind as it shifts up and down and in and out of various levels. Next question."

He was definitely determined not to dilly-dally with things he thought I should've known.

"The animals in the field. Did you have anything to do with their behaviour?"

"Yes. Next question."

"No, no, please; please expound on it a little."

"What is there to expound on? You are not all that keen on animals. They pick up on that. So, I helped them express their fondness and love for you."

I could feel the sarcasm oozing out of his words. He laughed.

"You were lucky I brought those crows in - they saved you from serious injury. The donkey was about to kick you and the goat was getting ready to head-butt you with all the love he could muster. Next question."

"Beethoven's fifth. Any connection?"

"Yes. The pause and then the opening bars."

He took a breath to represent the pause and then sang out the four notes in perfect pitch: ba-ba-ba-baaaam. He looked at me to see my reaction, and added:

"But then, subtlety is wasted on you. Look, this is not the time to go into it. I'll give you a few clues and then you go away and meditate on it in your own time: the pause, and the four notes and their relationship to the whole symphony. It was picked specially for you because of your particular fondness for the piece. Next question."

"'Go back'. What did you mean by that?"

"Well, that's something to keep you busy for the rest of this life and the next and the one after that. But you have already started and you're on the right track. Keep working on it. You can also *go back* to Beethoven's fifth for a few hints. Are we finished?"

"One more question, please. The hole in the rock and everything that took place there. I can't decide on the status of the whole experience. Was it real? Did it actually happen? At what level of consciousness did it occur, in what kind of reality? It seems to have taken place outside time."

"Ah, time, time. Do you honestly think that I'm going to answer this question, this multiple question, with a short answer? No, not possible. And I'm not going to answer it the long way either. It's for you to sort it out - remember, you came to me, I didn't come to you. But, if it did indeed take place, ask yourself: where? - in your head, in your heart, in your spleen, in your liver, in your bones?...."

He stopped momentarily and opened his eyes wide as he prepared for one more shot at my intellectual integrity. "....in your arse?"

And, as expected after such a comment, he guffawed. His laughter was so loud some birds in a nearby tree were woken from their sleep, not to mention the reaction from the crickets which went suddenly quiet. As if nothing had happened, he continued:

"Two hints to help you out here. As I've already said, you're on the right track. Look at the way you've asked your questions - you started at the end and moved backwards in time, the last event first: the old lady, the animals, Beethoven's fifth, the hole in the rock; that's hint number one. Two, reflect on the story of the wise holy man who pushed the head of his young disciple into a bowl of water. Now, reflect and meditate and then come back to me - and don't tell me about it, it's *your* exercise for *your* benefit."

He stretched his arms and the rest of his body in a limbering fashion and in an obviously concluding attitude, making ready to leave. I rushed to make sure I met him again.

"You said come back to you. When, where?"

"Tomorrow," he answered without hesitation.

"Tomorrow when?"

"Afternoon will be fine."

"Where?"

"Ah, let's make it interesting. I'll meet you at the *brother's*," he said, emphasising the last word. "And I'm not going to help you with any clues. You'll have to work it out by yourself. I'll be there. If you don't show up you'll never see me again. Enjoy the rest of your holiday."

And on that, he turned round and set off in the opposite direction to the one we had come from. I stood there watching him disappear behind a small boulder, justifiably numb at the suddenness of his departure and still wandering if I'd ever see him again. "Enjoy the rest of your holiday." It sounded so final. More like "enjoy the rest of your life" - if you can!

I walked over to the boulder to see where he was going. He'd already gone, disappeared. That side of the hill was precipitous, almost like a cliff, a place only for mountain goats to climb. No trace of him. The noise of falling soil and small stones pointed to the direction he had taken: downwards to the sea, to deep water. But, surely, he must know some path that led away from that vertical drop and towards the sandy tourist beach.

Quiet. Only the sound of the night crickets, which had now returned after the sudden interruption. But now, instead of being reassuring with their usual calming chirping, the crickets' repetitious beat had the effect of mounting suspense.

I had to take stock, and very quickly, before my friends gave up waiting for me, if they hadn't done so already.

I sat on the small boulder again and returned to my normal routine: making a list, revising and evaluating. I soon realised that there was a tremendous amount to go through and, as I didn't have the time to revisit the events of the whole evening, I decided to concentrate on what had been left out and what remained to be done.

Key questions regarding the status of my experience at the doughnut hole as well as the point - the meaning - of those hammering opening notes of Beethoven's fifth symphony, had been left frustratingly unanswered. Also, that elusive and ever repeating "go back" - a chorus that kept cropping up in ever increasing circles: elusive and yet proving more and more inclusive and central. And now, Yiannis had thrown in an additional puzzle: the wise old man and his disciple and the incident with the bowl of water. Naturally, I saw the obvious comparison with myself and Yiannis, but I was certain that wasn't the main reason for bringing it up: it was the actual event he was pointing at that mattered.

And then, his drawing my attention to the way I'd asked the questions, as if remembering them 'backwards' - his own word. I'd normally start at the beginning and work my way to the end chronologically, or pick out the most important question first; but this time I had done neither. Had I posed the questions in a chronologically indiscriminate manner it wouldn't have mattered either; but I hadn't done that - I'd done it in an orderly backwards way, without being aware that I was doing that.

Ah, and his poser as to 'where' the experience had taken place, in my head, in my heart, etc. He'd twisted it in the end to give it a humorous touch - to make me keep my feet on the ground - but, again, I was sure he was pointing at something else, something more important than just being crudely funny.

And the 'brother'. What 'brother'? Was this going to be another wild goose chase - this time looking for a 'brother' instead of a 'sister'? I noticed he hadn't said 'twin brother'. Was this a clue that it would be a different sort of goose chase?! And then, and then..... oh, damn! What was wrong with me? He'd said to meet in the afternoon. But what time? I'd forgotten to ask him the time - very unlike me.

Instinctively, I stood up ready to run after him - a stupid reaction. I remained standing and tried to collect myself. A Greek afternoon, I thought, didn't start until two o'clock - and, sometimes, even later, according to how a Greek felt! - and finished a little before sunset, giving way to that magical part of the day just prior to the start of the evening. Good, that cut it down to between two and six. Then I thought again: I'd better take no chances - I'd do it the English way: afternoon would begin at twelve noon; which meant that I would have to find the "brother's" place before noon the next day.

Oh, no! I looked at my watch - it was already next day, it had been for a while. That reduced the time for search to just a few hours. Wait, wait: he'd said "tomorrow" - what, exactly, did he mean by "tomorrow"? If he used the word in a literal sense, then I had more time than I'd thought I had - an extra day. But, if he used it in a normal, casual, sense, I was back to my original calculations - just a few hours. Oh, god! Panic set in again.

I took a few deep breaths and checked my priorities. On top of the list, in terms of time, were my two friends. They were leaving, and I'd promised to meet them at the disco. After that, I would attend to whatever pertained to Yiannis, beginning with the search for the "brother's" place.

– 12 –

Helen and Aphrodite - or was it Eve?
(Sex or Love?)

The disco wasn't very far, I could hear the music still playing. I just hoped that my friends hadn't left. I put on my intellectual blinkers and descended in the direction of the disco. Stumbling my way downwards through the thorny undergrowth and the ancient, loosely hanging boulders, I managed to reach the rocky seafront almost unscathed. There, I rolled my trouser legs up to my knees and washed my dusty feet and sandals in the sea before setting off on the two hundred metre or so walk to the disco.

Save for the moonlight, there was no other illumination on the path; no street lights and no houses - and the path wasn't all that smooth either. I wondered how people found their way to the disco when there was no moon - and the answer came when I ran into a couple walking in the opposite direction, returning to the village, carrying a small battery torch and picking their way over the lagunas and protruding stones. I hadn't been to this disco before, and I thought it considerate of whoever owned it to set it up so far away from the built-up areas, despite the dangers inherent in the unlit and uneven pathway.

At the disco, I was relieved and more than pleased to find that my friends were still there, drinking and dancing. I apologised for being so long in joining them, but declined to drink beer or anything else alcoholic. They teased me when I asked for a soft drink, and offered to get me a pint of goat's milk!

I had to explain that I couldn't afford to get drunk as I was seeing Yiannis later in the day and needed to be sober and have a head clear of the possibility of a hangover. My explanation was clearly not an excuse, and was intended to get me out of an awkward situation and allow me to enjoy their company for the rest of whatever time we had left to spend together. But it backfired. I expected them to press me for a little longer and then give up.

Which they did, but then latched onto my mentioning Yiannis and wanted to know more about him: who he was and how he knew so much about Mike and his uncle and what was the purpose of my meeting him again. Oh, and was that "horrible" mongrel really stray or did he belong to the old man, some kind of guard dog? - asked the girls who appeared to be still in fear of Athespodos even in his absence, reminding themselves of his "vicious" growl and casting their eyes around furtively to make sure he hadn't followed me into the disco and was now hiding under some table.

Once again, I skirted the issue and gave my friends as little information as possible, in spite of their apparently genuine interest in Yiannis and the general 'metaphysical' area. The girls seemed too flighty, and a disco wasn't exactly the best place to open up an involved discussion on the subject. But they were serious - Harry was even considering postponing his flight in order to stick around and find out more about Yiannis. I had mixed feelings about this, but said nothing - except promising to report to them anything 'interesting' that might take place during my meeting with the old man.

I spoke softly on purpose and complained that the music was too loud for them to hear clearly what I was saying. I was searching desperately for a way out. When in such situations, my 'desperation' radiated like an SOS signal and, usually, I received a response. But on this occasion the response, if there were to be any, was long coming.

And then there she was, standing in front of me, beaming an ear-to-ear smile, blonde and beautifully tanned, a modern Aphrodite.

"Hello. Nice to see you again," she said. "Thanks for the information."

She had an American accent. I couldn't place her. She looked familiar, very familiar, but I couldn't place her. Frustration and embarrassment are the usual feelings that surface at such moments.

I said "Oh, hello," and smiled stupidly, playing for time.

She must have read my frantic efforts to remember in my rather contradictory facial expression - smiling mouth, frowning forehead.

"Don't tell me - you don't recognise me with my clothes on," she blurted, bursting into a cheeky laughter.

My friends and their northern companions looked at me with eyes open wide, in a mixture of mock shock and approval.

I continued to smile in the same idiotic manner, all the while racking my brains, searching for the give-away clue. Was it the shock of being confronted with such a beautiful girl? She was not just beautiful: she radiated femininity, effused irresistible sexuality.

I was reminded of what the Teacher had said to me once when I declared that I did not intend to ever get married: "Just you wait," he said, "just you wait until the day arrives when someone turns up to make all thirty two of your teeth shake out of control!" - a Greek expression which meant total loss of control either because of fear or intense passion (or love?). Was this the "someone"?

"Shall I take my clothes off, then?" she teased, playing mercilessly on my feelings of frustration and sexual anticipation.

"Yes, please," tipsy Harry cut in. "*I* may be able to remember you. I sure--" and the rest of his sentence was mumbled as he fell off his chair and tumbled to the ground at the vigorous push from his female companion.

We all laughed at the silliness of the situation, and suddenly I recognised her - nothing in particular happened to trigger the recognition, just a glint in her eye. It was the girl on the beach, the one who had been roasting herself in the midday sun, who had asked me about the small ferries.

"Did you get back alright?" I asked, with a sigh of relief.

"Yes, thank you."

"Aren't you going to introduce us?" asked Mike.

I introduced Harry and Mike as my friends and the two girls as their girlfriends. I hesitated for a beat when I turned to the American girl because I didn't know her name, but suddenly I lost my inhibitions and introduced her simply as the girl who would cause the launching of a thousand ships!

As I said that, a very brief flash of the face of a 'doll' with four round red spots on it - on the forehead, chin, and cheeks - was superimposed on the girl's face. Nobody else seemed to notice it - it was not 'physical', or maybe the lights in the disco played tricks on me. Apparently oblivious, too, to this momentary 'hallucination' of mine, she laughed and thanked me for the compliment, and then proceeded to introduce herself.

"Helen. Pleased to meet you."

My friends thought she was just playing along with my description of her but she assured us that that was her actual name - and a shiver ran up my spine. I exerted myself to ignore it, along with the 'vision' of the doll's face....

We all danced for a while and drank a few beers - I gave in to pressure and agreed to have a beer which I sipped slowly for the rest of my stay there - and drifted towards the edge of the open air disco where it was less noisy. Harry wanted to talk, he said, have a serious discussion on memory, of all things. Why? Because of what had happened with me earlier - not recognising Helen, and yet somehow being able to offer a description that identified her as 'Helen'. He wanted to talk about some weird experiences he had had a while back. I was not in the mood but the rest of the group appeared supportive of this sudden interest of his and so, once again, I went along so as not to seem antisocial.

We sat on some rocks at the boundary of the disco and indulged in what developed into a series of accounts that resembled 'tales of the unexpected'. Harry did not disappoint us; he came up with experiences of false memory that sometimes got him into trouble, and 'memories' of people and events of the *déjà vu* type except that they had been dream images which eventually unfolded in the waking state.

An experience which all of us had had was one in which a person had been 'recognised' as someone we had met before, only to realise eventually that they had been merely lookalikes – albeit practically 'clones' of each other. The converse was, of course, true, that is, not recognising a person when we met them again out of the original context - as in my case with Helen. I was sorely tempted to mention memories of past lives but I resisted.

Helen kept glancing at me and flashing a smile every time the word recognition came up. At the beginning I thought she was doing that in order to remind me of not having recognised her earlier on but I soon realised those glances had a deeper meaning. I would shiver and get transported to 'places' and moods that I could only describe as inklings, as openings, to more powerful recognitions - the beginnings of remembering thrilling and meaningful experiences.

These were signposts leading to full memories, and I knew them very well. But, as with Yiannis at the beginning, I felt that there was something holding back these memories, these recognitions. I put it down to the noise and the crowd and the inappropriateness of the location.

After a long while we all agreed we'd had enough of the disco; also, my friends needed to catch some sleep before travelling up to Athens for their flight, not to mention the fact that I too needed to hit the pillow for a few hours. We walked away picking our steps carefully over the holes in the path, and by the time we reached the hotel I had already decided not to go in. I wanted to go and sit on a beach nearby to collect my thoughts, perhaps sleep there - something I'd done a few times before.

Besides, I wanted to be alone with Helen for a while, just a short while, before setting off in search of the "brother's" place where I was to meet Yiannis - I was sharing a three-bed room with the boys and there would have been no privacy. We said our goodbyes - with Harry again threatening with the possibility of postponing his flight - and promised to keep in touch. They went in accompanied by the two girls.

The beach I decided to go to in the end wasn't exactly nearby; it was some distance away but I felt I needed the walk to clear my head and the rest of my body of the alcohol and the reverberating noise of the disco. The beach itself was a small cove in the shape of a horseshoe, sandy in the middle part but pebbly round the arms, enclosed on all three sides by pine trees which, at places, practically dipped in the water. It was quiet and secluded. The locals called it "The cove of love" for obvious reasons. But we were lucky, there was nobody around at that time of night - or, perhaps, I should say day seeing that we were into the small hours.

We found a good spot at one end of the horseshoe, and sat on comfortable fine pebbles facing the sea and the setting moon.

I inhaled the freshness of the sea air, leant back, and asked her to talk to me about herself. I was pleased to hear that she had studied classical Greek at high school and that we shared a similar love for ancient Greek culture. She was in the middle of her undergraduate studies in psychology and was very keen to return to the subject of memory.

Worse luck, I thought. First I failed to recognise her and now she wanted to talk about memory! I'd thought that the subject had been disposed of at the disco but, in fact, Harry's interest in it had aroused her interest too. She assured me - with a cheeky smile - that she had already forgiven me for not remembering her at the disco but that she was deeply and genuinely interested in the subject as a psychology student.

As I wanted so much to be in her good books, I went along with her desire to discuss the subject - perhaps I might impress her, I thought, and promote my own interests which, at that point, had nothing whatsoever to do with memory!

She surprised me. She did not only possess knowledge of scientific experiments in this area but she also displayed unexpected philosophical acumen. I guided the exchange towards the philosophical approach which suited me best by temperament and felt I was well placed for discussion in that mode - and also because I was hardly aware of experiments in memory, neither the questionnaire type nor those regarding brain functioning.

We discussed the concept of the identity of a 'person' in relation to continuity of memory; which raised the central question: in the absence of continuity of memory (in the presence of sizeable gaps in memory) could one be certain of one's identity, of being one and the same individual in reference to the ownership of the 'remaining' distinct bits of purportedly 'remembered' events?

Once again, I was tempted to introduce into the discussion personal experiences and ideas talked about with Yiannis, including 'gaps' in memory in regards to past incarnations. But, again, I resisted. I was practically at the point of blurting out: "Isn't this amazing?! Only today I...I...". I bit my tongue. Just in time.

"Imagine this", she said, apparently oblivious to my efforts to conceal an ongoing internal struggle. "Imagine that all the physical evidence of your childhood is lost irretrievably, including the house you were born in, the places you visited and those you lived in, all your childhood belongings, your parents, relatives, and all the people you've ever met and everybody else who might be able to provide evidence of your childhood. All the evidence before the age of twelve is wiped out".

She'd been lying on her back staring at the starry sky when she spoke. She raised herself a little, dug her left elbow gently into the layer of fine pebble, and turned to face me.

"One, how would you go about proving that you had the experiences you believe you had in your childhood; two, how could you be certain you've had those experiences; three, how would you know that all those experiences were yours; four, how could you be certain that some if not all of those experiences were not fabrications of your imagination?"

She smiled and added: "Remember, you can have no recourse to external evidence, no external confirmation."

What a poser! I considered the first question to be a nonstarter as I took "proving" to have an external reference, but all the others were obviously aimed at eliciting some kind of internal criteria. I had to search for reasons that would justify an internal form of continuity, a core of awareness. And to do that, following the conventions of current logic and scientific requirements, I would have to show 'objective' proof which, in accordance with her request, should have no reference to the external/physical world.

These questions brought back to me the whole area of verification of past incarnations where there was no external evidence, or, more importantly, where I did not feel the need for external proof. How did I know I had had those particular incarnations? I always applied one or the other of two kinds of criteria, and sometimes both: the emotional reaction, and external evidence. I was now being asked to abandon the latter. Would emotional reaction be a sufficient criterion for the veracity of memories of everyday trivial events in this current incarnation? Obviously not. Most events were not remembered with any degree of emotion - they were just 'memory facts'.

Helen had opened a can of worms. In all honesty, I had no absolutely firm, unchallengeable, criterion for establishing an unwavering memory in the absence of external verification. For internal proof, which did not relate to incarnations, I had relied on three 'modes' of cognition, one of which was partly external: the feeling of certainty, confirmation by what I had come to appreciate as internal 'contacts' (including discarnate human and other beings) and rules or laws applicable to the internal landscape, and confirmation of internal events by other incarnate human beings who had shared/witnessed that particular situation.

Again, the last one had to be discarded because it involved external criteria. Regarding the first, the most potent and most reliable underpinning to all experiences, that of certainty, had already been shaken at its foundations by Yiannis earlier on. The second criterion-cum-form of cognition, once the certainty aspect had been removed or its potency undermined, began to shift into the realms of dream and hallucination.

If I had memories of a childhood which I could not prove that I had even to myself with absolute certainty, then...then...Was everything merely in my mind, built by my imagination? A solipsistic world... No, no; I couldn't even say that with certainty...

Oh, yes, a can of worms had been opened, and its emerging slithering creatures, corrosive images of doubt, were now eating away at the very core of Existence! For if the objective status of memory could not be established internally on unshakeable criteria, its continuity was also in doubt. And if veracity and continuity of memory were put into question, what of the status of consciousness, of our claim to existence as discrete units?....

Was she thrown in my path deliberately by Yiannis to reiterate my existential concerns? I was beginning to get a little paranoid again. She was beautiful and extremely desirable, and all I wanted was to be with her as a man, physically, perhaps emotionally too, but not particularly intellectually - not that I didn't want to associate with her at that level, but not now. I had already spent so many hours dealing with these questions, and now another part of me was laying claim to attention. Maybe I was too tired, maybe I wanted to let go... I was torn...

"I'm sorry. Were my questions too hard?" she said teasingly, almost whispering as if not to disrupt my inner struggle.

"Well, I..."

She was looking at me with eyes full of feminine softness, dripping sexuality. How could anyone be allowed the audacity to look so irresistibly sexual and at the same time so demanding intellectually? And that 'doll's' face again, seemingly calling from the distant past....

I had to make a decision, and very quickly. Should I concentrate on seeking answers to her questions or throw in the towel, admitting that I was incapable of functioning at an intellectual level when faced with overpowering sexual attraction?

And then I remembered what the rabbi had said to his son when the latter couldn't decide which one of two options to go for: "When faced with such a dilemma, my boy, always look for a third solution".

A third solution. Right. A third solution - I practically mumbled it to myself. Right. I stood up and walked a few short steps to the edge of the water. A third solution - but what? The whole star-studded sky was being reflected on the calm surface of the sea, and I felt compelled to be part of that sea and that sky - I found them irresistible.

And, all of a sudden, I began to take my clothes off: my shirt, my trousers and underpants, and then kicked my sandals off. I stood there stark naked. I didn't know why I was doing this but it felt right: strip myself of my clothes, of all acquired layers and ways of thinking and feeling, divest myself of my concerns. "We are all born naked, everything else is drag", somebody said once, probably intending it to be a witticism. But it had a deeper meaning for me right now.

I threw myself into the water and swam a few metres before turning round to face the land. The water was cool, refreshing; not that I had never swum in the nude before; and I knew that I hadn't thrown myself into the sea to cool my ardour - in fact, I now felt more aroused by my nakedness, the gentle caressing of the water.

I saw her stand up and shout: "Wow! What a wonderful idea!" before taking her clothes off and jumping in to join me. She swam and splashed around for a short while and then came and paddled gently in front of me. I had found a patch of the bottom of the sea clear of pebbles, and was standing shoulder deep. She swam around me making me turn to follow her encircling movement. Her hair was, surprisingly, still intact and mostly dry except for the edges that were touching the water. She giggled and splashed water at me.

"I like your answer", she laughed, and slowly laid on her back, her blond hair now dipped in the water, the whole front of her naked body gleaming in the fading moonlight, a veritable Aphrodite.

I think it was Zorba in the eponymous novel who said that if you can't swim against the current then let go, go with it, be with it. Was this the rabbi's third solution?

Helen straightened up from her supine position and swam closer to me.

"It's not fair", she pouted. "You're taller and can stand on the seabed while I have to swim to stay afloat. You should carry me". And on that she came and wrapped her arms and legs around me - and the rest became history, to paraphrase a much used expression!

It was sudden, unexpected in its suddenness, but totally welcome. It was a case of "If you can't make up your mind, let your mind make itself up for you" - a possible version of the rabbi's solution, although it wasn't my mind that was now making a decision. Was it my body? Yes. But not just my body; there was something else at work.

Normally, immediately after sex (after lovemaking?), as my body relaxed and I drifted contentedly into semi-somnolence, I would be inundated with the images of flowers, gardens, gentle and pleasant landscapes, grazing and playful animals, geometric designs and the like - images that were always accompanied by feelings of affection for the person I happened to be with at the time.

Now, however, all the imagery and affections I would experience after lovemaking were there right from the start, except that I was nowhere drifting into semi-sleep. It was more of a light trance in which my senses and emotions were heightened as the imagery unfolded and engulfed me in a quiet intensity.

The physical pleasure was extreme, to say the least, and the emotional side matched it equally. I was on a sexual high, more, much more than I had ever been before. For some inexplicable reason, however, my youthful, normally vigorous sexual thrusts, soon slowed down and came to a halt. I remained inside her motionless, in a tight embrace. At the beginning, I found it strange - I should have been thrusting to a climax, but instead I had stopped.

"That's right, that's right," she whispered under her breath and into my ear. "Take a deep breath and give it to me." I took a deep breath and wondered what she meant by "give it to me" - it didn't sound like the 'normal' sexual invitation.

But then, as I was about to exhale, she took my face in her hands and brought her mouth to mine, whispering urgently: "Give it to me!" She closed her lips over mine and I found myself exhaling into her mouth. She inhaled my breath with relish and said: "Do it again." I obliged by taking another breath and "giving it" to her. She asked me to reverse the procedure and again I obliged by inhaling her breath. I felt it coursing throughout my body.

Carbon monoxide is poison, and yet her breath was an injection of energy. We alternated, inhaling each other's breath. Under other circumstances I would have objected to this practice on health grounds, but it seemed natural at the time - and I was glad I hadn't eaten anything containing onion or garlic!

"I'm going to teach you how to have multiples," she declared whisperingly.

Multiples? Surely, she couldn't be referring to orgasms. I had heard about them but only that women had them - and I hadn't been with a girl who had had such experiences. But I, a man, having multiple orgasms?! A physiological impossibility.

"Concentrate down below," she said, and tightened her grip on me.

Down below? Where? My penis, of course. I followed her instructions, puzzled but with anticipation, like an apprentice listening to a master craftsman - and she was probably younger than me!

"No, no. Not there," she inerrupted. "Not on the bit you have inside me. The other bit."

"What other bit?" I, naturally, querried, even more puzzled.

She gave a short giggle. "Okay. Look. Concentrate on the part of the penis that's inside you."

What?! There was no penis inside me and, what was more to the point, I did not fancy the idea of having one inside me! Then I understood what she meant. Maybe it was the way she said it, or the fact that my pleasure at that moment was mostly gathered in the area of mutual sexual contact - inside her vagina. But I couldn't shift my attention to where she suggested.

"Okay," she sighed gently, "concentrate on the base of your penis and tighten the muscles there."

That was easier. I found the spot and contracted the muscles.

"Now let go."

I did. She got me to repeat this procedure a few times and I began to feel the pleasure spreading in both directions: towards the tip of my penis and inside me.

"Forget the penis," she said. "Concentrate on the base and where it leads inside you. Whatever you do forget the penis."

Easier said than done. But I tried. She held me gently and gave me a full, slow, smouldering kiss. Then, with our lips locked together, we went back to breathing into each other's mouth. I kept my concentration, tightening and letting go, tightening and letting go...

Gradually, it became more of a syphoning, sucking, kind of activity which helped my attention stay away from the penis round which she was now contracting and relaxing her own muscles ever so imperceptibly. I was aware that she was watching my reactions and adjusting her actions accordingly - stopping and starting every now and then. She was, clearly, leading me higher and higher into this wonderful experience but careful not to let me peak into an ejaculation.

My whole body was now tingling, and the pleasure was spreading throughout, further heightened by the imagery which had returned and was flooding me. I started to experience the tingling sensation in visual terms: brilliant crimson energy around the genital area which rose towards the heart where it changed to a delicate shade of rose-white that carried with it an enormous outpouring of joy. Tears were welling in my eyes and my chest heaved in sharp intakes of air. Every cell in my body seemed to be energised.

I could see and feel the two columns of energy flanking my spine - those columns which I had experienced on the hill earlier on - rushing upwards and pouring themselves into my arms which were wrapped round Helen's body. Likewise, I could see and feel hers around me - sparkling passionately and lovingly, with her left column complementing and augmenting my right column and my left column doing the same with her right, and vice versa. And the middle column, oh the middle column! My middle column had joined hers to form a U shape, with energy coursing up and down from one end to the other - from her heart to her genitals to my genitals to my heart and back the other way.

And then, the U shape collapsed into one straight, vertical column like an 'I', which we both shared: my middle column was not any longer simply joined to hers but the two had become one - strongly reminiscent of the experience with the Pharaonic sceptre at Yianna's house. The moment this happened, we both exploded into an idescribable orgasm that went on and on. After a while it reached a plateau and, to my utter delight, it did not collapse, it did not come to an end.

Helen appeared to be encouraging this process with minute movements of her vaginal muscles that acted as a cue to the contraction and relaxation of my own muscles which led to another orgasm, and then to another and another... The whole process had now become automatic and out of my control. I seemed to have reached a high plateau on which there were only minor undulations between great pleasure and extreme pleasure - like small waves on the surface of a deep sea, where the bottom would be the normal place for me to be after an orgasm. I was entranced.

Two other developments in this state of affairs were also totally unexpected. As the orgasms continued - or, perhaps, it was only one orgasm that went on and on - I noticed that my penis began to soften and shrink until it returned to its normal non-sexually aroused, floppy, state. But the orgasms, or orgasm, continued: they, or it, had become totally internal. At the same time I was aware of a tremendous scintillating energy rushing up my body, from my genitals to my head. It gave me a wonderful sense of euphoria, lifted me into a realm of fine emotions, and, as it reached the head, flooded my mind with exquisite clarity of thought and depth of awareness.

This awareness enabled me to see what was also going on in Helen's body and mind. I could see that she was having similar experiences to mine - which, I felt, absolved me of the possibility of selfishness! Indeed, I felt that she was much deeper into it than I was.

I made an effort to 'perceive' whether this was due to a greater capacity on her part or that it was, perhaps, by reason of her being female - after all, until that moment I'd thought that only women were capable of multiple orgasms, not to mention the depth and pervasiveness of the experience. But I could not gain an insight into this: at some point I'd lost the distinction between male and female - was I not, in a sense, having a sexual experience more or less as a woman?! (admittedly, a frightful thought to a normal 'male' state of mind!).

But by this time, the ecstatic pleasure I was experiencing was not exclusively sexual. It had moved and spread to other regions of my consciousness. The clarity of thought was especially astounding. I felt that I was in possession of a vast store of knowledge - no, no, wisdom would be a more appropriate word. And my pattern of thinking had changed: it was augmented and 'liberated', it had shed many of the barriers by which it was rendered recognisable as mine, and had begun to acquire mannerisms which were clearly 'external' to its normal functioning.

I was pleased but puzzled by this development, and felt totally disempowered, as if something or somebody were taking over my personality. I thought I heard Yiannis' voice, I sensed his presence, although he was nowhere to be seen physically. But he was there, I felt him in my bones - literally; he was overshadowing me, taking over, I was being 'pushed out'.

This was not a case of me coordinating myself with Yiannis - something I had done a few times before in order to get under his skin, so to speeak, and comprehend what he was trying to convey to me. I had not initiated this, although I would have more than welcomed it in different circumstances.

There seemed to be two processes in action here: on the one hand, I felt Yiannis entering and taking over my physical body and, to an extent, my personality, while at the same time imprinting his own brand of thinking and behaving on me. I understood this to be an extreme case of overshadowing. I felt I was slowly acquiring his mannerisms - the way he talked, laughed, gestured. But I did not feel old. On the contrary, I was filled with a great deal of energy, and experienced an unfamiliar sharpness and high degree of mental clarity and agility.

But then, all of a sudden, I had the clear sensation of being 'beside myself', of being dispossessed, deprived of my physical body. I stood two or three metres outside my body, with the water gently undulating through me, and observed 'it' as it continued to make love to Helen. Some of the sensations were still being conveyed to me as if by relay, but they were tentative. The old man was now in possession - not old any longer but youthful and energetic. His general mental attitude felt connected to me so intimately that I knew his thoughts and intentions just before they became externalised: a *déjà vu* of someone else's experiences!

However, I did not like the idea of someone taking over my body without my consent, let alone using it to make love to Helen. I reacted by trying to get back into it, only to be met by Yiannis' offhand dismissal before I got anywhere near it. I made another effort, this time using as much force as I could muster, but again without success. It was obvious I could not compete with the shaman's much greater abilities. I felt him laugh and tease me with: "Oh, you want to get back in, then?", to which I simply responded in the affirmative. "Okay, then, come in," I felt him say. I took him on his word and proceeded with my third attempt.

What I hadn't realised, however, was that with the two bodies being so intimately entwined it was hardly possible for me to distinguish their boundaries - their mental counterparts, their emotional and mental bodies, being practically meshed together. But being naturally more in tune with my own physical body, notwithstanding the fact that Yiannis was in possession of it, I picked out the connection and made a move towards it. Yiannis appeared to be more agreeable this time, even obliging. As I thought I was beginning to re-enter my body, however, I received a push and felt myself enter-ing Helen's body instead. I was, momentarily, inside it, sharing it with her. And for that very brief moment I shared some of her per-sonality and history, too.

In personality terms, she was even more beautiful than I'd thought, and she had, indeed, been the historical Helen of Troy, but not the one portrayed in history books. More interesting for me were her numerous incarnations as a priestess, an artist, a philosopher, and as a man, some of which she had shared with me. The closeness I had felt towards her throughout the preceding hours now gained a deeper meaning.

I felt the need to be with her and with her alone - this threesome situation, with Yiannis shanting me around and usurping my per-sonality, did not sit well with me. Besides, by staying inside Helen's body, wasn't I being literally screwed by the old shaman?! No mat-ter how much I liked him, I was certainly not prepared or willing for this kind of intimacy!

The moment I formulated this thought I blanked out. When I came to I found myself lying with Helen on the fine pebbles of the beach, still entwined in a loving embrace. She was asleep in my arms, and Yiannis' presence had vanished. I had no recollection of how we got there. I disentangled myself as gently as I possibly could so as not to wake her, and lay beside her. It was already dawn.

I looked down at my soft penis and wondered if I had ejaculated. I couldn't tell and it didn't matter, although I was still amazed, and feeling great, by the experience with Helen. I pulled a little farther back and looked at her, looked at this gloriously beautiful young woman lying next to me. I'd passed her by on a beach, run into her at a disco and ended up by visiting paradise with her. Could life be more unpredictable and 'coincidences' more designed? I had ad-mired her and loved her in centuries past: in temples, in public and in private philosophical debates, in Mystery schools - a sister/ brother soul and eternal companion pilgrim in the search for the ultimate truth. As ever, beautiful in body and in 'soul', whatever the latter word might mean.

I looked up at the morning sky to catch sight of the Morning Star hanging alone in the vastness of the heavens - Aphrodite. How appropriate. The goddess of love high above and her priestess lying on the beach having come out of the sea after the very act of love. Everything was still, quiet, as if to freeze this moment in time for ever. I was overwhelmed by joy and sadness at the same time, and began to weep silently. Why was I given these glimpses of happiness that lasted so briefly? Why would they not last for ever? Had I asked Yiannis these questions he would probably have said that it was due to my lack of ability or, more likely, that the questions were irrelevant. Irrelevant?! - he would have a lot to answer, explanations to give.

I wanted to scream, but I would have woken her. Let her sleep. Instead, I reflected on how this situation had arisen. It all started, apparently, with questions of memory and identity. Identity... Yes. Right. What would be the case if...? Was this another ruse meted out by Yiannis as a kind of test? Test for what? Was Helen in on this? No, no she couldn't have been. She was lying there, in front of me, with all the connections from the past; I knew her. This was not exactly a case like Yianna's - or was it? There were similarities.... No, no... Yiannis should have the answers.

Ah, Yiannis. I was supposed to meet him at the "brother's" - today, in the afternoon. I looked at my wrist watch and reminded myself that there wasn't that much time. I should be going. But I couldn't tear myself away from her. I wanted to talk to her, ask her questions, tell her how I felt, make plans for later. I was being torn. Oh, no, not another dilemma, not another rabbinical solution.

She stirred; she turned her head towards me and half-opened her eyes. I wondered if she knew what I knew, if she remembered what I remembered - maybe more.

"Morning".

"Morning," she responded. She smiled, rubbed her eyes and cast a look around. "Been up long?"

"A couple of minutes."

She stretched out on her back and looked at the sky. "Did the earth move for you too?" she asked, in an obvious cheeky tease.

"No."

She turned and gave me a disappointed look.

"But the rest of the universe did," I returned the tease, and leant forward and kissed her tenderly, exerting a great effort to resist a powerful urge to throw my arms round her and kiss her passionately. I knew that if I let go I'd be powerless to pull away for the rest of the day - and, probably, the day after and the day after that...

"Wow!" she exclaimed. "It sounds like you had a much better time than I did." And then added: "No complaint intended."

I expected her to inquire about my orgasms, seeing that she was the one who proposed the whole idea and, in a way, set herself up as the expert - which she, undoubtedly, was. But she said nothing, being confident, I suppose, in her expertise, treating the whole experience as an everyday event. Nor did she offer to enlighten me on how we had conveyed ourselves from the water to the beach - was she as much in the dark as I was? And she did not say anything regarding the more transcendent part of the experience, either. I waited in vain for her to come forward with something.

Instead, she sat up and listened to the dawn chorus, a smile of delight spreading on her beautiful face. She became so absorbed in it that I didn't want to disturb her by talking. I joined her. It had always been one of my favourite pastimes, in fact - listening to nature.

I knew, from practising the direct method, that relaxing my physical body and quietening my mind (thoughts and emotions) put me into a receptive state which, depending on the next move, could either continue to be receptive as in the original mood or break into another, deeper, state. To function in the former state all I had to do was simply concentrate gently on the subject of my interest. For the latter state, a much more focused attention was required: it implied 'going against nature', somewhat against or above or 'outside' the normal functioning of our mental faculties.

I had understood, from my teenage meditative experiences, that the world of Existence came about by means of movement/vibration and that this movement/vibration was also absolutely necessary for its continuing maintenance. In other words, if the world became still it would cease to exist - which, according to the Teachings, and now also Yiannis, was what happened periodically. What took place next, or 'where' the world would be before re-emerging - if, indeed, it was the same world that re-emerged - I had no intimations.

It followed, of course, that we humans, being part of the world, depended entirely on this movement/vibration for our continuing existence, and that we too 'disappeared', along with the rest of the world, when movement/vibration came to a halt. However, the

Teachings also suggested that there were ways of escaping this fate since we as humans were linked to aspects of Consciousness that 'predated' the world of Existence! - we *were* before we *existed*, and continued to *be* as we *existed*. For this reason, by means of *being* as distinct from merely *existing*, we could survive annihilation. But how exactly? The theory put forward a number of graded techniques all of which had the same core element: one-pointed, total concentration.

The rationale behind this was that in order to break the powerful hold of Existence we had to learn to switch to *being*, and cease to be concerned with *existing*. To achieve this, we must attack the very essence of Existence: movement/vibration. Continuous, one-pointed concentration would lead to that goal. One example cited in support of the strength and veracity of this approach was that if the eyes of a person were totally immobilised then that person could not see - the eyeballs being normally in a state of constant, minute, vibration even when we think they are absolutely still. By the same token, and further along the line, total psychological stillness would break the vicious circle of incessant chattering, thinking, imaging, and so on that pervaded our minds and kept us bound to that process.

Whether by arriving at pure *being* we ceased to *exist*, was a question I had never been given a satisfactory answer to. Yiannis had spoken of becoming Light in order to survive Darkness, although he had also proposed that we had started from the condition of an amalgam, a kind of agglutination of psychological bits and pieces, which worked on the possibility of acquiring individuality and thus surviving Darkness - a view that appeared to be at variance with the theory that we *were* before we *existed* (a point I would have to take up with Yiannis when I saw him next).

My personal experiences and abilities, however, lay in the 'lower' level of relaxation and concentration, that in which I could connect, quite often successfully, with my surroundings - including people - in a direct manner, bypassing deductive and inductive reasoning. Which was what I began to engage in as soon as I pulled myself out of these reflections.

Helen was still listening to the birds, mostly sparrows, as they twittered the day in. The smell of pine was beginning to ooze out of the early morning dew. All I had to do was allow myself to slide into any part of the environment I chose to and stay with it, checking stray personal thoughts from claiming my attention and pulling me into daydreaming and fantasy - what many so-called psychoanalysts pride themselves on encouraging their patients to do.

A small lizard that had come out to salute the dawn light became the focus of my attention for a short while. And, as I 'concentrated' on her, she turned into an enormous animal, a true dinosaur. I could hear the rustling noise of her scaly skin, the rhythmic booming of her heart, the hissing of her blood as it began to warm up and race in her body. She flicked her tongue and caught an insect. I heard a dry crunch and tasted the squirting insect in her mouth. Momentarily, it tasted vile, but then, as I overcame my human reaction, I was delighted with it. The same happened when I attended to a noisy 'pre-historic' sparrow. And, again, as I shed my human 'judgmental' attitude, I enjoyed my insect breakfast enormously.

The smell of the pine resin had become increasingly deeper and more delicate - I could taste it, as well as the scent of the aromatic bushes and the seaweeds and the saltiness of the sea water. My eyes and ears - the distant sense receptors - were functioning as tactile sense organs. I could smell and 'taste' the presence of minute insects weaving their way amongst the pebbles, even though I was not looking at them.

It brought back similar experiences I had had, the latest of which had taken place on the mountainside above the lemon groves a few days earlier. I had sat under a gigantic cypress tree and stared out across the orchards and towards the vast expanse of the sea. After a while, as I relaxed, quietened my mind, and became absorbed in the panoramic view, I felt myself expanding and taking in the whole vista in its totality and in its individual parts - the trees, the birds, the insects, the goats, the donkeys and so on, as well as the sounds that rose out of this land-seascape. And, again, the experience was not solely visual - it crossed the boundaries of the senses: what I saw I also heard and smelled and tasted and felt in a tactile sense.

These were experiential confirmations of what I had already been taught: given the correct approach, I could - anyone could - taste and smell sights and sounds as well as see and hear olfactory, tactile and taste sensations. The sensory organs were simply picking out individual aspects or vibrations of nature. Behind them lay a 'common sense', a synaesthetic way of perceiving.

Then, I remembered a theory of perception, circulated in the ancient Greek world, which argued that, in the act of seeing, something (etheric fire) goes out from the eye to meet the object of sight while "effluences" from the object reach the eye itself. I had always taken this to mean attention, that without attending to an object we don't see it: we see something either because we direct our attention to it voluntarily or because the object itself 'draws' or 'catches' our attention - no matter how weak, fleeting or passing our attention might be at the time.

But what I hadn't understood - or, rather, experienced in full cognizance of the fact - were the mechanics of the process. Attention should be understood as 'putting oneself into it', being absorbed into one's object of attention - something I had practised on numerous occasions and at various levels but without being fully aware of the actual logic of the process until now.

According to this, the senses function separately from one another not simply because of their physiology - separate neural pathways, differently developed kinds of sensors, different brain locations - but also because of insufficient attention. If enough attention of the right kind were to be applied, then 'common sense' would kick in - 'common sense' being synaesthetic not only in that it transfers from one sense to another but also in that it functions as a central core of perception, as one 'sense' whose activity engages all the senses simultaneously in one all-inclusive 'sensation'....

Suddenly, I thought I heard distant barking. It felt like a gentle reminder, like a muffled alarm clock. Athespodos sprang to mind with mild urgency. I couldn't tell from which direction the barking came from, but as I pondered I felt it right in front of me, right in my face! There was no Athespodos, only his barking. It took away my 'common sense' and brought me back to my individual senses. The world around me was still beautiful but, somewhat, fragmented: I would have to take it in by means of separate feelers now, each one bringing in distinct bits of data, like spies scouting different parts of the world to extract information for my attention to sieve through. What a drag!...

Helen was looking at me, smiling, watching me come out of my reverie.

"Do you always do this?" she asked.

"What?"

"Disappearing on your girlfriends."

"No. I was following your lead," I said, returning the smile. After all, she was the one who started this lark, listening to the sparrows and the rest of the surroundings.

She was as beautiful as ever. No, more beautiful. Her beauty was transcendent. I'd fallen in love before but that love was a mixture of physical, sexual, attraction and emotional bonding. Wonderful though those occasions had been, this one felt different. Looking back at her, sitting in her naked beauty as she did, I gradually became aware that the powerful sexual attraction I'd felt earlier had transformed itself, it was not sexual in the ordinary sense any longer but more of a passionate spiritual sort of friendship. Sibling souls. There was an unremitting tenderness and unconditional love exuding from that wonderful form. It took me back to the hilltop where I had experienced the meaning of friendship.

Once again, I was filled with joy. But there was a tinge of sadness. I did not understand it at first - why sadness? I recalled old Yiannis' admonition not to indulge in such feelings - which were usually associated with my innate way of looking at beauty and happiness as merely transient - but to concentrate on joy and happiness instead. I tried, and I succeeded. But only temporarily. I soon realised that the sadness I was experiencing, while springing from the same source, had an even more personal dimension to it. I was sensing/realising that she wouldn't be with me long, that this would not be like any of the other associations I had had with her.

Quickly, I stood up and walked to the edge of the water to hide the look on my face, and to try and arrange my thoughts and feelings. Feelings of loss, of impending loss, or imaginary loss: they were all the offspring of fear, resulting from attachment and inadequacy as an individual. I was losing the battle. I was supposed to learn to love with detachment. And there I was swimming in a sea of emotion.

I exerted a supreme effort to distance myself, to gain a perspective - not to sever the connection but to view it as one of many, to deprioritise it. I took a deep breath, then another. I dispensed the breath throughout my body, and loosened my bonds with it. With some confidence I then turned to face her.

She was staring at me, as if waiting for an answer, for a verdict, still smiling lovingly. I desperately resisted her radiating charm and directed my gaze through her, as if she were a transparency. I did not concentrate on her but to a space through her and beyond her. "Either allow yourself to be sucked in by the phenomenal display, studying it in the process, or look through it, directing yourself to its core and ignoring the periphery" was the instruction I was following: either would do. I chose the latter.

And it worked. It wasn't Helen any longer - she had become Aphrodite herself. She was the goddess in all her glory - unbelievably glorious! The epitome of womanhood. And, yes, she was breathtaking in her beauty but she still carried a veiled sadness. It wasn't so much a sadness within herself, within Helen or Aphrodite, as much as the effect of sadness on the 'onlooker'. As expected, I dismissed it as merely a personal reaction - the 'onlooker' obviously being me.

However, I slowly came to appreciate that the effect of sadness was not all that personal. It affected me as a man, as a human, but - and this was the earthshaking aspect of it - 'I' stood for mankind, for the whole of Humanity! I had become the representative of humankind!

As I gazed at her, on that empty beach at the crack of dawn in the midst of awakening nature, the relationship became universal: I was humankind and she was a principle, the principle that expressed itself as the goddess Aphrodite, a living universal principle that had a far-reaching effect on humanity.

She had taken the ever-present sense of Love and particularised it. She had deprived 'me' of certain qualities and abilities which she now called 'feminine' and which I had to struggle to regain. She split me. She made it impossible for me to procreate by myself, to create new forms of life from within myself by myself. I was forced to gain a sense of 'externality'. She was sexual: she had invented sex, gender. There was guile and necessity involved here.

Love was 'unique' before the emergence of Aphrodite - it was whole, so pervasive that you could not see it. She split it into millions of ways of expressing itself; and mostly 'sexual', not simply in the ordinary sense of physical sexuality but in deeper and difficult to discern ways: on emotional and intellectual levels.

Because of her, 'I' needed to experience all these millions of different ways in order to become whole, complete - "completed", as the ancient hierophants would have said.

She displayed charm, which conveyed a meaning of irresistible attraction and guile, the guile of Existence, and the 'cause' of losing sight of the whole so that 'I' would struggle, and in that struggle acquire individuality.

Yiannis was right! Struggle was the implication of Existence. A curse and a blessing (?) - a curse because of the struggle entailed and a blessing because of the individuality to be gained.

Being 'thrown out' of paradise. What paradise? The paradise of having no core, no centre of consciousness? Obviously - being blissful in ignorance. In which case, Aphrodite was none other than Eve: the cause of my 'fall' and of my 'resurrection'....

But Helen was there in front of me as a person now, not as a principle. I was reminded of Yiannis picking up a small stone on the hilltop and throwing open the whole process of creation for me. And now Helen, with all her vast background and experience as an 'old soul', has been doing something similar - or, so it seemed.

She moved, she stretched out an arm to pick up her clothes which lay beside her. The movement had an air of finality about it. She glanced at her watch.

"I'm going to be late."

"Late? Late for what?" I asked, and began to collect my own clothes which I had scattered all over the beach hours earlier.

"I'm catching a flight to Paris, and I'm cutting it fine," she answered in a cool, natural, tone of voice as if announcing her decision to do a manicure or have a new hairdo done. And she began to put her clothes on.

I felt as if I were standing at the edge of a precipice with my internal organs disappearing down the cliff. I was gutted. True, I myself wanted to move on and get ready for my day's task - to find the "brother's" place and meet Yiannis - but that was for part of the day only. I was hoping to see her again later and the following day and the day after that perhaps. I hadn't anticipated this to be the shortest encounter I had ever had with her - even though I had sensed it. I'd expected it to be short, but not this short.

"Then Berlin and Moscow," she continued, before noticing my reaction and making an attempt to soften the blow. "But I'll return before flying back home. We'll meet up again. What do you say?" she asked as she put her sandals on and stood up fully dressed.

What could I say? I slowly regained my composure and said

"Yes, fine," and finished putting my clothes on. We hugged closely and kissed, kissed deeply and passionately, and my disappointment began to wane, and the yearning increase. The sadness, too, started to creep back in but I fought it. It turned into nostalgia. I took a deep breath and gave her an affectionate squeeze. Why should I feel sad, or even nostalgic? I should be grateful for the love and the insights she had brought me, and I told her so.

"Same here," she said, and beamed with joy.

But we couldn't dilly-dally on the beach any longer. She had to get back for the boat to Piraeus. I would have liked to walk back, as I was feeling so full of energy despite the lack of sleep, but that would have taken too long.

We walked on the beach, under the "golden pines", as Pindar would have put it, to a little boat tied to a small jetty. A young man was busying himself with the boat's motor. We approached and asked him if there was a quick way to return to the village. He said that if we didn't mind waiting for him to fill up the tank he would take us there. We couldn't wish for better luck. He poured in the petrol from a plastic container and we were off.

As we chugged away and out of the Cove of Love, we gazed back at the pine-clad little bay with affection, and smiled to each other.

Back at the village, we went straight to our respective hotels to shower and change. My friends had already left on an earlier boat and I had to make arrangements to move to a single room. That done, I walked down to the seafront just in time to have coffee and breakfast with Helen before her boat pulled in. Goodbyes are terrible things, tearing and hurtful. We kept our cool as much as we could. But I'm sure I saw her eyes brimming over as we parted. Would I see her again? - in this life? We'd agreed to meet at the Cove of Love in two weeks' time. Failing that... Well, life's not always predictable.

As she waved goodbye from the upper deck, I thought I saw someone else waving to me - or I could have been mistaken; there were quite a few people up there waving to their friends. From that distance though, and for a moment, he looked very much like Bob the Australian! Surely not. Would he leave his restaurant in the hands of children?

– 13 –

The Suicidal Girl
(A puzzling 're-enactment')

I sat down to have another cup of coffee and work out a plan for the day. But I found it hard to concentrate. Helen was still so much in my thoughts. I decided to trick my mind in order to free it from those thoughts. I knew two ways of achieving that: one was to promise myself to return to the subject - in this case, to think about Helen - later on, perhaps later the same day or the day after; the second way was to busy myself with something altogether unrelated to the subject, preferably external, physical. I had found that employing both methods on each occasion yielded stronger results than using them in isolation of each other.

So, first I made the promise and then looked around for some physical activity to occupy my mind. There were various landlords and landladies at the seafront offering rooms for rent to newly arrived tourists. I watched them as they blurbed their spiel to prospective tenants, and tried to guess, from where I was sitting, the language and nationality of the visitors. They were mostly Germans, with a sprinkling of Scandinavians and a few Americans. Not many. The boat was returning to Pireaus and most of the passengers were on their way to Athens to catch a plane. I dwelt on this game for a short while and then went back to the real task of organising my day.

My problem was, of course, to understand what Yiannis had meant by "brother" and then go to meet him at this person's house. Nobody had said that he had a blood brother, so it stood to reason that he had meant a 'metaphorical' brother, somebody who was like a brother - as it had been explained to me the previous day. The only two people I knew who fitted that description were Mr Zeno and Bob the Australian. It had to be one or the other. Mr Zeno's taverna was only down the road, and I decided to start from there.

An old lady in black was sweeping the courtyard in front of the taverna. She turned out to be Mr Zeno's mother. I didn't exactly expect to see Mr Zeno around at that time of day, knowing that as a taverna owner he would have been up most of the night, and wouldn't need to get up this early. But I wanted to know when he was going to be around.

I was a bit surprised when the old lady said that he had got up a long while ago and gone to the mainland to drive with a friend to Athens for business. He wouldn't be back until some time in the evening, or maybe next day. Tavernas are not open during the day, and that more or less ruled him out: Yiannis had said to meet him in the afternoon, and, surely, he would not have set up a meeting at the empty courtyard of someone's closed taverna. And the old lady didn't know anything about any meeting. I thanked her and left.

Bob, then, was the only alternative "brother". I walked back to my hotel, picked up my swimming trunks and a towel and returned to the seafront to catch a small ferry to get across to Bob's place. It was early in the day and, just in case Bob's café-restaurant was not open yet, I could have a swim and relax. The meeting with Yiannis wasn't until the afternoon, anyway.

The little boat I jumped into, as it was departing, was practically full of people getting to the beach before the heat of the day became uncomfortable (most of them had come for the sun but didn't like the heat!). The journey to the beach was hardly a kilometre away.

First we passed through the strait between the mainland and the island, which was also used by ships, and then continued sailing close to the mainland coast on our right. Halfway down our journey, the sea opened out into a wide channel to our left - the route of the big passenger ships - whereas, on the right - our route - there was another, shorter, strait, this time between the mainland and a minute island less than a hundred metres long, mostly rocky with two or three shady pine trees and a few small bushes growing where some meagre soil had managed to attach itself amongst the rocks.

There were no sandy beaches, and the waters were deep except on a part of the strait where there was a reef which the small ferries had to nagotiate very carefully. I'd done that journey a few times before and I knew that no ferry stopped at the small island - although, I suppose anybody could get onto it either by swimming or by private boat.

That's why I was surprised to see people on it as we passed by this time. I could make out two couples under a pine tree, and they were fully clothed. Maybe they were having a picnic. But, suddenly, as I took another look, I thought I saw Yiannis. One of them looked very much like old Yiannis! Oh, no - was I getting into some fantasy state in which I was seeing people that were not there? First I saw - I thought I saw - Bob on the ship travelling to Piraeus, and now Yiannis on a small rocky island that nobody seemed to visit. Whatever was going on required investigation.

As soon as we docked at Bob's restaurant I went straight in and asked to see him - only to be told that he had caught an early boat to Pireaus and that he would not be back till the evening! Disappointed? Yes, but at least I knew I hadn't been hallucinating. Would that mean that I was also right about Yiannis being on the small island? I hoped so. And there was only one way to find out. I asked the man who ran the small ferry if he wouldn't mind dropping me off at the island on his way back but, as I expected, he refused to. Was there any small boat I could hire? No. Was there any other way I could get onto the island?

"Swim," came the laconic response from the ferryman.

After a short consideration, I decided to walk to the spot on the mainland opposite the island and ask around for any more bright ideas! It was the same path I had taken the day before when I had left Bob's restaurant in search of Yianna's house. But there was nobody there to render practical assistance or offer viable suggestions - even the donkeys were already on their way to the lemon groves, laden with obese tourists, and their owner simply shrugged her shoulders.

Standing there on the beach facing the island, I could see the four figures engaged in some sort of verbal exchange, but the manner in which they were relating to one another seemed strange: one of them, a young woman from what I could make out, sat facing in my direction with her head bent and listening to an old man - the one I took to be Yiannis - who sat on her left. To the left of the old man and slightly behind him sat a middle-aged couple who were also more or less facing in my direction but didn't seem to be communicating with anybody - maybe they were listening to the old man too; I couldn't tell. They were all sitting on low flat rocks in the shade of a pine tree.

I reconsidered the boatman's advice. The strait in front of me didn't look more than one hundred metres wide - no distance to swim. And, if I were careful, I could negotiate the reef. But where would I leave my clothes? The beach I stood on was practically a thoroughfare. Then I remembered an old story in which a Greek sailor won a bet against the devil. It sounded like the best idea - well, the only viable idea - so far. And I proceeded to act on it.

I withdrew behind some bushes and put my swimmming trunks on and emerged on the beach with my clothes and the towel bundled up into a ball. Now, if the waters turned out to be shallow enough for me to walk, I would do just that all the way to the island, holding the bundle high above my head - I still wore my sandals, of course, to avoid cuts on the reef. If, on the other hand, the waters were too deep to walk, I would swim using only my legs and feet - and possibly one arm - to float and propel myself. I could do it; well, I could try.

By zig-zagging and deviating here and there to avoid obvious drops in the reef, I managed to walk half of the distance to the island. I couldn't spot with precision the canal cut in the reef where the small boats passed on their way to and from the tourist beach, but I saw another boat coming this way and waited for it to pick it out for me. As the boat approached, the tourists in it began to cheer and clap and laugh and egg me on - standing in the middle of the strait holding my clothes above my head must have looked quite amusing. And the wash that nearly knocked me over did nothing to lessen their glee or bolster my dignity!

When the waters settled, I made a dash across the cut, swimming as I had planned, but only for a few metres before returning to walking again. I'd made it, with my clothes still dry, nearly as good as the Greek sailor - although, in his case, he had to keep his clothes dry from the rain as well; and the prize for winning the bet is un-mentionable!

I'd come out just a few metres away from that group of four people. They hadn't noticed me as I was hidden from them by the rocks. I didn't know what to do next: pop out and introduce myself or stay hidden and eavesdrop? In fact, I didn't have to eavesdrop because I could already hear them very clearly - and it *was* Yiannis. I peered briefly and cautiously to make certain that it was him and then sat back trying to decide what to do.

Maybe I should not interrupt them, maybe I should go back. Go back and try and work out this "brother" lark. Go back? I took a look at my sandals which had been butchered on the reef. No way.

If I was going to get off the island it would have to be by forcing one of the small ferries to stop and pick me up. For now, I would stay there, get my breath back, and see what happens.

I could hear what was being said quite clearly. Yiannis was talking to the girl, and his voice sounded rather impersonal. He was speaking in English.

"It's entirely up to you. *You* are the one who'll have to come to terms with it sooner or later. I've given you my advice. I can't solve your problem for you."

There was no response from the girl or the others. I waited for a beat or two and then decided to have another peak.

The girl, in her early twenties, was looking at the ground between her feet, and appeared dejected. The other two were deep in thought. There was something familiar about the three of them - not their physical appearance so much as the overall atmosphere that seemed to envelop them.

"Look, my dear: You're either extremely incompetent or you're not serious about it," Yiannis spoke again.

The girl was taken aback. "What?" she said, lifting her head a little. She spoke with a German-sounding accent, but I wasn't certain - it could have been Dutch.

"Let's face it: You've tried to top yourself half a dozen times," Yiannis continued. "Obviously, without success." Then, he became blunt. "Now, do you want to live or do you want to die?"

She remained silent, looking very despondent. Yiannis continued in the same blunt manner.

"Let me put it another way: Do you want me to help you get through your problem and live or do you want me to show you a foolproof way to do yourself in? I'll help you either way?"

They were aghast, all three of them. They appeared unable to utter a word. The suggestion must have shocked them into a locked jaw. This was getting interesting, and my scruples about eavesdropping began to wane.

"Well?" said Yiannis, waiting patiently for an answer.

But still none was coming. Instead, the girl lowered her head and began to sob quietly.

Yiannis sighed in a show of impatience. "Dear god! Am I talking to myself?"

"But, sir! You can't be serious!" intervened the older woman, in

The Suicidal Girl (ch.13)   261

a slight Dutch accent.

"I'm dead serious, madam - if you pardon the expression," came the response from Yiannis.

"But--"

Yiannis cut her short by turning to the girl. "Do you really love him?"

The girl sniffled and continued to sob. The woman came back with more force.

"She hates the bastard!"

Yiannis ignored her and addressed the girl again. "Do you hate him?"

The girl lifted her shoulders weakly in an indecisive response. Yiannis continued. "Do you think he's worth it?"

"Nobody is worth dying over - least of all him!" growled the woman.

The old man ignored her and continued speaking to the girl.

"I mean, is he worth your love, d'you think?"

The girl sniffled again and nodded affirmatively, but almost imperceptibly.

The woman nearly blew her top. "Are you totally insane?!" she practically shouted at the girl. "The son-of-a-bitch is screwing all over the place like a rabbit, and you still love him?!" Then turned to Yiannis. "Is she or is she not insane? I ask you?"

Yiannis kept ignoring her and concentrating on the girl.

"What'll happen if you manage to kill yourself? What about all your plans?"

She shrugged her shoulders and continued to sniffle.

"What about your *drawings*?" he said, stressing the last word.

She lifted her head, still sniffling, and looked at Yiannis.

"What?" she said, not quite certain of what he was talking about.

Yiannis leant towards her and spoke as if in confidence.

"Your drawings. And the plans. Those marvellous plans. Those plans for wonderfully beautiful buildings you've been drawing."

The woman cut in. "Plans? Drawings? What drawings?" She moved a little to her left to face the girl more squarely, and spoke to her. "You never said anything about plans and drawings."

Suddenly, I felt as if shifting into another time zone. The familiarity I had sensed earlier regarding these three people's concerns, began to turn into a weird flashback, a playback of a prerecorded scene: the middle-aged couple and their daughter at the Teacher's house, the unfaithful boyfriend, being an architect in a previous incarnation, the attempted suicides.... I was 'reliving' their conversations in the Teacher's lounge - conversations I had not been a witness to! I primed myself to take in every detail.

The girl looked bemused. Her interest had been aroused and she stopped sniffling.

"How did you know? I never told you."

"I know. How I know is irrelevant," Yiannis responded.

"But I never told anyone," she persisted.

"That's neither here nor there. The important thing is that these drawings, these visions, is what caused you to bungle your suicide attempts. Right?" He looked her firmly in the eye and continued. "Right in the middle of your trying to top yourself you would have a brilliant flash of one of these visions, of these marvellous buildings. Later, as you recovered, you made colour drawings of them. And worked out plans for building them. Right?"

The girl burst into tears. The woman - her mother, I now knew - turned to her husband:

"Did you know any of this?"

The man was just as surprised. "No. Nothing."

"What are these drawings?" she asked Yiannis, and then swept her eyes over to her daughter with the same questioning look.

Yiannis turned to face both parents.

"You didn't know your daughter was a budding architect, did you?" and then turned back to the girl: "And a very talented one, too, I might add."

"Well, we knew she could draw at school, but..."

"But an architect?!" the husband complemented the sentiment.

Yiannis addressed the girl again. "Do you want to throw all this away? A wonderful talent? Down the drain?" He waited for a beat and asked her again. "Do you?" No response. One more beat, and then: "Because if you do, I'll show you how to kill yourself. Quickly and efficiently. Do you want me to show you how?"

The girl shook her head.

"What? I didn't hear you."

"No," she practically whispered. Then, more positively: "No. I don't want to die."

"Good. Now, do you love him?"

She hesitated, fidgeted, and then whispered what I took to be "Yes."

"Give me your hands," he said firmly, and opened his palms before her.

The girl placed her hands inside his palms. He closed his hands over hers gently. I saw her shivering momentarily as if electric current coursed through her body. I knew the feeling.

"Do you hate him?"

"No," she said in a low voice, almost whimpering. "I don't know. I don't think so."

Yiannis then began to speak slowly and gently but continued to be firm and authoritative.

"Now, I want you to expel all hatred, all possible hatred towards him from your heart. To achieve this we do the opposite of hating: we make love. Come, let's make love."

The girl's hands tensed up, her eyelids fluttered. She opened her eyes and looked apprehensive. The parents exchanged looks with a sense of alarm.

"Close your eyes, my dear, and relax. We're going to make love now," Yiannis continued.

"Sir! What's going on here?! What are you doing?!" interrupted the mother, her voice full of alarm.

"Not *doing*, madam, *making*: *making love*," came Yiannis' response, before turning his attention to the girl again. "Now, close your eyes, and relax. Go on."

The girl glanced at her parents for support, but they were indecisive, trying to work out what the old man meant by 'making love'.

"Come, close your eyes. We'll make love," came Yiannis' voice, soft, inviting, authoritative.

The girl looked totally confused, and ready to fall under the old shaman's spell. She slowly closed her eyes. Yiannis kept his eyes on her, vigilant but relaxed.

"Good. Relax."

He continued to speak slowly and gently but with increased firmness and authority.

"We're going to make love now, my dear: *produce* love, *generate* love from the depths of your heart."

He sat up in the manner of the Teacher. And it was, indeed, the Teacher speaking now - the mannerisms of his voice, the tone, the inflections. The parents watched bemused as the old man continued.

"Open your heart. Fill it with compassion and love. Open your heart and take him in, smother him with love. It doesn't matter whether *he* loves you or not. Love, real love, is unconditional. Open up. Love him unconditionally."

He carried on repeating this mantra of 'unconditional love' with small variations.

"You don't have to be with him any longer, if you don't want to. But don't hate him. Love him and leave him. Yes. That's the best for you. Leave him but love him. Open your heart, my dear. And love him. Fill your heart with love. And fill *his* heart with *your* love."

I was by then falling into a trance myself. And I could see what was happening to the girl. There was a cloud of dark brown and black enveloping her chest, filled with pain and despair, which gradually began to thin out and dissipate, giving way to a thick pink which itself changed to rose and then to rose-white. I could feel her mood changing along with the colours: the despair slowly disappearing to be replaced by joy, as white energy rose up in her middle column and flushed her heart clean of all signs of darkness.

Her body began to shake, and she burst into tears. But these were not tears of pain, they were tears of relief, catharsis, joy; they ran down her cheeks uncontrollably. The parents looked bewildered, moved, concerned.

The old man let go of the girl's hands, took a deep breath, and slapped his thigh in the manner of the Teacher.

"Yes. She's done it. She's cured herself," he said, his voice raised a little, and exhaling as if to indicate the end of a task carried out satisfactorily. I practically expected him to call out for a cup of coffee in the usual tone of the Teacher.

"Thank god for that!" exclaimed the mother with relief. "Are you sure she's completely cured of him?" she added, with some reserve.

"What? No, no," snapped Yiannis. "You misunderstood. She's not cured of *him*. He's not some kind of illness she could be cured of. You shouldn't think of people that way, madam."

"What was she cured of, then?" she asked, puzzled.

"Her illness. Her cancer."

The parents were thunderstruck. The girl's sobbing and shaking slowed down; she took a deep breath and stared at Yiannis in disbelief and bewilderment.

"Her what?!" the mother shrilled.

"She went into hospital for tests the other day, didn't she?"

"Yes..."

"She had some Xrays taken."

"Yes..."

"And the doctor said that he wasn't sure of the results, that he wanted the consultant's opinion. She has an appointment to see the consultant in a couple of weeks. Is that right?"

The woman was totally bemused, flabbergasted.

"Yes, yes. But how did you know? What's this got to do with her situation?" she asked when she managed to get her speech back.

"Everything, my dear. It has everything to do with it. It's her *situation*, as you put it, that caused it."

"Caused what?"

"The cancer, of course."

"What cancer?!" came the scream from the girl.

"The one the doctors saw in the Xrays, the one you'd brought about with your feelings and thoughts and frustrations, the one you've got rid of just now, my dear," Yiannis explained, and added, with a broad smile. "You've just had open-heart surgery."

"What?!" jumped the girl, and looked down at her chest instinctively as if to check the old man's statement.

Yiannis chuckled quietly. "You've just opened your heart and dissolved the cancer."

"The doctors didn't say anything about any cancer," stated the woman, still in disbelief.

"They will," Yiannis assured her, "when she goes in for her appointment. But ask them to check again. They'll find nothing." And then turned to the girl. "Because you dissolved it, my dear. With your love. And you must try and keep this up. Don't allow negative feelings and thoughts to lodge themselves in your heart ever again, or you'll bring the tumour back. Be happy. And be creative. You have so much going for you."

And on that he stood up in a clear indication that the meeting had come to an end. The family followed suit.

What happened next was even more astounding for me than what had taken place so far on that rocky little island. The young woman, filled with obvious relief and joy, and with moist eyes and intermit-

tent sniffle, grabbed Yiannis' hand and began kissing it and thanking him profusely - exactly as in the scene on the Teacher's veranda so long ago; and the remainder of that scene unfolded in precise detail, an exact re-enactment of those activities, down to the
attempt to pay the Teacher for his services, his refusal to accept any
money, and the joke about his knuckles being worn by the kissing.

But what was even more intriguing was the manner in which I
experienced those last few events. Even though the language spoken
was English, I could also hear the whole exchange in Greek, as in
the original scene! It was like a movie which I had already seen but
I was now watching a dubbed version of - except that I was hearing
both languages at the same time. It was disconcerting momentarily
but it felt quite natural after the initial shock.

And then, as if in a dream, I saw a small boat arrive - not one of
the normal small ferries but a much smaller one - which took the
visitors away. Yiannis waved them goodbye and went and sat under
the pine tree.

I leant back against a rock, trying to take in what had taken
place, and decide what to do next. The experience on this island had
been another confusing broadside to my efforts to come to grips
with the concept of time. Ever since I met Yiannis in the doughnut
hole, it had been an intermittent - no, a continuous - battle to understand time. I felt like Sisyphos, pushing up a rock towards the sum-
mit of a mountain, only for the rock to keep slipping and making me
start over from another side of the mountain - too many angles, too
many slippery mountainsides. And I had never asked for this, time
had not been one of my prime concerns. I had been *forced* to grap-
ple with it.

And what about Mr Zeno and Bob? Was it merely a coincidence
that they both had to be away?

The sound of a passing small ferry laden with tourists pulled me
out of my considerations. I had to decide how to confront the old
man. The scruples had returned. I knew that the Teacher would not
have approved of my eavesdropping. His approach had a strong
moral ingredient: you never broke into someone's private life -
physical and psychological make-up and history - unless you had
been invited to by that person or the situation absolutely warranted
the intervention.

Yiannis, on the other hand, when he was not behaving like the

Teacher, had a different approach, or so he appeared to. There were times when I thought of him as a loveable rogue - but appearances could be deceptive, as I had come to appreciate in the few hours since our meeting in the doughnut hole.

"You can come out now," I heard him call in his familiar jocular tone of voice.

He knew. Of course he knew. But, at least, he didn't sound judgmental. I came out of my hiding place, the bundle under my arm, ready to apologise. He took one look at me and I could tell he was trying hard not to laugh. He held back for a beat or two and then burst into a raucous laughter.

"Oh, god! Oh, god! You're a real blessing. My life would be intolerably dull without you!" he uttered, in between bouts of roaring laughter.

What now? Did I really look that amusing? His reaction was strongly reminiscent of scenes in the rock and on the hill.

"You and your scruples. You look like shit." And then. "What's that you're carrying under your arm - your dowry?" (a Greek in-joke).

I wasn't sure whether his hilarity was due to my physical appearance or his perception of my concerns over eavesdropping - in either case, I couldn't see the funny side.

"Come and sit down," he pointed casually to a rock near him.

I sat and placed the bundle on my lap. He glanced at it and shook his head as he lowered himself onto a rock next to me.

"Let go of your worldly goods and tell me why you're here."

"I've been looking for the 'brother's' house where we're supposed to meet," I said as I put the bundle on a rock beside me.

"What, here, on this desert island?" he querried, his face readying itself for another bout of jollity.

I ignored the touch of sarcasm and narrated my unsuccessful attempts to find Mr Zeno and Bob. How come they had both disappeared for the day?

"How should I know? I'm not their keeper," he dismissed my inquiry.

"But... I thought you and...."

"Me and what?"

"Oh, never mind." I realised I wasn't going to get any help in that direction; no use probing any further.

"In any case, we're not to meet until the afternoon," he said, and looked across to the mainland, his statement sounding like a polite way of asking me to vacate the island - but I couldn't, I had nowhere to turn to.

Except... Except Bob's restaurant. Of course! The arrangement had been to meet *at* the "brother's". It didn't mean that Bob had to be present. The restaurant would not normally serve food between two thirty and seven but it stayed open serving coffee and soft drinks. We could sit in the courtyard, under a tree. That was it! Why hadn't I thought of this earlier? In all the rush to come over to the little island, I hadn't stopped to consider it. Did Yiannis just put this into my head? - possibly, probably.

"Before you go," he continued, making it abundantly clear he was dismissing me, "please tell me why you torture youself by indulging in scruples?" He was, of course, referring to my feelings of guilt regarding the eavesdropping.

"Well, it was inadvertent, actually," I mumbled.

"Rubbish. You could have left. Nobody was stopping you. Did Athespodos growl at you?"

"No," was my sheepish reply. Athespodos? Why mention Athespodos? Oh, yes: my 'guardian angel' - or my Nemesis?

"Inadvertent, my foot! Is this an explanation or a justification? Don't answer that. My question was 'why do you torture yourself with scruples?'"

"Well, I felt I was doing something wrong."

"Why?"

"I was eavesdropping, I was listening to a private conversation."

"So?"

"I...hm...."

"Where would knowledge be if we all held to such scruples? Where would science be? How would we get to the *truth*? - in whatever way you might understand truth."

Only a few minutes earlier he was behaving like the Teacher, he *was* the Teacher, down to the slapping of his thigh. And now there was this divergence - back to the original Yiannis.

"Did you intend harm?"

"No."

"There you go, then. Why waste energy by applying man-made cultural rules?"

"But they're wholesome rules designed to protect."

"True. But you just admitted that you did not intend harm. So who is being protected from whom here?"

He was right. My scruples were unnecessary, a waste of energy. I felt relieved. I was about to apologise for being such a fool when I noticed the edges of his mouth raising themselves into a trace of a smile; and I could see his tongue rolling inside his mouth against his cheek. Tongue in cheek! He was pulling my leg. I went through his argument again in my head and realised he was leaving something out, something important: me, me as consciousness. He saw the realisation in my eyes.

"You nearly missed it," he said, and gave a little chuckle.

Yes. It was one thing making rules to protect people from harm by others, but what about the perpetrator himself? There was damage in that direction too. 'Thou shalt not kill', for instance, was not a rule only to protect people from being killed but also to prevent a person - the perpetrator - from creating adverse conditions in the development of himself as consciousness. I was reminded of an incident reported in the local press a long time ago in which a twenty-year-old man had attacked and raped a sixty-five-year-old widow. When I mentioned this to the Teacher and expressed my sympathy for the victim by saying "poor woman!", his response was "yes, but also 'poor man!'".

The old Socratic admonition again. Every time you hurt someone, you create conditions within yourself that slow down your development as consciousness - it's a subtle stage in the process of realising the Delphic exhortation: Know Thyself.

But how did all this relate to my eavesdropping? I had done nothing to hurt anybody. Curiosity? Thirst for knowledge? Was this detrimental in any way?

"Only in that you might be creating elementals which would bolster a self-serving attitude; you need to examine that," he responded to my question. "Having noted that, however, you then get on and stop wasting energy."

I took his advice on board. I should meditate on it, analyse it, take stock, and move on: one of the Society's seven promises, and one of Pythagoras' conditions on entering his School. I'd forgotten, I'd slipped up.

– 14 –

The Teiresias Dilemma
(On the Cusp: Male/Female, Existent/Non-existent)

"Let me ask *you* a question now. May I?" I chanced it.

He looked towards the mainland again. "Could it wait till the afternoon"?

"Well...". I knew I was pushing it, but now that I'd got him there I might as well have a go - at least with one question. There were many questions I wanted to raise with him, including this latest weird 'time-warp-repeat' with the Dutch family, but I was prepared to shelve them for later, in the afternoon.

He glanced at me out of the corner of his eye.

"Go on. So long as it doesn't take all day."

"Why did you interfere... No, no. It's not the right word. Why were you present when I was making love to the girl?" There, I said it.

He turned to me, and his eyes nearly popped out of their sockets with surprise - mock surprise, as I'd come to identify by now.

"What? Are you accusing me of having hidden behind some bushes or rocks - as you have just done yourself - and watched you have sex with someone?"

I was not shaken by his display. "No. It was more serious than that. You know what I mean."

"No, I don't. What is it you're saying?"

"You got in the middle, you nearly took over."

"Whom did I nearly take over?"

That was a difficult question to answer because his 'overshadowing' had gone in both directions: me *and* Helen.

"Was it you or her or both?" he expanded on his question. But he didn't wait for me to confirm or deny. He threw his head back and laughed. "You're obsessed. You have too many obsessions, in fact."

"What obsessions?"

"Sex, for a start. You're obsessed with sex."

"No, I'm not." I knew he was baiting me.

"I mean, you're obsessed with sexual distinctions."

"I don't understand."

"D'you remember yesterday at the rock when you got scared shitless because you thought I wanted to have sex with you?"

Did I remember? Of course I did. But I refused to take the bait.

"So?"

"You're so obsessed with distinctions: who does what to whom, who is male, who is female. Why should it matter to you so much?"

It did matter to me. But since the experience with Helen I had begun to wonder. Right now, however, I wasn't sure how to phrase my response.

"Well...". I dithered.

"You're obsessed with definitions and concepts and time - the concept of time. Defining, distinguishing, discriminating - this is all good practice, but too much of it restricts the growth of consciousness."

He saw me withering under his 'chiding' and, as if taking pity on me, he added: "We'll talk about sex and time later, more deeply and in a wider perspective."

These were concluding remarks, and I took the hint. I was about to pick up my bundle, when he spoke again.

"Look. I'll take you through something very briefly, and then we leave it for now, okay?"

It was not a question but an ultimatum, and I felt I had to accede to it. "Okay."

He leant forward and began to draw something in the dust using his index finger. It was an erect penis! - vertical and sketchy, in the fashion of pornographic graffiti.

"You know what this is, don't you?"

"Yes - pornography."

"Ha, ha." He dismissed my comment and continued. "Watch."

He drew a long vertical slit, an oval opening, below the base of the penis where the scrotum would normally be: it looked like the opening of a vagina with a penis stuck on the top end of it!

"Are you watching?" he asekd without raising his head.

I whispered "Yes...?" as I tried to make sense of it.

He scratched a replica of this sketch next to it. "Now watch carefully. Imagine this shrinking to this," he said. He rubbed off the penis and replaced it with what looked like a small glans - a clitoris.

"You are following, right?" he asked again.

I looked at the strange scratchings on the ground and mumbled "Right...," not being exactly certain what this imaginary mutilation was supposed to mean.

He drew another representation, another replica of the penis with the vagina below it. He raised his head and looked at me.

"You've drawn the same thing as the one before," I said, in obvious puzzlement, and pointed to the relevant sketch.

"Ah, but look," he responded. With a little twig he picked up from the ground, he began to scratch zig-zag lines between the labia of the vagina, starting at the bottom end and finishing at the base of the penis, every now and then lifting and dipping the twig daintily in the manner of sewing. He was having fun.

"What do you think of my surgical talents?" he chuckled, and proceeded to enlarge the lower part of the sealed labia turning it into a little bag in the shape of an overripe fig! He then picked up a couple of small pebbles and placed them next to each other within the bag – the scrotum! He leant back and laughed.

I looked at the three drawings: the first one included both sexes - from which the other two, the female and the male, developed.

Yes, he was, once more, making his point on definitions - but also on physiology and biology, drawing my attention to the sexual differentiation of the genders.

"You see? It's all a matter of emphasis - physiological, biological, and hormonal emphasis. You are not only a mongrel, my boy, but also an inherent, and potential, hermaphrodite."

He chuckled, and continued with a series of questions.

"Why else would you have nipples - which serve no purpose? And why would women have orgasms and, even, ejaculations - whose biological functions are practically insignificant? And what about the G spots, and your having multiple orgasms and retrograde ejaculations? Do you think that all those ancient Greeks who propounded the idea that humans were originally hermaphrodite were just idle drifters into fantasy-land?"

He was bombarding me with information, and questions which I took to be rhetorical, and expected him to procced with answers to them - presumably to point out in detail the defferentiation, or lack of it, regarding the sexes. But he continued:

"Did you know you could get pregnant?"

"What?!"

"Genetic manipulation will be doing that, before long - not to mention the creation of part-human-part-animal forms."

He saw the frozen, puzzled (horrified!) look on my face and laughed his head off. Then, he stopped abruptly, slapped his thigh, in the manner of the Teacher, and added:

"Enough for now. Later. Now, tell me: do you ever go fishing?"

What a question! Out of the blue. "What?"

"Fishing. Do you fish?"

"Sometimes. Not recently. When I was a child I used to cast a line a lot. Why?"

"No reason. What about octopus? Ever fished octopus?"

"Yes. A few times."

I had, actually, fished octopus using a spear gun but not very successfully.

"Come with me," he said abruptly, and stood up.

I stretched my hand towards my bundle but he stopped me.

"Leave it. Come."

He led me near to where I had got out of the sea earlier, and squatted by the edge of the water, inviting me to join him.

"See if you can spot one," he said casually.

I struggled to adjust to the new situation. I pushed all questions regarding sex and gender to the back of my mind - I would, though, hold him to his promise to discuss questions of "sex and time more deeply and in a wider perspective later."

The water in front of me was just over half a metre deep and crystal clear. I looked into it wondering what he was up to this time. Small fish were darting around but no octopus in sight. They prefer rocky, cavernous places, but even in the open they're very hard to pick out from their surroundings when they're lying somewhere motionless. The bottom was covered with pebbles, small boulders and weeds - perfect for camouflage.

"See any?" he asked.

"No."

"There. Over there."

He pointed to some weeds at the bottom of the sea. I looked hard, trying to pick out the shape of an octopus - the tentacles, the head, the eyes perhaps - but without success. It was all weeds and pebbles. I thought of switching to the direct method to pick out differences in colours and vibrations, but I felt him holding me back, preventing me from doing so. I began to see why he was putting me through this: it seemed like a lesson, a lesson on discrimination - on definitions! Ah! - as in the rock, looking for boundaries. I smiled to myself, I'd rumbled him.

I continued to look, however, searching for the elusive octopus when, suddenly, he plunged a hand into the calm waters and pulled one out, a baby one (what the Greeks consider a delicacy because of its tender flesh!?). He placed it on a rock beside him.

"Now it's your turn; you catch one," he said, and leant back.

For a brief moment I wished my youngest brother had been there; he was very good at this - he would dive and pick them out of the bottom of the sea and shove them into his swimming trunks and store them there until he had caught enough. No, thank you!

I looked and looked but I couldn't see any.

"Look! There's one!" he called out.

"Where, where?!" I couldn't see it.

"There! Look!"

I followed where his finger was pointing but I still couldn't see the blessed mollusc.

"Get closer," he suggested. "Look. There."

I bent over as far as I could, my nose practically touching the water. And, then, I felt his hand on top of my head. What was he doing? Before I had a chance to turn to face him, he slid his hand down to the back of my neck and squeezed it, pressing with his thumb on the nape and with his fingers round my throat; I had a fleeting mixed feeling of pain and pleasure before he pushed my head into the water. I struggled to lift it out, to breathe, but he had a firm grip on my neck and was holding it under. Why?!

Was he trying to drown me?! He could have done a better job at the other side of the island. Here, we were squatting by a busy lane, boats going to and fro - in fact, I'd seen one coming up from Bob's place just before he'd pushed my head in; it would be right in front of us in a minute or so.

Then, just as suddenly, I went blank. I lost all memory, I forgot who I was. I found myself in a limbo. I was not even sure that I existed.

Gradually, however, I began to be aware of the presence of 'entities' and people I thought I knew, I *felt* I knew.... There was a Hall of Justice, decisions were being made. Everything was moving, nothing was stationary.... It was a very fast, impressionistic, sequence of events.... Then, I blanked out again....

At some point, I seemed to come to, to regain consciousness. I lifted my head out of the water with a sharp intake of air. I was in a bathtub, and I was testing myself to see how long I could keep my head under water. I was about six years old - and I was a girl.

Mother called from another room and came in to get me out of the bath because I was taking too long. We were going visiting and we shouldn't be late. I was the only child of a well-to-do French family and lived in Paris in the seventeenth century. We had connections to the aristocracy and enjoyed an enviable social life.

What followed was a whole, complete, incarnation which I experienced in every minute detail, day by day, hour by hour, minute by minute. Strictly speaking, I should say I *re*-experienced this life since it was one I had already lived, but there was a crucial difference between this and any other incarnation I had visited: I did not relive it as a memory. On all other occasions, no matter how vivid the incarnation I was visiting, I was always aware that I was experiencing it as a memory, from the present to the past - powerful, vivid, alive, though it might have been, it was, nonetheless, a memory.

As I lived this particular one, however, I had no memories of incarnations I had had before it and had no connections with or awareness of my present self in Greece. I lived and breathed like any other normal female in France at that time.

I grew up to become a very beautiful young woman, with boys and men always seeking my company - and I had great difficulty in saying no to them. The family did all they could to rein me in, but I liked men too much. Being very attractive, I was spoilt for choice. But I soon realised I did not have to choose, and so I ended up with a string of lovers.

At the beginning, there were duels among the men who sought my favours, until I made it a condition that no man would go to bed with me who had the slightest intention of monopolising me. This was not a rule simply to save lives, but more to keep my lovers alive! I loved every one of them and never cast off any one for the sake of another. Greedy? No. Lusty.

There were times when I was scared of myself, scared of what I might do if men turned away from me - I knew I would go after them, and cheapen myself by revealing how much I needed them. But while I was young and healthy and beautiful there was no fear of that happening. I was coy, and enticing. I never went after men in any overt way. I knew how much power I swayed over them.

The next stage was an obvious progression: I would go to bed with a number of men at the same time. My lovers enjoyed having me but had no conception of how much pleasure they were giving me. They were so wrapped up in themselves, in deriving pleasure from taking me, as males do, that I let them carry on pleasing themselves, reminding them every now and then how lucky they were to have me - not knowing that taking me the way they did was exactly what I wanted them to do. Instead, they showered me with all manner of gifts for my favours - bless them!

The physical aspect of being taken by men was only one part of the wonderful pleasure of sex I was having; another part was psychological: the sense of pleasure I derived from pleasing men, of making myself available to them to use me for their pleasure, and the knowledge that they were satisfied having me.

As time went by, and I grew more mature, I began to have an urge that had been absent in my life in earlier years: I wanted to have children, and I wanted them to be brought up properly, in a proper family environment. So, when the opportunity arose, I 'gave in' to one of my favourite lovers whom I had prepared with a series of innuendos over a period of time. I 'gave in' and accepted his third proposal.

We got married and left Paris to settle in Vienna, away from my, now, ex-lovers. Giving up all my other lovers to become monogamous proved a very difficult move, but once I had the first child my character seemed to change dramatically. I liked being pregnant and hated going through labour but when the child arrived I was over the moon - and wanted more. I went on to have four children in all and lived to a ripe old age, surrounded by grandchildren. I died a very, very happy old woman.

As I lay in my deathbed, with my children and grandchildren around me, my life, my happy life as a woman, flashed before me, from that last scene in bed to my childhood and beyond, to when I was born to my beloved parents who were now waiting for me to join them. And, tucked at the end of that flashback, was a vague and peculiar, almost inappropriate, 'memory' of me having had an incarnation as a man in Greece during which I had met an old man by the name of Yiannis who.... One last breath. As I lay in my deathbed, I began to exhale my last breath when my body suddenly shook and I felt choking....

....And I jerked my head backwards, and out of the water with a sharp intake of much needed air. I gulped for dear life and turned to see Yiannis squatting next to me and smiling cheekily. I heard and saw a boat approaching from Bob's place and passing by on its way to the port - the very same small ferry I'd noticed coming up just before Yiannis pushed my head into the water. I began to adjust.

"No, no! Don't do that!" shouted Yiannis, raising an alarm. "Don't come back! Stay! Stay!"

I felt myself going back into that incarnation, sliding in and out of it. But this time it was me, with my full present consciousness - and my perception of that earlier life was different. For a start, I didn't take easily to the idea of lying on my back with my legs wide open and up in the air and a man riding me! - not to mention all the other things I had participated in with groups of men! I felt faint.

Yiannis helped me up and guided me to the shade of a pine tree. I sat down and he sat next to me, urging me all the while to return to that female incarnation with my present consciousness. I followed his instructions only to continue feeling averse and becoming more confused.

"Take it easy, do it slowly, bit by bit," he encouraged me.

I took a deep breath and tried again, and again. Slowly, I gained some control over the process. It was a procedure akin to the one used for dealing with phobias: a gradual exposure to the problem situation.

Yiannis' advice to do it gradually concerned partly the adjusting of the two consciousnesses to one another. I had never experienced a past incarnation in the absence of my present consciousness. In fact, I had never thought it possible. It would be like a dream in which normal logic was totally suspended and connections with the three-dimensional world severed, or a split personality.

The task at hand, as I perceived it, was to retain the vividness and reality of the female incarnation while viewing it and re-experiencing it from my present position. In other words, to feel like a female while still in a male body!

As I continued with the exercise, I was reminded of my experience with Helen: the way in which I did not only have multiple orgasms but, towards the end, without an erection. Although the physiology was different, the experience had similarities with my experiences as a woman. And the fact that, following Helen's instructions, I had concentrated not on the penis itself but farther inside my body, brought the two sets of experience closer together. Also, Yiannis' sketches on the ground and his pointing out that the differences between the sexes were primarily a matter of 'emphasis' on 'developmental' physiology, biology and hormonal secretions - not to mention the female ejaculatory experiences - confounded the traditional polarisation of the genders even further.

Ah, wait a minute! Was the encounter with Helen a calculated prelude perhaps, easing me into sexual experiences as an 'actual' female incarnation? Were those two - Yiannis and Helen - in cahoots? Was Helen a figment of my imagination?! Wait, wait! I'm getting paranoid again!....

I took a deep breath, then another, and went into a patterned breathing exercise to calm my darting mind and bring it under my control. I returned to the present, and continued with the process of adjusting.

The explicit sexual activities in that incarnation, and the strong identity of femaleness they carried with them, were not the only interesting and important elements in it. There was an equally strong psychological component, an integral constituent of the personality: the loving and caring that became abundantly obvious in my role as a mother - even in my relationships with my lovers.

Although I was aware that a female cannot justifiably lay claim to loving and caring as an exclusive characteristic of her gender, having a life experience as a woman in the manner I had done had given me the opportunity to inhabit a system of feelings, thoughts, needs and attitude which appeared to spring from a source that showed a predilection for the female nature in regards to expressing love, care and service. At times, it felt sacrificial. Whether the physical/sexual features gave rise to the psychology or vice versa, or the two were inextricably bound, feeding off and enriching each other, I could not fathom. I felt certain, however, that Yiannis would have something to say on this.

Gradually, as my initial strong reaction softened and the confusion dissipated, I began to feel a kind of elation - for want of another word - in which I had the sense of being cocooned and looked after, of living in happy abandonment, without worries, in the secure knowledge that I 'belonged' and was guided and protected. This was a far cry from the loneliness 'promised' me by old Yiannis on different occasions and in a variety of ways. But then....

A boatload of tourists raised a hell of a cheer as they passed by on their way to the beach. They brought me back. Yiannis was now sitting a couple of metres away, looking at me, observing me.

"Well?" he said, with relaxed anticipation.

"Well what?" was my response.

I sensed he was expecting a report but I had questions to ask instead: How was it that I had the experience of a whole lifetime in minute detail in the space of seconds? How was it that, while living in a past incarnation, I had 'memories' of a future one? How was it that I had experienced a complete incarnation totally disconnected from my present consciousness? What was the relevance of femaleness in the life of a man and in the wider scheme of things? What was the 'real' nature of sex? What--?

"One shock at a time," he interrupted the flow of my mental questioning. "Another time. We'll discuss all these things another time." He looked at me and offered me one of his cheeky smiles again. "Now, answer me this - and be careful what you say lest the fate of Teiresias befalls you, too: who enjoys the greatest sexual pleasure, a man or a woman?"

I did not expect this kind of question, and I could not see its relevance. He didn't seem to be interested in my other concerns at that moment. Was he making light of the situation - as usual? My immediate response would have been "a woman", but I hesitated. The sexual pleasure I'd had with Helen was, well, just as great. Or was it? A tad less? Debatable. There were other dimensions to that experience - but the same would apply to my sexual experiences as a woman. Would it? There were additional aspects to being a woman that enhanced sexual pleasure to beyond anything a man would imagine. Definitely a woman, then. Ah, but what about poor old Teiresias. I must be careful here.

Teiresias was an ancient Greek priest, a good man, beloved of the gods. One day, Zeus and his wife Hera became embroiled in a heated argument each asserting that their opposite gender enjoyed sex more than their own. To resolve the ensuing impasse, they decided on changing Teiresias, the devout priest, into a woman, allowing him to have a normal life in his new gender, then reinstating him to his original gender and asking him to report in which gender he had had the best sex.

Teiresias, innocently and truthfully, reported that he enjoyed sex much more as a woman than as a man - an answer which invited the wrath of Hera who blinded him for daring to disagree with her. Zeus, then, taking pity on the poor man, endowed him with the gift of second sight and turned him into an oracle to compensate for the loss of his physical sight.

I weighed the odds for a while and then decided to assuage my concerns by treating the Teiresias story as just that, a story - without consequences for telling the truth.

"Promise I won't go blind?" I joked.

"Physical blindness is the least of your worries," he said, putting on a serious face.

"What?!"

He chuckled in his usual manner. "You've missed the point," he said, shaking his head. "There are two processes involved here: the blinding and the gaining of second sight."

He stared at me waiting for the penny to drop. I stared back blankly.

"Go back to your experiences earlier today with the girl - to Eve and Aphrodite. And think of attachment, physical and psychological, of the universal and the particular. It will help you make a start. Meditate on it. We'll talk about it later." He passed me my bundle.

"When?"

"Later. In the afternoon. As we said."

"Yes, but what time?" I wasn't prepared to hang around Bob's restaurant for the rest of the day.

"Ah, time, time. Another of your obsessions." He sounded disappointed. "Alright, I'll give you a time. How about three o'clock?"

At last! I got him to commit to an exact time - none of that loose 'afternoon' talk.

"Good. Great. I'll be there." I got up to go. "Ehm. How do I get off this island?"

"The same way you got on it."

"Surely, there must be a better way."

He shrugged his shoulders.

"How about you, how are you getting off this place?" I inquired.

"I don't know. I haven't thought about it yet." It was obvious he wasn't going to help.

I walked to the edge of the water and looked around for a possibly better way than the one I had used. (I noticed, incidentally, that the little octopus Yiannis had caught earlier wasn't anywhere to be seen - he must have put it back in the water when I was 'out', or, perhaps, caused it to dematerialise! (?)).

"Why don't you walk across - *on* the water?" he teased. "All you need is sustained accurate visualisation, unwavering attention, and total conviction." He was teasing alright, but he was also reminding me of basic training requirements - which he knew I fell short of. "Ah, and bring a small battery torch with you; don't forget."

A battery torch? What for? This was new, he hadn't mentioned this on the hill. Eh, well, I wasn't going to stop and inquire. I said "Okay." I'd have to go and buy one.

In the end, I decided to return the same way I'd come: wading through and swimming. I was up to my knees in the water when he called out to ask me if I spoke Turkish! I said I had a smattering, and turned to find out why he wanted to know.

"Güle, güle," he said, and began to walk away, towards the other side of the island, before I had a chance to say anything else to him.

"Güle, güle," I muttered to myself. Why start speaking Turkish all of a sudden? One thing I was certain about, he wouldn't have done so unless he was alluding to something, or providing me with a clue. A clue to what? I would have to apply the 'knock and wait' procedure: concentrating hard and long and then letting go. Later.

I managed to cross to the mainland with my clothes and beach towel bone dry. I thanked my few holiday-making fans for their clapping and cheering, and set about deciding what to do next.

My tatty sandals needed changing and a battery torch had to be purchased. That meant getting back to the village and returning as soon as possible. Then, I would stay close to Bob's place until three o'clock - swimming, meditating, analysing, and organising and trying to unravel the 'Turkish' puzzle and make sense of the day's events so far.

In order to get to the village I had to walk back to Bob's for the small ferry. As soon as I started walking, I heard Athespodos growling. It was a distinct growl-bark I could not mistake. It came from around the 'donkey stand' - the spot where the donkeys for the rides to the lemon groves were stationed. I looked but couldn't see him. I went to the donkey stand and checked around. I could hear him but could not see him. As I didn't want to waste time, I headed for Bob's, with Athespodos' growling following me from the donkey stand. I made a mental note to investigate this weird phenomenon as soon as I'd finished with the other, more important, items on my list.

In the village, I bought a new pair of sandals and a small pocket-size battery torch, and returned to Bob's place, and from there I went down to the beach - equipped with a couple of sandwiches and a bottle of water from Bob's restaurant. Passing by the donkey stand - opposite the small island - on the way to and from the village, I had heard Athespodos' growl-bark again loud and clear, but still I could not see him. I would definitely have to investigate.

The beach was crowded, so I made for the doughnut hole. I could swim and rest there for a while. But it was occupied by two couples. I turned round and walked up the hill towards where Yiannis the Baptist had sat the previous day shaking his hand and swearing. I found an old olive tree and sat under it, leaning against its ancient trunk, surrounded by thyme and origanum and other dried up fragrant bushes. It was moving up to midday and soon the tourists would be disappearing back to their hotels to get away from the hot sun.

I had a clear view of the whole beach from up there, with Bob's restaurant at one end and the small mound at the right end, behind which stood the rock with the doughnut hole. I could also see the small island in the distance. I wondered if Yiannis was still there, and how he would get off it - if he hadn't already done so. By walking on the water? I shouldn't wonder!

I decided to stay up there for a while, and reflect and meditate on some of the events that had taken place and the issues which had come up. Besides the latest, that is, the female incarnation, the episode with the Dutch family and my encounter with Helen, there was also the more general subject of time which cut through all the above - and the way it kept cropping up in all manner of warped, 'condensed' and twisted ways, ever since my first meeting with old shaman Yiannis at the rock.

I had begun to reflect on these matters, trying to decide which one to deal with first, when the opening bars of Beethoven's fifth symphony came back unexpectedly and with a rage, demanding my attention: ba ba ba baaaam! ba ba ba baaaam! As on the previous occasion, I couldn't see the relevance. Was there some sort of conditioning, perhaps, so that whenever one thing happened another followed? I searched in that direction but, again, there was nothing obvious.

I went into patterned breathing and examined the music itself. Was it the key? No. Was it the development, the inversions, the transpositions...?...ehm... There was something there but I was not able to put my finger on it...ehm... No, Bach was much better at this; and yet there was some connection there. I went back to the opening: the theme, the first five bars, the clarinets and the strings, then the strings further developing it... No, no.

I remembered Yiannis pointing out the opening rest and the first four notes, and also saying that the piece had been specifically picked for me because of my fondness for it... Ah, it was a personal kind of message - a philosophical one (?). Of course! - not so much the music as the philosophy. Now, this required a very different approach.

I let myself drift into it, veering gently away from the strictly musical aspect and leading into the abstract: the rest, the four notes, the development...the rest, the four notes, the development... Those opening bars!... They came back again and again, like a broken record, and louder and louder! Then, the rest again! A rest filled with silence - like a pregnant pause....

That was it! That rest was not an empty rest: it was full, full and waiting, full and ready to burst. Minute, insignificant, timeless - not a rest between notes, but a rest with nothing preceding it, out of nowhere, out of nothing. Yes! Out of Nothing! Non-existence! Full and ready to burst - and it burst: into three short notes (quavers) followed by a long one (minim) - the latter being of the same length as the opening rest and the first three notes taken together, with a musical sign placed above it (fermata) signifying dramatic lengthening of the note!...

Time that stretched, that was suspended... And then the development.... Here was creation - Existence out of Nothing.... I was taken back to my teenage years, to my experience with numbers, to one (as zero/rest), to one (as two), and so on. The first bar contained both Non-existence and Existence, the latter further represented by the second bar of a longer, sustained, lower note, establishing and consolidating Creation... The fourth note - solid, grounded Existence.... And, then, the opening theme cropping up throughout the symphony, returning to the Beginning, as if 'going back'... Pythagorean numbers and sounds....?

A trick of the mind? Perhaps. Beethoven didn't have me in mind when he wrote this, and he hadn't been philosophising either, as far as I knew. Yiannis was picking up on my obsessions and finding ways to entice me into experiences and types of understanding that I hadn't always been open to. He knew I would fall into this kind of analysis, and he knew how I would react and absorb the 'message'. Wasn't this in the same vein as my 'being sent' to drama school in order to enhance the activities of my solar plexus centre, as the Teacher had put it? And that advice to "go back" nearly always tacked on to the end of my inquiries.

Ah, now I was really beginning to see. The female incarnation, for instance, besides the many other layers of experience and comprehension it had provided, also introduced me to, and induced in me, a state of existence and understanding which had been far apart from my normal male approach and way of viewing life.

Was it an actual past incarnation of mine? The moment I posed that question, I heard Yiannis laughing and throwing at me his wellworn response: "Is it relevant?" The exposition he had given me up on the hill regarding the distinction between incarnations that were mine and those that were not but which I could - one could - experience at will and in detail once a certain level of ability had been achieved, was falling into place. Why should I be concerned with the question of whether that particular incarnation was mine or not? All incarnations could be mine, and yours, and his, and hers.

I'd had the experience so totally and completely that the question was, indeed, not relevant. At the time, I *was* a woman, cut off from my present consciousness. I was happy being a female, all the way from childhood to old age. I, as present consciousness, felt enormously enriched, not only for having been a woman but also for gaining insights into what would be called femaleness - insights which had begun to impinge on my awareness during my time with

Helen at the Cove of Love and which culminated at the incarnation as a woman. Interestingly, as I noted when I was still on the small island, this hadn't been the first time I'd had experiences and insights into femaleness from past incarnations, but those had all been snippets and they had always been viewed from the perspective of my present consciousness.

Was it an actual incarnation or a construction erected by Yiannis for my benefit? I received a similar reaction to my question: "Is it relevant?" If an experience had been so pervasive, so whole, why should it matter whether it had been an incarnation or a construction? After all, what was an incarnation if not a mere construction that enabled us to gain individuality through 'living' it, like all other experiences? And I did live this particular one.

Yiannis' dipping my head into the water was partly an in-joke, playing on the story of the wise man and his disciple - which he had drawn my attention to on the hilltop - but also a shamanistic trick: by nearly drowning me, he had forced both my body and mind into a condition of fear and struggle, a vulnerable situation conducive to an altered state of consciousness. What's more, I was now convinced that his pressing the top of my spine and my throat in the manner he had done was the cause of that weird sexual pleasure I had felt - a factor that had thrown me off balance even more. Was that strange, momentary, pleasure connected with the switching of genders, I wondered; and I could feel Yiannis' discarnate smile floating around me cheekily at the thought.

Time. Time and memory. Confusing - and very intriguing. When I was on my deathbed in the 'female incarnation', my whole life flashed before me - backwards. On the hilltop, Yiannis offered me encouragement by saying that I was on the right track, and drew my attention to the way I had recounted the events of my day - backwards. In the Pythagorean schools of antiquity, the disciples were required, on retiring at night, to review the events of their day - backwards. And the same discipline was required of the Teacher's 'brothers' and 'sisters'.

Remembering backwards. Unravelling the linear, unidirectional, continuity of time. Breaking and reversing the continuum. "Go back", was Yiannis' mantra. Could it, also, have meant "go backwards?" - as if the process, by being reversed, placed, what had become the future, at the very beginning, turning it into the cause of the past? Not in the normal sense of the word 'cause' but more in the sense of 'purpose', or 'final' cause, as Aristotle would have put it - the form and shape of a tree, for example, 'causing' the seed to unfold it.

Years earlier, I had been impressed by how old people seemed to possess a much better long term memory compared to their short term one - they couldn't remember what they had for breakfast but could recall in detail a childhood experience. This prompted me to initiate an exercise that would, I believed, enable me to "go back" to my birth. Using as cues information I had garnered from my parents and other relatives, I embarked on a journey to discover the exact time of my birth, which mother could not recall, and nobody had taken the trouble to record. I was surprised by the ease with which I had arrived at the precise time - a time which was later agreed by all concerned that 'must' have been correct.

However, what I had not foreseen was the way in which the process I had initiated would take over and carry on beyond my control. I found myself re-entering the birth canal and diminishing in size to the extent that I was not aware any longer of inhabiting a body. I was simply conscious that I existed.

'I' drifted into what felt like a waterfall - I was in the middle of a column of a moving indefinable substance in which flowed, as in a waterfall, a succession of prehistoric creatures. They were flowing by me and through me and I was feeling an affinity with them. And there were plants and trees flowing in a similar manner. At some point, I became aware of myself being a form of life that resembled a plant, with a stem for a body and a flower for a head.

Revisiting this experience, I wondered how far it had gone in fulfilling Yiannis' advice to "go back". It certainly qualified as being, at least, part of the search.

In his response to my query regarding my experiences in the doughnut hole, Yiannis had not confirmed their veracity outright but had indicated that I should look at certain 'locations' in order to decide their status - 'locations' such as my heart, my solar plexus, my spleen, my liver, etc, even my arse! This I could see now revealing all sorts of connections in terms of time and levels of communication.

On examination, I could see how active my solar plexus centre had been when I was dealing with the crab, how delicate emotions and intuitive understanding seemed to localise themselves in the area around my heart, how, in dealing with 'knowing' and 'understanding', I was practically lost in my head.... And in experiences outside the hole I could now identify the activities of certain 'locations': the genitals, solar plexus, heart and head during my time with Helen, my neck, heart and genitals when Yiannis pushed my head into the water, my whole spine when dealing with the sceptre/walking stick at Yianna's, and so on.

The sequences of events in all these experiences carried a sense of timelessness, the kind experienced by a child involved in an absorbing activity. During the actual experiences, events appeared mostly to transpire in 'real' time - sequential, that is - although in terms of physical time they occupied only seconds, if that. Activities in these 'locations' also revealed a predilection for affinities with certain life forms: animals and plants, for instance, seemed to be more connected with activities of the solar plexus centre.

Concerning the meaning and sense of time, Yiannis had also suggested I should consider the opening of Beethoven's fifth again. That I had done, and I could now see that reversing the sequence, going backwards to the Beginning, I was touching that split moment between Existence and Non-existence, a no-man's land where time and space were....were not.... were.... were not.... Was this what the old shaman was advising me to do? Beethoven's fifth was like a parable: I had to distill the meaning by means of my own understanding. These were exercises for my own benefit, he had said, and I shouldn't go back to him with my solutions. Would I not?!

Deep into my meditations as I was, I heard Athespodos' growl again. It was distant but very distinct, although I couldn't detect where it was coming from. But it definitely brought me out of the state I was in. I noticed that the crowd on the beach was thinning out. Two small ferries had arrived to evacuate the rest of the roasted tourists who were lazily wending their way to the small docking area next to Bob's restaurant. I looked at my wrist watch and realised I didn't have enough time for the swim I had planned. It was just gone two o'clock, and I wanted to be ready for Yiannis.

I walked down to Bob's place where his nephew was taking care of the last few customers - very efficiently, by the look of things - and asked if there was a chance of having a shower around there. He said there was a tap and a hose out the back and I was welcome to it. I thanked him and availed myself of it - cool and refreshing. I dried myself and put my clothes on, and I was making my way back to the courtyard when I heard Athespodos' growl-bark again.

This time round, it sounded much closer and more persistent. I could tell it was coming from a place opposite the small island, the donkey stand - the same spot it had come from earlier, when I had passed by in the boat to and from the village. I walked to the edge of the restaurant courtyard, right by the sea, and gazed in that direction. I was right, it did come from there: a dog was pacing up and down excitedly (with anticipation?) and barking his head off.

He sounded very much like Athespodos, although I couldn't identify him visually with absolute certainty from that distance. I glanced at my watch. There was time. I could walk over and investigate. It was only two or three hundred metres away. In any case, Yiannis wasn't anywhere to be seen beyond Bob's place, and if he were to come from the village or the small island I would see him.

I hastened to get there, walking as fast as I could on the uneven, stoney, beach. When I was about one hundred metres away, I saw the mongrel - definitely Athespodos - walk off the beach and towards the donkey stand, which was just out of my view. He continued to bark but when I got there I couldn't find him. There was a short stretch of a low wall where he could have hidden but, again, he was not there either. And still I could hear him; he was growling, and he sounded as if he were inside the wall! I turned to the middle-aged woman in charge of the donkeys and asked her if she'd just seen a dog near there.

"Yes," she said. "He was here a minute ago. He pissed on the post and cleared off," she elaborated, pointing at a wooden post which was attached to the wall and carried a sign with the name of a restaurant and an arrow indicating the direction to it. The restaurant itself sat at a prominent position on the mountainside, at the top end of the lemon groves, and had long been established as the destination of the donkey-riding tourists who journeyed up there for a meal and the view.

"But he's still around," I said to the woman. "Can't you hear him?"

She gave me a side look as if to say that I needed either my ears checked or my sanity. Clearly, she could not hear him, and I did not think it a good idea to challenge her. I stood there staring at the signpost and listening to Athespodos' growling. Why was I staring at a piece of wood where a dog had urinated? I looked up at the sign in order to divert the woman's attention from my preoccupation.

The moment I cast my eyes on the sign, Athespodos' growl-bark nearly blasted my ear drums. I was immobilised, and kept staring at the sign. It read: "Kardasee's restaurant", in Greek. I'd seen it before, when I'd gone up to the restaurant a few days earlier. There was, however, something unusual about it on this occasion. I read it again, but my reading of it was a little different from what was written on the board. And, suddenly, it struck me! Of course! That was it! I wasn't going to meet Yiannis at Bob's restaurant - *this* was the place! And Athespodos' growling ceased abruptly.

The name on the sign was a Greek rendering of the Turkish word *kardes* which meant 'brother'! I was flooded by a rush of certainty. Athespodos' barking and growling around the spot made sense now, and so did Yiannis' unexpected interest in the Turkish language. I must have appeared extremely thick to both of them.

"The Brother's restaurant" said on the board. Why the Turkish for brother? Nothing unusual there. The Turks had occupied Greece for four hundred years and a number of Turkish words had inevitably seeped into the Greek language - much to the consternation of various contemporary Greek purists.

I checked my watch again: it was two thirty. Too close for comfort. The woman in charge of the donkeys gave me a dismissive glance, shook her head, and turned to tend to her animals. My unexpected realisation that I had finally found the answer to Yiannis' puzzle had come with a sudden jerk of my body and a pronounced intake of air, and the woman, justifiably perhaps, thought my behaviour a bit peculiar. In an attempt to modify her opinion of me, I explained that I needed to get to Kardasee's restaurant by three o'clock but that I did not want to run in the heat of the day.

"Take a donkey," she said, seeing an opportunity for business.

"Donkeys are slow going uphill. I can walk faster than a donkey," I said, falling back on past experience.

"Not faster than this one," she retorted, pointing to a small donkey that didn't look like it could carry the weight of a young child.

"Are you sure?" I querried.

"Am I sure? Of course I'm sure," she responded boastfully. "Look!" she added with determination, and whipped the animal violently with the stick she was carrying.

The poor thing jumped out of its skin and raced up the path. I was furious. I felt like grabbing the stick out of her hand and giving her a hefty taste of her own medicine. But just then a bunch of tourists turned up to hire the donkeys for the journey to the restaurant, and the situation changed. I couldn't afford any delays, so I agreed to hire the small animal. The woman's routine was to hire the donkeys and walk alongside them to the restaurant and back.

We set off, but less than halfway up the lemon groves I couldn't continue riding the poor thing: he was sagging under my modest weight and my dangling feet were almost touching the ground. I could feel the great effort he was making to carry me up the uneven winding path. I dismounted and walked along beside it. The woman shook her head again and glanced at me with a carping smile.

"You're not getting your money back, you know," she said. "No refund."

I shrugged my shoulders and dismissed her silly comment.

We arrived at the restaurant at five minutes past three. It was quiet. The owner came out to greet us and apologise that no meals were being served at that time of the day; we could have soft drinks and coffee and some home-made cakes. There were no other customers around. Yiannis was not there either. I asked the man about him but he simply opened his arms and swang them slowly around to show me the empty place. I sat down and ordered coffee and cake and wondered if I'd missed him - I was only five minutes late.

Then, there he was, coming down a path that led up from the restaurant and into the mountain. He was carrying a small traditional leather bag over one shoulder.

"You've made it," he said, and sat at my table.

"Only just," I sighed with relief.

The woman with the donkeys was sorting out her animals at one end of the courtyard and preparing to bring water to them.

"Is he with you, then?" she asked Yiannis, indicating with her head in my direction.

"Not if I can help it. Has he been misbehaving again?" he asked with a put-on strictness.

"Weird. You need to watch him," she said, and went back to shaking her head.

"Why? What has he done?"

"He paid for the animal and then walked alongside it all the way - not to mention going around checking on dogs' piss and hearing dogs barking in his head."

The old man burst out laughing. "Is that all? That's nothing. I thought you were going to say he carried the donkey on his back."

"Well, I wouldn't have put it past him," she said, and bent down to pick up a small blanket which had fallen off the back of one of the animals.

And that's when it happened. The donkey standing on her left kicked her. Right in her left forearm. There was a clear, loud, snap as the bone broke in two. She screamed and swore at the animal. Everybody rushed to help her. Yiannis, too, stood up, said a calm "Oh, dear," and went over to her. I was probably the only one left sitting. I was almost paralysed by a strange feeling of guilt that swept over me as the bone snapped. I felt her pain and her anger, and the anger of the donkey that kicked her. It was as if we formed a triangle at the moment of the kick: I, the woman, and the animal.

I saw Yiannis pulling apart the two sections of the broken bone and then bringing them together to join. He asked for two pieces of wood to make a splint and a piece of cloth or string to hold them round the injured arm. The woman continued to issue unmentionable expletives mixed with appeals to Virgin Mary for help. Yiannis was cool, impersonal, occasionally telling her to pipe down and go easy with her cursing. When he had finished, he advised her to get on a donkey and go to see the village doctor right away. It was a real spectacle to see that arrogant woman cowering and following his advice in the end.

"You should be ashamed of yourself!" he reprimanded me as he resumed his seat opposite me at the table.

"Why? What have I done?" I retorted, naturally surprised at this sudden and undefined accusation.

"You know very well what you've done: you broke the woman's arm."

What? It was the donkey, not me. I had nothing to do with.... He was staring at me with scolding eyes. It began to dawn on me: the feeling of guilt, the connection with both the woman and the animal....

"You should've known better - you are not supposed to go around shooting angry thoughts and nasty intentions at people," he explained. His voice was clear and firm.

I knew what he was talking about: my anger at the woman when she beat the donkey and my thought of hitting her back - and it was in her left hand she held the stick, and it was the left arm she had broken! Proof enough of my guilt (?). He was perfectly right: I shouldn't have thought those thoughts and projected those intentions. I should've known better - thoughts, desires, intentions are real things, substantial and effective packets of energy, always effective.

"In a way, she's been lucky. Had your anger and intentions been coupled with a more pointed attention, you might have killed her," he concluded.

I was shocked. I'd never hurt anybody 'intentionally' - but, then, intentions vary according to degree, ranging from fully conscious to totally unconscious.

"And your visualisation leaves much to be desired," he added, completing an interim report on my abilities. Anything else?

"And wipe the guilt off your heart."

I was about to open my mouth to speak but he stopped me.

"And don't apologise. Don't waste energy." And then, by way of explaining, as if to attenuate his trenchant language, he added: "She was ripe for it." And he smiled. "But don't think for a moment that you're let off."

Yes. I should acknowledge my error and be more careful with my reactions in the future. And make amends. But how?

"You've already started. You're more sympathetic to animals."

"What about the woman?"

"What about her?"

"Shouldn't I be doing something to help her, seeing that I was responsible--?"

"No, no, leave her alone," he interrupted. "Disconnect from her."

That was another surprise - disconnect? But I was now more interested in *his* behaviour. I wanted to know why he did not even attempt to heal her; and what did he mean by saying she was ripe for it?

"She's been building into her character unpleasant habits, nasty thoughts and intentions, for quite a while. How else do you think she had responded to *your* thoughts and intentions? Remember: like attracts like. I would not try to heal her the way you expected me to.

It wouldn't have worked. And I would be interfering too much. She was not ready."

The restaurant owner arrived with my coffee and cake. I asked Yiannis if he would like anything from the restaurant but he politely declined.

"Don't eat that," he said, as soon as the man left. "I don't want you to be sick."

"Be sick, why?" I asked, looking suspiciously at the cake.

"Never mind. I'll explain later," he said, and stood up decisively. "You can take the cake with you, if you like. Let's go."

I couldn't make out what this cake business was about. But it looked enticing. I went inside to pay and have the cake wrapped in a piece of paper. When I came out, Yiannis was already walking away, up towards the path from where he had come. I quickened my step to catch up with him. The woman was on a donkey and practically on her way down the lemon groves. As I passed close by her, she glanced at me: there was a tangible cry for help on her face. My heart went out to her.

15

At the Old Cypress Tree
(On Unconditional Love: an Exercise)

"No remorse," Yiannis whispered loudly to me. "Don't indulge. Let's go."

"Where are we going?" I asked, and fell in behind him, as the path was too narrow to walk in double file.

"Not far. Just up ahead."

It was a two hundred metre winding hike up the mountain. There were no lemon groves in this area. The orchards were filled with vegetable beds, pomegranate and pear trees, and hedged in with rose bushes. And there was the occasional vineyard, sprawled decoratively round the undulating folds of the mountainside. Farther out was wilderness. I'd been up there before, and had sat under the enormous cypress tree to enjoy the panoramic view and meditate. And that was where Yiannis was leading me to. Although I was dying to talk to him, to try and get answers to my host of questions, I managed to keep quiet, enjoying the hike and absorbing the beauty of the surroundings.

"You might've told me this was where you were taking me," I said, sounding a tad disappointed, as we stood under that splendid specimen of a tree.

"Taking you where did you say?"

"Here."

"Oh, no, this is a temporary stop. We can stay here only for a while."

"And then, where to?"

"A bit farther up," he said casually, indicating with his head in a general direction up the mountain. "Let us sit and enjoy the view for a few minutes. May we use your beautiful blue towel to sit on?" he teased.

"By all means. Be my guest."

I swept the ground with my feet and laid the towel down in the shade of the tree. We sat facing the lemon groves and the sea in the distance. It was the same spot I had sat in days earlier, and a feeling of comfort and familiarity began to envelop me.

"May I speak, or do you simply want to enjoy the view?" I inquired.

"By all means. Be my guest," he quipped, copying my earlier response. And then, as an aside: "Do you ever do anything else?" He sneaked a smile.

I ignored the friendly snipe. I wanted to ask him about the torch and the cake but changed my mind.

"You said I might have killed that woman if my attention was more pointed."

"Yes...?"

"I take it *you* could?"

"Why should I?"

"Hypothetically speaking."

"No - such hypothesis is impossible."

"What?"

"I am incapable of hurting anybody."

"You mean, you're not so inclined."

"No. I mean I cannot. It is not possible for me."

"Ehm. I don't understand."

He looked up at the light blue sky and then down across the lemon groves and the deep blue sea.

"You're not enjoying the view," he said, in a half-jesting attempt to digress.

"The view will still be there. Please."

He deliberated for a beat or two before he spoke. "It's part of consciousness development."

"What is?"

"The non-hurting. It's a stage." We were sitting less than a metre away from each other. He turned to face me. "There comes a time when you lose the need, or tendency, to attack - or, even, defend yourself - in order to survive. You don't need to. The fear is gone," he said.

"What do you do when someone tries to harm you?"

"Nothing."

"Nothing?"

"Kind of."

I leant back and stared at him. I didn't say anything. I waited for him to elaborate.

"As I said, it's a stage. There are many stages." He stopped and glanced at the sea and then turned back to me. "How do you get rid of bad habits, of negative elementals?"

"By dwelling on positive ones, and ignoring, starving the negative ones of energy-attention."

"Good. It's a similar process."

He was not being explicit enough.

"But you still haven't told me how doing nothing is going to help you if someone is out to hurt you?"

"But nobody wants to hurt me."

I felt he was being deliberately economical with his responses, and was beginning to frustrate me.

"What about Yiannis the Baptist, then?"

He burst out into another one of his laughs.

"Yiannis the Baptist. I like the nickname. Poor chap. How could you possibly think he wants to hurt me?"

"He was very clearly angry yesterday, very threatening. And he intends to take you to court."

"Empty threats; I told you. He shouts from a distance. He never really intends doing anything. He is getting things off his chest. I'm not his problem."

He saw from my frowning reaction that his explanation hadn't gone far enough to satisfy my inquiry.

"Look, it's like kicking at stones when you get angry or frustrated. The man is obsessive, a control freak, what people now call anal retentive. He wants his rock and he chases everyone off it."

He saw me smiling and asked me why. I told him about the tourists I'd seen in the rock earlier and the scene I'd imagined with the Baptist. Would he get them out of there? Of course he would; tourists were there to enjoy themselves, they wouldn't want to ruin their holidays by fighting unnecessarily.

"He can't get rid of you, though, can he?" I poked a little.

"No, he can't. Too much light."

"What?"

He smiled and gazed at a passenger ship in the far distance before turning back to me.

"Stay with me and try and see this by the direct method. Take a deep breath."

I followed his instructions and went into patterned breathing.

"Now, you asked me what would I do if someone wanted to hurt me and I said 'nothing, kind of.' I also said that 'nobody wants to hurt me'. Let me unpack these statements while you follow the un-ravelling both by perceiving their unfolding logic and their internal status.

"Consciousness development, after a certain stage, requires the total abandoning of everything negative and the expanding of every-thing positive. It's a two-pronged process. You do it externally by constant checking and controlling of your thoughts, emotions, inten-tions, desires and so on, and internally by exercises of conscious-ness expansion. You know the theory of these things and some of the practice, but not all of it. You've had glimpses, but they have been short and temporary. In *constant* consciousness expansion, you experience everything and everybody as part of you, they are *literally* part of you."

While he was talking I was having a 'psycho-perceptual' experi-ence of the content of his explanation. It started with revisiting my experience up there a few days earlier, only now it was greatly en-hanced by Yiannis' presence. To this were added the 'creative en-tities' I had encountered on the hilltop - they brought a powerful sense of service and love of what they were doing; and, again, that wonderful feeling of the lack of a sense of sacrifice, even though all their work was being carried out 'through' their bodies.

And then, I 'saw' the same process taking place in Yiannis - and in me! The love of service, quiet service, unobtrusive. There was an almost abstract-impressionistic perception of innumerable things and people inside me. I saw the Baptist face to face with Yiannis. But the relationship was different now. Yiannis was a Body of Light and the Baptist couldn't get anywhere near him - too much light!

His reaction, however, was not hostile, more of puzzlement - and the mere suspicion of understanding, of relaxing, a chink of light entering the armour of the man's obsessiveness. Yiannis' doing 'nothing, kind of' was a psychological game, a technique, to help the man 'see the light'. And while the man was standing facing Yiannis, a 'duplicate' of him was also inside the old shaman!

"When everybody is part of you, you cannot possibly want to hurt them, and vice versa. When you are fully projecting, radiating, this knowledge through your whole being, nobody would want to hurt you - they, instinctively, subconsciously, know their relationship with you. What you feel in this state is pure, unadulterated, unconditional love for everything and everybody."

As he spoke those words, I was, once again, inundated by the joy and bliss that came with them. More powerful now than anytime before. I thought I was about to pass out when I felt him 'pulling' me down, out of that marvellous state.

"As I said: now and then you get glimpses - continuity of expanded consciousness comes later," he remarked, as I began my struggle to readjust to everyday 'reality'. "Now, go back. A bit. Stay on the border."

It was a balancing act, and not easy to maintain, but afforded an understanding of the two sides. Actually, they were not two sides, only the one, but a graded one. And there were many gradations, the physical being just one of them.

"Do unto others as you would have them do unto you."

He spoke those words as if reciting from a page - cool, unemotional. Nothing else. And waited. He gave them to me as a *koan*. To study them, to understand them. They were not strange or contradictory like a *koan*, but I could feel his intention to view them as contradictory.

On the face of it, they constituted a good moral admonition: be good to people if you want them to be good to you, don't hurt people if you don't want them to hurt you... No, no. This had nothing to do with morality. It was advice for the construction of a social contract, like the concept of democracy: for the protection of people against one another. No, no. It contained too much self-centredness, it was *conditional*.

I shifted gently to 'the other side', to the expanded consciousness. And the difference was vast. Here, the enormously expanded self, ego, individual, was 'selfless'; and it had set itself up to serve - *unconditionally*. Service was the key feature, and all activity flowed from that. "Do unto others", and so on, did not feature in it. It was a stage, as Yiannis had said, an entirely natural stage of total goodness but devoid of sentimentality: natural, matter-of-fact.

I was reminded of the Teacher's admonition to "practise goodness until it became second nature to you" which, at the time, sounded like the practice of self-suggestion. But now I knew what he had meant: it was not an acquired 'second nature': it was the *real* nature of consciousness.

And now the contradiction: in that state of consciousness the individual was consumed by the burning desire to be of service, yet the service which he rendered by means of his whole being was a cool offering of himself in accordance with natural laws!

"Do you understand the *unconditional* bit now?" the old man asked, bringing me altogether back to physical reality.

"Yes, I do."

"It is important to know it in your bones, in your blood. It is essential, of the *essence* of existence. Along with memory, they are the *sine qua non* of creation. Healing, for example, proper healing, cannot be carried out without unconditional love."

"What do you mean by proper healing?"

"There are all kinds and grades of healing. You're performing a healing act every time you form a positive thought, for instance. Many so-called healers are out for themselves, either to make a quick buck or to satisfy their own psychological needs. Proper healing comprises two ingredients: unconditional love and a knowhow."

"A knowhow?"

"Yes. Knowledge of a person's bodies and how to apply the right kind of energy. Sometimes this alone is enough. Likewise, unconditional love may be sufficient. But in an expanded consciousness they always go together."

He paused, and smiled at me. I knew that smile, it was an expectant smile, a prompt. All those explanations concerning healing, and the experience of unconditional love and service... He sounded so much like the Teacher.

"Okay. I'll do it," I announced, all of a sudden.

"Do what?"

"Healing, of course. In full consciousness. Not just sending out a vague positive thought."

"Well..." He pretended surprise.

I was raring to go. I felt the need to do just that: to be of service. Inexplicably, I also felt a curious connection with the French female incarnation!

"I know I don't qualify. My knowledge of anatomy is rudimentary, and as for loving unconditionally... And who am I to heal, anyway? But....."

"Well, this request has taken me by surprise," he continued pretending. "I don't know what to say." He, then, changed his tone, he became solemn. "You don't know what you're asking. This is serious and demanding work, and could be painful."

"Painful? Why?"

"You've said it yourself. You won't be sending out a vague positive thought. The healing will have to be done *through* you, not *by* you."

I reflected very briefly, and consented. "Okay. Who am I going to heal?"

"The woman with the broken arm, of course," came the prompt answer.

"What?!"

"Perfect case. You don't like her much - so here's you chance to practise unconditional love."

I was in it now. "Hm. I don't know where to start."

"Easy. Two things. Visualise her left arm - here, do it on your own arm, easy to build up the picture. Then expand yourself and fill her with unconditional love. Formulate your intention, and the rest will take care of itself."

It all sounded very easy the way he put it, but saying it was one thing doing it was another. Nonetheless, I began to prepare myself, and then I remembered.

"Wait a minute. If it's so easy why didn't you do it yourself down there? You said that you would be interfering too much, that she was not ready, that I should disconnect from her."

"Oh, yes. And if you believed that you'd believe anything."

"What?!"

He chortled. "I'm only pulling your leg. But you're right. She was not ready - for me. For you it's different, though. You have an affinity with her - you both have obsessions." I could see the sneer forming on his mouth. "Besides, you are the cause of her injury. You owe it to her." He was piling it on a bit thick and tugging at my chain teasingly at the same time.

I sat up straight and followed a breathing pattern for a few minutes. When I reckoned I was ready, I gazed at my left forearm for a further few minutes and then concentrated on visualising its internal anatomy: the bones, the nerves, the veins and arteries - especially around the area of the broken bone in the woman's forearm.

Then I did two things at the same time: I concentrated on the woman and opened up, expanding myself. I aimed to reach the stage

I had been in earlier. It took a while. I kept going in and out. But I got there in the end. I had the woman standing right in front of me. I felt the connection with her. She was not at the doctor's surgery. She was still riding her donkey - with Yiannis' splint secured on her forearm. I could see the pain in her face. The silly woman had decided to save money by not catching a boat to the village! The moment I thought that, I was back to square one.

"Don't criticise!" I heard Yiannis whisper loudly. "Just do it. Be a conduit. Keep out personal feelings."

I started from scratch. This time, I began by inundating myself with joy and love - it was easy, sitting up there with all that beauty of nature spreading out before me. I raised the joyful energy from the base of my spine and took it through my solar plexus and my heart. I sensed Yiannis was helping me out, guiding me. I realised that the approach in this second attempt was better, more appropriate. I did not even need to visualise the woman's forearm, it simply happened: I could see the break and what needed to be done.

But then, unexpectedly, I was presented with two alternative ways of conducting the healing. The first one required concentrating and directing energy into the break - energy which floated around in nature and in the woman's body and in mine. The whole activity hinged on will-power, my will-power. I could do it. It called up past experiences of will-application.

The second way of healing, like the first, called for concentration and direction of energy, but my will-power had to be diverted and subjugated to something universal, to a will that was communal and superseded my own personal will, a will which I experienced as unconditional love: will-powered pervasive love. I had never thought of love as powered by will - on the contrary, I always considered love as yielding and passive. Yes, it was yielding and passive but at a deeper level it was will-powered - a will that held Existence together.

The choice was mine; but it was not a real choice. I knew I had to abandon the first alternative: that was the old, 'personal', application of will. I plunged for the second and gave myself to the task. I expanded as consciousness and concentrated and felt the energy pouring through me and into the woman's forearm. I could see the healing taking place: the bone was mending as in a speeded-up cinematic film.

And then the pain hit me. It was excruciating. The whole of my left forearm hurt, particularly at the point where the woman's forearm had been broken. I ignored the pain and managed to control it, and it seemed to dissipate for a short while. But then it returned. And I felt sick, about to vomit. I persisted, but at the fourth attempt I could not bear it any longer. I was back at my usual self. The pain was still there in my forearm but dull.

"You asked for it," said Yiannis, offering me a comforting smile.

"Yes, I did," I agreed, not entirely certain as to who had initiated this activity. "But you coaxed me into it."

"Maybe. But you're the one who started it, you're the one who called," he retorted. "You may not remember. You need to go back to previous incarnations. A powerful call is always answered - when the time is right. You may not have called *me* in particular, but that's neither here nor there." He was widening the issue, and giving it a much longer, and deeper, perspective. I took the point.

"Was it a failure?" I inquired, rubbing my hurting forearm.

"There are no failures in this game," he responded.

A game? What was I - a masochist?

"You threw yourself in at the deep end," he continued, "at a very deep end. But, as the old saying goes, no sailor learns his craft in calm waters." He was not answering my question.

"How successful was it, then?" I persisted.

"First of all, you must learn not to ask such questions. They betray self-interest, they are contrary to unconditional love and service. You should not be concerned with results." I understood what he was saying. And then he relented. "But for the sake of a better understanding you need to know the various factors involved."

I prepared myself to take down a list.

"The person to be healed may not be ready: too many elementals creating strong habits and an unyielding personality, and making it difficult for physical injuries to heal - not to mention causing such injuries in the first place.

"And then it's the law of retribution, too complex to go into right now.

"Next, the level of the healer's abilities: concentration, visualisation, knowhow, capacity for unconditional love and service.

"And then it's pain. Usually a sign that the bodies of the person are not functioning as they should: the causes vary - external injury, psychological, also known as psychosomatic, retribution."

He paused, looked me straight in the eye, and added: "But it can also be a function of unconditional love."

He moved closer to me and touched my left forearm. "This is a gift to you, your badge of unconditional love," he said, and I could feel the love pouring out of his whole being; I shivered with joy.

"Is it always like this?" I asked.

"What, the pain?"

"Yes."

"No, not always. But you'll learn. She's a difficult case, and you willed it too much. You're taking on her pain - well, some of it. It's an honour, a reward. Wear it with love, as I'm sure you will."

He stroked my forearm gently and stood up. His stroking wasn't just a comforting or congratulatory gesture: he shared, he lifted off most of my pain.

I was almost in tears - the love, the joyful love that radiated from this unpretentious little old man was unbelievable. His love acted as a trigger on me to release a gush of corresponding feelings, although 'feelings' was not exactly the right word since he affected me similarly on emotional and intellectual levels and beyond - and physically, too: the times I felt the compulsion to hug him!

I watched him as he walked to the edge of the clearing and stood by the low dry wall that demarcated that plot of land and provided protection against falling down the three metre drop over the other side. He gazed across the tree-clad mountainside for a few seconds and then turned round and looked up and down the cypress tree a couple of times before going for his leather bag. He took out a piece of dry bread and a bottle of water with which he sprinkled the bread to moisten it a bit, and gave it to me.

"Eat it," he said, "and wash it down with a little water - not too much, just a little."

He rested the bottle on the ground, next to me. I was thirsty and hungry, and suddenly remembered the cake.

"Thanks. What about the cake?"

"Leave it for now. Eat your bread."

"Why did you stop me from eating it at the restaurant? You said it would have made me sick."

He was standing a metre or so away in front of me, and stared at me when he spoke. "Yes, it would have," he said, and continued to stare - until the penny dropped.

Of course! I would have been sick during the healing practice! Was there anything he had not planned? He'd used the word "game" earlier. Was everything just a game? He smiled at me. I took a bite of the bread: beneath the moist surface it was dry but crispy.

"Aren't you going to have some?"

"No, I don't eat," he answered casually, and moved away a little.

"But I saw you eat." I knew his statement was glaringly untrue.

"Well, I do a little, sometimes. For social reasons and to keep my alimentary canal in order." He had moved out to the low wall again.

"What do you live on, then?" I asked.

"Light."

I waited for him to elaborate but he kept looking out across to the distant sea, with his back to me. I knew that certain types of breathing practices could provide a tremendous amount of energy - I myself used some of them. I had also heard from the Teacher that at the next rung of evolution humans would be living on light, but I'd never come across anyone who would claim that to be their main source of sustenance.

"How?"

He turned round to face me.

"Through here," he said, and, lifting his right hand, he touched his forehead. "And here and here and here and here and here and here." And, with those words, he successively touched his genitals, his heart, solar plexus, throat, right shoulder and left shoulder. To an extent, the whole gesture resembled that of making the sign of the cross - with the inclusion of some additional parts of the body which would not normally be touched in a religious context!

"And here," he added, bringing the palms of his hands together, in an oriental manner, and placing them at the top of his head, like a closed clam. For a brief moment I thought I saw his hands opening, with the open palms facing me, and giving the impression of the horns of the Egyptian goddess Hathor.

"Could you be more explicit, please?"

"There isn't much to be explicit about. Everything is light. It's a matter of degree and state of functioning. You eat bread, for example, which is light, and which your physical body turns into another form of light. It's all light. All I do is bypass the process and take light directly." He looked at me as usual to see how much of what he had said was sinking in. "Come here. I'll show you," he added abruptly.

I swallowed the last bit of bread as I stood up, and walked over to him.

"Look up here," he instructed, lifting a hand about half a metre in front and above me. "Concentrate in this area," he continued, and moved his hand in a wide circular movement. He dropped his hand and waited for a couple of minutes. "What do you see?"

The sparkling, flickering, light energy had begun to fill my field of vision. I had experimented with this simple little exercise before and was convinced that everybody could do it with immediate success, but I'd never seen the energy so brilliant and so loaded with vitality on any of those other occasions. As I continued to concentrate, the silvery sparks multiplied and the air became dense with them, and they were not only in front of me but everywhere. I was surrounded, and penetrated, by a sea of light energy. I felt so very charged, energised.

"And you're not even attempting to take it in consciously. Imagine. One day." He sounded as if promising to teach me how to breathe in light through my body - one day.

"Let's sit down," he said, and sat on a clean slab next to the wall, facing in the opposite direction, with the lemon groves and the sea behind him.

I joined him on another slab beside him. We were now looking west, still in the shade, and facing the cypress tree about seven or so metres away from us. It was really enormous. It would have taken two grown men to embrace it. I saw Yiannis leaning back to take in it's whole height. It was tall, very tall.

"What do you think of it?" he asked, admiringly.

I leant back and looked at it. It stood there tall, upright, motionless, like a gigantic exclamation mark, its rich, heavy, foliage and scores of small cones quiescent in the lull of mid-afternoon. The birds in it were silent, too, resting away from the sun and the heat.

Cypress trees and daffodils have always been associated with death and the 'nether' world. One would be hard put to find a Greek cemetery which was not adorned with cypress trees. They are dark green and solemn-looking, and when they are in clumps, they have been likened to a gathering of monks or widows clad in black - especially at dusk.

There was hardly a breeze, and the quiet was underscored by the monotonous sizz-sizzing of the cicadas. One great thing about cypress trees, and conifers in general, is the way heat brings out their wonderful health enhancing scent. It spread all around and descended on us like a balm. As I relaxed and allowed myself to be drawn into the tree, I began to sense a marvellous contradiction in its nature....

As in re-winding a cinema film, the cypress tree gradually got smaller, younger, until it was a seedling. The scene of the countryside around it was, also, different now: there were no lemon groves, no houses, no people - just wilderness. Then the tree began to grow, and, as it grew, the surroundings underwent great trasformation. Trees and bushes were cleared, and orchards replaced them. There was a sizeable natural stream running nearby which was diverted to water the cultivated areas. People came and went, had picnics under the tree, children played with its cones.

In all this time, the tree was like a backbone - everything changing while it simply grew, taller and taller. And yet, it remained the same. I could see a structure within it that dictated its growth - a blueprint of its future, something permanent and yet unfolding. Around its base not much could grow - its fallen leaves would give off their invigorating scent but their resinous content would prevent most plants from taking root. And yet, its resin was preservative. It acted like a connection between physical life and life after life - denying life to plants at its base and yet breathing out vitalising energy, and preserving with its resin.

Its tall, solid, trunk exuded dignity and confidence, quiet strength and the certainty of permanence... I became absorbed in it - literally: assimilated into its nature.

The cicadas fell silent... The whole of nature seemed to hold her breath. Nothing was moving - not even my chest: I'd breathed out, and that was it - like a freeze frame in a film. Time stood still. Time ceased to exist...Time....

"Time to get a move on," I heard Yiannis call. He was already standing and preparing to continue with the hike.

"All I said was 'what do you think of it?' not 'do an analysis of the nature of time'."

"Ah, but I would like to talk with you about time," I retorted, as I made my way to the towel.

He threw his bag over his left shoulder and began to walk.

"We'll talk about time when we talk about space," he responded.

"When?"

"Soon."

I shook the leaves and soil off the towel and folded it hurriedly under my arm as I rushed to catch up with him. I shoved the torch into my pocket and the cake, in its wrapping, into the folds of the towel - I didn't fancy the idea of spending the rest of the day on bread and water! There wouldn't have any point asking him where we were going. He would probably have said something vague, like 'Up over there'. So, I just walked quietly behind him.

We walked west, into the sun, with the sea far behind us and to our right. After a while, we veered off to our left a bit, to southwest, and right into the steeper side of the mountain. I could see a stream running down below to our right, quite a distance away. Curiously enough, although I hadn't had much to eat, I didn't feel particularly hungry; but as the terrain got rougher, I found it increasingly hard to walk in sandals. Yiannis had asked me to bring a torch (for whatever purpose) but had not seen it fit to mention hiking shoes - mind you, *he* didn't seem to have any problems with his sandals. I watched him walk through the bushes and the boulders with the ease of a mountain goat.

He kept telling me to follow the path but, for the life of me, I couldn't see any path - unless he meant 'goats' path', thin traces on the ground mostly marked by goat droppings. At a certain point, we did in fact come to a stretch of recognisable path. I breathed a sigh of appreciation. By that time he was ahead of me by ten metres or so and I saw my opportunity to catch up with him.

I hardly managed half a dozen hurried paces when this snake suddenly slithered right onto the path. I stopped in my tracks, and waited for him to pass. But the blessed thing didn't seem to be in any hurry. He stopped in the middle of the path, curled himself up nice and comfortable, raised his head and flicked his tongue in my direction. I couldn't tell whether he was poisonous or not, and I didn't want to take any chances. I called out to Yiannis. He turned back a few steps and looked to see.

"Oh, don't worry. He's harmless," he said.

But I was still not altogether comfortable with this encounter.

"What do you mean?" I asked, needing more assurance.

"He's not poisonous. He's harmless," he reassured me. "He's probably hungry. Give him something to eat."

"Give him what to eat?"

"Let him have some of your cake." He laughed.

"Cake? Do snakes eat cake?" Surely, he was having me on.

"Why not? There is egg and cheese in that cake - and, knowing Kardasee, I wouldn't be surprised if there was some other stuff attractive to omnivores in there," he said and chuckled again.

The snake turned and flicked his tongue towards Yiannis, and then turned back to me again.

"I think he's taken a shine to you," he continued to laugh.

I ignored his teasing remark. "What shall I do, then?"

"As I said, give him some cake."

I took the cake out, unwrapped it, cut a piece and threw it on the ground close to the snake. He flicked his tongue a few times but didn't care to go for it.

"See? I knew it. Snakes don't eat cake. You're just having me on," I concluded.

"No, silly. Look: would you eat it if I threw it at you?"

"What - you want me to put it in his mouth?"

"I've told you, he's harmless."

"Next thing you'll tell me he's an old acquaintance of yours."

"Of course he is."

"Why don't you give it to him yourself, then?"

"Because he wants to make friends with you. Look, he doesn't even bother to look at me."

I couldn't quite make my mind up whether Yiannis was being serious or just making fun. It was a challenge, though. I was not exactly enamoured with this category of reptiles, in spite of the fact that in past incarnations I had been somewhat associated with them - and still used their symbolic imagery in meditations in this life. But, somehow, I'd lost the knack of dealing with situations that involved physical encounters with them.

"Well? He's not likely to budge until you feed him. Are we going to spend the rest of the day here?" he goaded me.

I decided to act. I took a couple of deep breaths and relaxed. I got myself into the same state of mind I had entered when dealing with the crab in the doughnut hole. I took the remainder of the cake and approached the snake. He kept staring at me and flicking his tongue. I stretched my hand out and offered it to him, like I would to a domestic animal. He opened his mouth and took it. It was like the old days in the temple. It was all familiar now. He dislocated his jaw to swallow, and then slithered away into the nearest bush.

"Good," Yiannis approved. "Pick up the piece you threw on the ground and let's go. You'll give it to the tortoise."

"Any more friendly reptilians around?" I asked.

"Oh, yes. Quite a few. But none as venomous as the one you've just fed," he quipped, as he set off on his way up the path.

"What?!"

"That's right. One bite and you'd have been a goner." He had a belly laugh at my expense. "Couldn't you tell by the markings?" No, I couldn't. "Such a short memory. You'll never get anywhere this way. You'll never get to the truth."

Memory? Truth? What was he talking about? These were subjects I was dying to discuss with him. Fancy throwing them at me at a time like this. As soon as we reached where we were going, I would definitely bring them up for discussion, first thing. For now, I picked up the piece of cake and followed him.

And he was right. It didn't take long to meet up with his other acquaintance, the tortoise, winding his way laboriously across our path. Naturally, I offered him the rest of the cake, which he politely declined.

"Never mind," said Yiannis, in a mock comforting tone, "the fox will have it."

We continued our arduous journey, running into various other friends of his: hares, moles, crows, ah, and a fox who was most appreciative of the remainder of the cake.

An eagle flew by very low and glided westwards before plunging downwards, seemingly into the earth.

"Here you are," said Yiannis. "He's showing us the way."

"What - how to plunge into the ground headlong?"

"You'll see," he said cryptically.

For a while now I'd been wondering what these animals were doing out in the scorching sun. They should have been resting in the shade somewhere, in trees, in dens or in deep cool burrows. Yiannis said I was being discourteous and ungrateful towards them seeing that they had come out to greet us! Okay, okay, they'd come out to greet us, Dr Dolittle! But I was getting hot and bothered. We must have covered a distance of about three kilometres - as the crow flies, that is, and we were not crows. The possibility hadn't escaped me, however, that all this had been deliberately planned, not just the hike but the details - some sort of test. So, I had better pull myself together and rise to the challenge with at least a semblance of patience.

16

The Devil's Gorge
(Space and Time)

"We're here," he announced.

We were in a very green patch, close to where the eagle had dived. I looked around wondering what was so special about that place to have warranted a hike in the searing heat. As if to answer my question, Yiannis pointed to an area about one hundred metres ahead - a strip of land covered in bushes. I still couldn't see anything particularly interesting.

When I followed him there, however, I was suddenly confronted by this wild spectacle of a ravine: sharp, mostly vertical, cliffs with sporadic vegetation seemingly growing out of the rock faces like hanging gardens. Farther down, towards the bottom, there were fruit trees too, all growing wild. The bottom of the ravine itself was mostly covered in pebbles and boulders, and scored by a gurgling stream of clear water.

"Wow!" I exclaimed with admiration.

"Yes," Yiannis agreed. "Are you ready?"

"For what?"

"To climb down, of course."

"Yes, yes." All my vexation and tiredness had evaporated, and I couldn't wait to reach that stream of fresh water.

"But first, we must pay our respects."

"Pay our respects to whom?"

"The devil," was his laconic answer.

"The who?!"

"You've heard: the devil. This is his territory: the Devil's Gorge. Come."

He walked ahead along the edge of the cliff. I dragged my feet behind him.

"Here," he said. "Come and pay your respects."

He'd stopped in front of a big sprawling rock that rose up to his waist in height. I approached more out of curiosity than trepidation.

"Here. Place your hand over his mark and ask for permission to enter his abode," he continued.

On the rock, there was the deep imprint of a hoof, of a cloven foot - cut or pressed into the rock very clearly and precisely.

"And you must swear allegiance first. Don't forget. Go on," he urged me.

I was aware of the old saying 'many a true word spoken in jest', which Yiannis had been practising on me on and off ever since I'd met him, but I was also aware that, on occasion, he had reversed the adage so as to present something false as true, in convincing solemnity, but with an underlying, often undetectable, smirking irony. I couldn't tell which way he was playing now. And I knew that an oath was a serious commitment, extremely difficult to undo - the elementals created would be terrifyingly binding.

Now, would the devil, if such thing existed, appear to me as the paradigm of love - in the guise of Yiannis? Of course he/she would: perfect deception would be his/her ultimate weapon. Ah, but in that case, two could play the same game. I placed my hand on the imprint and waited.

"Repeat after me: I swear allegiance,..."

I flooded myself with brilliant white light and all the love I could muster, and waited for him to complete his sentence; but *he* was waiting for me to begin the oath; *I* waited for him to continue.... Instead he screamed a command:

"NOW!"

I jumped out of my skin, and the birds in the trees and the cliffs flew in panic. His voice echoed and reverberated throughout the gorge. When, eventually, the sound of his voice and the general commotion had died down, he laughed heartily and patted me on the back.

"You're getting to be too good for me. You're depriving me of my amusement."

He was back to his friendly self again, and I was relieved. He stopped patting my back but he kept his hand between my shoulder blades a little longer than I felt warranted, and made an apparently incongruous remark just before he removed it.

"How's the old spine? Healthy. Good, good."

As I turned to face him, he flashed a big, caring, smile and repeated "good, good" like an echo, in the Teacher's voice - and, once again, the Teacher's personality was strongly present. It shot me back to the reason for the remark.

Some years earlier, I had an accident on the beach. As is the case with many other young teenagers, I took chances with daredevil exhibitions of athleticism. My speciality at the time was to stand at the edge of the pier, place my arms straight on the sides of my body, spring myself upwards, and dive into the sea head first. On one occasion, however, I failed to take notice of the fact that the tide was unusually low, so when I dived I went straight in and hit my unprotected head on the, luckily sandy, bottom of the sea. I came to the surface unable to move my head and with my left arm paralysed.

At the hospital, they put my whole torso and head in plaster but couldn't tell exactly what the problem was, except that there had been some damage to the spine - they talked to my family of the possibility of my left arm remaining paralysed and of some other complications. In the meantime, I had contacted the Teacher who was at my bedside in no time.

"Silly boy!" he reprimanded me, " what are you trying to do - kill yourself before your time?"

He took a good look at me and made his own diagnosis.

"There is a hairline crack on the fifth vertebra, a nerve has been damaged, and there's a great deal of internal bruising in the area."

He shook his head reproachingly. "You're one lucky young man for you're being protected. You could've been paralysed for life. But don't worry, you'll be alright. We'll work on it. All I want from you is to concentrate on the bruised area and cleanse it. You'll see it as a small, darkened, expanse, a black splotch: use visualisation and turn it into flowing light red. Do it tonight, tomorrow morning and at midday. We'll do the rest."

Next day, when the Xrays arrived, the doctors confirmed the Teacher's diagnosis, except that their prognosis was not as positive - they still feared permanent paralysis. But, with the Teacher's intervention, the crisis was overcome.

"Thank you for your concern," I responded to his, now, not so incongruous remark, "but what's all this business with the devil?"

He laughed. "Who knows?" he shrugged his shoulders and began to walk through the shrubs. I followed him. "It's part of the folklore around here. And the local boys swear by it."

"Why?"

"Because it works like a treat, or so they say."

"What are you talking about?" He was talking in riddles again.

He paused momentarily and spoke as if in confidence.

"A boy would bring a girl up here, scare her breathless with stories about the devil, and then pretend to protect her and - guess what? - comfort her with sex." He nodded a couple of times in mock bewilderment. "Yes. Such things do happen. Hard to believe, eh?" he said, as he resumed walking.

My bewilderment, however, was that any girl in her right mind would undertake such a toilsome trek, in the first place. I didn't have time to ask him how the hoofprint got there - he was rushing ahead and I was trying to catch up with him.

"Mind you don't slip on any condoms and fall down the cliff," he advised me casually.

I followed close behind him, heeding his advice half-heartedly. At first, I thought he was kidding me again, until I came across some evidence - how did they manage not to get scratched all over in those thorny bushes?! Or, maybe, that was part of the attraction!

At last, we came to what looked like a path on a part of the gorge that was not so vertical. It was a long climb down but did not look unmanageable. We descended slowly and carefully, with me stopping every now and then to admire the view and inhale the rising aroma of the rhododendrons. At the bed of the gorge we strode over the little stream and got into the shaded area, at the foot of the cliff. Oh, it was cool. The contrast!

"Ah, before settling down too comfortably, would you mind picking a few figs - seeing that you missed your lunch and you are probably starving?" Yiannis said, pointing at a fig tree, and taking out of his leather bag a plasic carrier bag.

"What else are you carrying in there?" I was curious to know.

"Nothing," he replied, and handed me the plastic bag before sitting down by the water.

I was more than happy to climb up the tree and start picking those delicious fruit. It took me back to my childhood.

"Don't pick too many - the crows might take objection to it. It's their tree, after all," he called out.

I had already noticed a number of crows darting around and cawing. Okay, I'll go easy with the figs! High up on the cliff I also caught sight of an eagle resting on a ledge and wondered if it was the same one I'd seen earlier.

When I returned with the fruit, Yiannis wasn't there. I cast about for him and called out a couple of times, and waited - maybe he was answering a call of nature. After a bit he called me from somewhere farther down the stream. I walked over and found him having a wash in a sizeable pool of water created by a small waterfall.

"Come in," he invited me, "you'll love it."

I didn't need to wait for him to repeat the invitation. I jumped in - clothes, sandals and all.

He laughed. "You're being silly. Now you'll have to wait for your clothes to dry."

"So? What's the hurry? We've arrived at our destination," I said, splashing water around like a child.

"Oh, no. We're not there yet. This is just a stop: for you to rest - and talk for a while, if you like. And wash - you must wash before going in."

"Going in where?"

"The place we have come to go into. Why do you think we've made this laborious journey - to sit by a stream and enjoy the scenery?"

"Where are we going to?"

"Not far from here."

"You've said that every time I asked you."

"Yes. And I'm not one to change my mind," he said, and got out of the water to dry himself with my towel which he had brought down there with him.

He put his clothes on and returned to our original spot. I soaked for a little longer, then got out, took my clothes off, dried myself, wrapped the towel round my waist, threw my clothes on some bushes in the sun to dry, and joined him for a fig meal. In the meantime, he had cut some wild mint and inserted it into the bottle which he had filled with water and then shaken to make an instant cold 'mint tea'. He had, also, brought to our sumptuous feast of figs a few bunches of grapes which he had picked from a vine I had totally overlooked on our way down the path - a surprising addition, since it was not the season for grapes yet. He said they were a special early variety growing wild in that area.

I ate the fruit and drank the water with relish. He nibbled. I could tell he was waiting for me to raise questions. On my part, I could have sat there saying nothing till kingdom come; I felt so comfortable. Wasn't it ironic? I chased him around just to get him on his own to press him with my stack of questions and now I was simply content to be in his company. Not for long, though. It wasn't in my nature. The question of time had to be dealt with, and he had promised to discuss it together with that of space; and now both cropped up in a rather unexpected way - or so I thought at the start.

"How far do you reckon we walked from the restaurant?" he asked.

"Ooh, I don't know. Two, three kilometres?"

"And how long did it take us to get here?"

I automatically looked at my watch. It was quarter past three! Oh, no, not again!

"Your watch playing up again?" he remarked, with an obvious smirk. "You'll need to have it checked when you get back," he needled.

"Yes... I will." I said, refusing to take the bait.

"So, what's your guess? Two hours, one hour, five minutes?"

"I don't know. What's *your* guess?"

"I'm asking *you*."

"Well, I don't know."

He was sitting at the edge of the stream, with his feet soaking in the water. He picked up a twig from the ground and placed it in the stream in such a way that the running water was forced to flow over it forming a small arch. It was a beautiful sight: translucent and fluid and yet giving the impression of a constant shape.

"What do you see here?" he asked me.

"An arch."

He touched it with another twig and split it into two almost parallel arches.

"Now?"

"Two arches."

He moved the second twig to another position and created two consecutive arches. He asked me and I confirmed the shape. He removed both twigs and the arches disappeared.

Then, he 'recreated' the first arch, but without the help of a twig, and asked me to observe it closely. As I watched it, it began to solidify into ice. It continued to be translucent but now it had become solid. He asked me to touch it, which I did, and confirmed that it was indeed solid. Then it returned to being liquid again. I watched it flowing as before, but then it gradually lost its liquidity and, when I touched it, my finger went through it. It felt like steam, it was airy, insubstantial - but it retained the original form, and it was also semi-transparent. As I continued to watch it, it lost its steam-like appearance and became totally transparent, while remaining translucent. In fact, it had become even more translucent, or, rather, it was not so much letting light through it as emitting it - it was fiery.

I watched it with excitement as it went through those transformations again, this time starting with being solid then liquid, airy, then fire and light, before it simply disappeared altogether. It was an act of 'magic'. He was exhibiting his control over matter, and I expressed my admiration to him.

"No. It is not magic: it is nature, it's all there is - out there and in here," he said, pointing outwards for 'there' and towards his body for 'here'. I pondered on it.

"What did you see?" he asked.

I described what I had seen.

"Where did it take place?"

"There," I said, pointing to the stream.

"Is it still there?"

"No."

"Where is it now?"

"Nowhere. It's vanished."

"But you've just described it - a whole sequence. It must be somewhere. Unless you're describing something that doesn't exist."

"Yes. I've described something that doesn't exist physically any longer." As soon as I said that I realised that what I had described was not something really physical, it was an illusion.

"What of the previous ones, the arches I had created with the twigs? Can you describe them to me?" I did. "And where are they now?"

"Gone."

"So, you're, again, describing something that doesn't exist."

I was beginning to catch on. He was pointing to 'inner' space, to elementals. I asked him if that was what he was driving at.

"Yes and no. Elementals are always involved. How else could we exist? But it's one of your favourite obsessions I'm bringing up."

"Time."

He nodded. "How do we conceive time?"

"As a flow of events: past, present and future.

"Ah, let us examine this a little more carefully. What is past?"

"Events that have taken place, that happened."

"How do you know that?"

"Because they happened; there are records."

"Where are these records?"

"Well, some are around us, others are in our memories."

"Fine. But how do you refer to past events and memories?"

"Well..." I wasn't sure of what he meant by "refer to".

"I'll tell you how," he stepped in to make his point. "You've just said it yourself: there are records. You said *are*, not *were*. So, the records are present, they exist *now*, they are not in the past - whatever the word 'past' might mean. How about the records that are inside you, your memories?"

"How do you mean?"

"When you talk about memories, are these memories past or present?"

"Past, of course."

"Are you sure?"

"Of course I'm sure."

"Okay, tell me this: what are you actually doing when you're remembering?"

"I recall, I bring to my mind the images - visual, auditory, and so on - and feelings and sensations of what I'm remembering." I began to see now what he was getting at.

"So, if I said to you 'what did you see a few minutes ago?' you'll have in front of you, or in your mind, the relevant images."

"Yes."

"In other words, these images will be in the *present* while you're engaged in the act of remembering. Right?"

"Yes, naturally."

"And where are these images when you're not engaged in the act of remembering them?"

"Floating around, inside or outside of me."

It was the ever-present elementals he was, clearly, presenting as the material of memories. And he went on to make it more explicit.

"So, when you are remembering, your memory images are in the present, and when you're not involved in the act of remembering, those images are floating around, always present for you to recall whenever you want to. Right?"

"Right."

"So, where is the past, then?"

I couldn't help but laugh. "You've just said it yourself: *is* - the past *is*. It's in the present."

"No, not *in* the present. It *is* the present - an aspect of it."

"What of the future?"

"What of it?"

"What is the status of the future?"

"What do you think it is?"

"It hasn't happened yet, it doesn't exist."

"Are you sure?"

"Yes." I followed his own logic. "All we can do is build up images in the present and project them as possibilities in the future - but they are always in the present. The future never happens."

"So, the future, like the past, is an aspect of the present.

"Yes. It must be."

"And what of the present itself?"

"What of it?"

"When and how is the present the present?"

I had to stop and think about this: Anything I do or feel or think or imagine is literally done, felt, thought or imagined the very moment these acts are taking place; in other words, the present is constantly receding into the past which itself does not exist as such! How far could I divide and subdivide space and time to reach the point where and when something *is present*?

I was thrown back to earlier meditations and experiences, to the One that is also Zero, that it exists and does not exist, to the pause at the opening of Beethoven's fifth, to the stillness of time at the cypress tree; to the events that had taken place in the rock in 'no time', and to the 're-playing' of the Greek/Dutch families' healing sequence.... But, most importantly, to my experiences with Athespodos and Hermanubis on the hill.

I was not answering his question - I was struggling for an unequivocal answer, and holding out, waiting for him to make the move. Which he did - and very elegantly, too! He looked at me without saying anything for a bit and, when he realised I wasn't going to answer his question, he leant forward and caught a walnut which was floating down the stream. He held it up high and pointed it towards a walnut tree fifty or so metres upstream.

"Here's your answer," he said.

I looked at the tree and then at the walnut and then back at the tree again, trying to see the connection - apart from the obvious one.

"You've pushed logic to its absurd limit," he continued. "Now break through it."

I gazed at the walnut, which he was holding practically in front of my face, for a short while, and then I took it off his hand. He let go of it as if expecting me to take it. I held it in my right hand, closed my fingers round it and held it there for a short while, then shifted it to my left hand and did the same there before returning it to my right hand. It was a method I had been taught to use in order to get into the atmophere of an object.

I turned to my right to face the tree. When I felt I was in the right position, I sat cross-legged and relaxed, concentrating on the walnut in my hand and creating a connecting 'feeling' line between it and the tree. I sat there for a while, practising patterned breathing and seeking an inner link with both the tree and the walnut.

The practice itself required that one should not try and work out intellectually the link or the nature of the object, but simply formulate the research intention and then relax over the object, preventing one's attention from wandering, and wait. The intention to forge a close link with the object is essential - a kind of internalisation of the object would then occur. As the procedure progresses, further formulations of intentions and/or questions are inserted from which answers/responses are elicited.

Next thing, I found myself sitting under the tree, which was now gigantic. A process, similar to the one I had undergone with the cypress tree, then took place for a spell, before I was back holding the walnut in my hand again. I felt it growing in size until it enclosed me like a cocoon. I was inside it. I felt the hardness of its shell and the softness and oiliness of its inside. I tasted it and smelled it and entered into a state of synaesthesia.

Sitting inside the walnut, I saw it and felt it growing into a tree: it grew all around me and inside me, as I was part of it. It was like sugar dissolving in water: I was everywhere within it and it was everywhere within me. The astonishing thing was that it was growing and yet not growing, developing and yet being static. From my 'understanding' position, the situation was incomprehensible, in my 'knowing' state, however, it was perfectly clear.

Moreover, I could perceive numerous 'static' stages: stages that carried a sense of permanency while growth was taking place. The growth was unfolding throughout the tree, down to its most infinitesimal parts - which themselves were not 'parts' but mere concentrations of energy. Being one with the walnut, I felt myself growing with it into a tree but, at the same time, I had the clear sense of being already a grown tree which had come to the end of its life then died and was reborn inside the walnut, and so on, the whole process being repeated again and again. There was permanency, the overall permanency of the cycle, and the sense of permanency in its stages.

As I prodded further, I came to realise that the permanency of this cycle was only an effect, an impression. The permanency was itself impermanent. There seemed to be something else beyond it that 'caused' it, like a wider cycle, a magnificently powerful attraction - but I could not grasp it. I was not dealing with one particular walnut any longer but with all walnuts, a universal sort of walnut. And then I 'saw' this whole process repeated throughout nature, with all plants and animals - and humans.

There was beginning and end, but, because the process was cyclical, the end was also the beginning. There was no literal end, but without the end there would be no beginning: the beginning was the end and the end was the beginning. When I looked for cause and effect, I was given the impression that the query was irrelevant. I could see the cause at the beginning but I could also see it at the end. In fact, the end itself acquired a double meaning: it was 'end' in the sense of final but also in the sense of purpose - the 'end' was the cause of the beginning. And all through this was the totality of the process which provided the 'false' sense of permanence. There was an intimation of 'real' permanence but this lay beyond my comprehension.

The cycles also engendered a strangely contradictory sense of security and imprisonment: I felt secure within the repetitions but at the same time I could not escape the feeling of containment, of constraint. Nonetheless, there was something intriguing in the human cycle, into the structure of which I was drawn by natural affinity. Although the cycle was unbreakable, it appeared like a circle whose circumference could - would? - thin out and dissolve.

Was I experiencing the dissolution of human individuality into Nothing or the expansion of it, its conscious identification with the Darkness - taking on the Darkness, becoming consciously one with it: the ultimate contradiction: Light and Darkness being one and the same? Suddenly, all contradictions were resolved - there were no contradictions, in the first place. The human mind, the *current* human mind, was unable to comprehend that opposites were not contradictory, that, in fact, they were the same. 'Going back' was 'going forward'. Ah, the ultimate permanency!

"You've ruined that walnut," he said, in a soft voice. He was standing next to me holding my clothes in his left hand. "And put your clothes on - you're upsetting the crows. You've already stolen their figs as it is."

He dropped the clothes on the shingle, near me. In his right hand he was holding the bottle half-full of water and peppermint leaves. "Here, drink this first." He handed me the bottle.

I was still not fully back. I was in a sort of daze. The last thing that struck me in the state I was in was the realisation that a corollary of the statement 'all things are the same' was that there was no movement, and if there was no movement there was no space, and if there was no space there was no time...

"Come on, drink it," he insisted.

I drank some. It was as if I had never drunk anything before. I felt the water in my mouth, my throat, my gullet, and all the way down to my stomach as if someone else were drinking it - I was 'travelling' along with the water from the mouth to the stomach as an outsider.

"No, no. All of it. Drink all of it."

I drank the rest of the water and slowly began to adjust.

"When you go, you go, don't you?" he commented on my 'walnut adventure'.

I didn't feel the need to ask him to elucidate any aspects of my experience as I knew that, on the contrary, the use of verbal language would have confused it. But, for some inexplicable reason, as I was putting my clothes on I thought of Helen - perhaps the fact that I'd been naked with her... I don't know. I had intended, however, to raise the question of sex with Yiannis, and I thought this might be as good a time as any.

17

A Dionysian Initiation
(Dionysos, Wine, and Sex)

"One plunge at a time," he said, when I mentioned it. "The subject is vast and I don't know if we have time to even scratch the surface."

Time? What was he talking about? Was he leaving? Besides, hadn't we just abolished time?

"On second thought," he continued, "we may be able to tackle at least part of it before we go in." Go in? In where? I was about to ask him, when he cut in. "Okay. You go across the stream to the vine over there; do you see it?"

"Yes..."

"Bring back a bunch of grapes and a few leaves. I'll get the ivy," he said, and pointed to the leafy climber crawling up the cliff behind us. He didn't give me time to ask him what he was planning to do - he was already on his way to the cliff.

I waded across the shallow stream wondering what he was up to, picked a bunch of ripe golden grapes and some leaves, as he had instructed, and returned. He was weaving a wreath of ivy.

"Who died?" I asked.

"Nobody yet," he replied, and glanced at me suggestively.

I gave him the vine leaves which he interlaced with the ivy into the wreath. I noticed that he had also woven into the wreath a few laurel leaves, which he must have picked from the laurel bush a few metres away. When he had finished weaving, he placed the wreath on my head and stood back one step.

"A perfect fit," he said with satisfaction. "Now, if only we had a straight stick and a cone to place on top, to make a *thýrsos*, we might just about be able to turn you into an acceptable Dionysos."

I liked the game. "I could go back across and look for one," I suggested with some enthusiasm, pointing at the trees on the other side of the stream.

"No, forget it; it won't be necessary. You have your own *real thýrsos*," he decided, and touched my spine just below the shoulder blades. I had an instant flash of the Pharaonic sceptre, and knew exactly what he meant.

He asked me to sit down and be comfortable, then picked out a few grapes off the bunch and gave them to me. He sat nearby.

"Eat two grapes the normal way," he instructed me, "and put a third one in your mouth and wait."

I followed his instructions, and waited.

"Do your breathing preparations and then start turning the third grape in your mouth. Don't bite it yet but concentrate on it."

He let me carry on for a short while and then told me to bite the grape slowly, feeling my teeth cutting through it, and tasting the juice. As I did that, I began to feel a bit light-headed, a little tipsy, as if I were getting drunk. It was a pleasant feeling; it filled me with a sense of bonhomie and gregariousness. Then, he said I should chew the pips, the skin and the rest of the grape, but not swallow them yet.

At this point, my tipsiness was elevated to high spirits. I was not drunk - I was uplifted. Drunkenness would have clouded my mind; on the contrary, now I was enjoying great clarity of mind and a verve for life.

"Are you feeling enthusiastic?" he asked.

A strange question, I thought, but yes I did feel a bit that way. And then I realised what he really meant. He was using the word 'enthusiastic' in its literal sense, which meant 'inspired', 'having the god inside' you - he was not joking when he mentioned Dionysos (Dionysus) a few minutes earlier.

I said a tentative "yes", and he told me to swallow the remains of the grape I had in my mouth.

He placed two more grapes, one in each of my hands, and told me to repeat with each one what I had done with the previous grape: roll it in my mouth, bite it slowly, chew and then swallow.

I was getting high, very high. My whole body was sensitised. I could feel the juice of each grape spreading to all the cells of my body - even the pips, the skins and the fleshy parts of the grapes seem to contribute to my sensitisation. Indeed, as I chewed them, after I had swallowed the juice, I had the sensation of some substance flowing out of them, an extra energetic substance that invigorated me even further.

I was electrified by this powerful energy which, having spread throughout my body, then began to concentrate in stages at various parts, beginning at my feet. I felt it tingling in my toes, the arches, the heels, the ankles, giving rise to a sensation of flight, as if I were being lifted off the ground, as if there were wings or wheels at my ankles propelling me and enabling me to travel round the world(s), like Hermes - to carry some message or other.

As it moved through my legs and thighs, I felt the need to get up and dance - and I believed that had I done so I would have performed a most vigorous and intricate dance. When it reached the base of my spine, it intensified immensely and generated almost unbearable heat. I felt it rising up my spine and partly distributing itself to the rest of my body, at various strategic points, on its way upwards.

At the region of my genitals, it caused a most tremendous erection which was accompanied by an almost uncontrollable urge to copulate and, frighteningly, by the need to engage in acts of brutality - I could have torn anybody and anything to pieces, raped and pillaged; I revelled in a mood of violence and sexual craving.

I was stunned both by the unleashing of such devastating tendencies and by the fact that I relished their acceptace as normal and 'good'. I decided to leave that area before losing my control totally, which I did by formulating the strong intention to move towards my solar plexus - but, for the rest of the 'experiment', I found myself being pulled back to the genital region again and again, with revelations of other aspects of its nature each time.

The energy at the solar plexus brought out an overwhelmingly varied world of 'creatures' and activities. There were nymphs, fairies, satyrs, sylphs, undines, salamanders, gnomes... All engaged in peculiar and confusing actions. I watched for a while and then tried to make sense of all this. The moment I posed the mental questions of who they were and what they were doing, the picture changed in character and an understanding began to dawn on me.

Some of them were elementals, imaginary 'creatures', given form by human desire and thought, which acquired a semblance of consciousness over many years of continuous supply of energy by the human mind - and they varied from beautiful to grotesque.

Others, and more interesting they were, comprised nature groups - and these were out there in the gorge: literally. They displayed semi-human forms, and they varied from minute to gigantic. There were small brown gnomes, half-submerged in the ground, digging and turning the soil; there were fairies and tree nymphs tending the vegetation, some of them partly inside the trees and plants to which they were literally attached; there were undines in the stream, flowing in and out of the water; sylphs were flying in the air above the water, in between boulders, around the cliffs. In the sunny parts of the gorge, were salamanders apparently basking in the sun.

All these creatures looked gossamer in substance, reminiscent of the transparent and translucent arches Yiannis had created earlier in the water. They were all happy and playful and carrying on with their appointed tasks: assisting in the growth of vegetation, cleansing the water and sustaining life in it, clearing the air of pollutants, controlling the generation of heat on the ground, and so on.

They appeared to be working according to a plan, from a blueprint. They repaired accidental 'digressions' from the blueprint but, interestingly, when these digressions seemed to work in favour of the survival and well-being of their wards, they supported it. In fact, at a closer look, these were not real digressions - they had already been built into the blueprint as 'possibilities' (which made me wonder for a brief moment what some strict interpreters of Darwin might make of it).

I was surprised to see some of these creatures copulating and seemingly deriving pleasure from the act. On closer investigation, however, I discovered that they had no idea what they were doing! They were simply imitating humans and animals they had caught sight of engaging in such activities. Even the pleasure they displayed was an imitation. They had no reproductive organs and they did not procreate: they 'belonged' to entities like the ones I had become familiar with back on the hilltop. I observed them for a while and saw them undergoing a series of 'emotions' none of which were real - they even looked as if they were in deep thought at times!

The tenor of the scene changed dramatically when certain other creatures made their appearance. They were satyrs and sileni and centaurs, all of them half-human-and-half-animal creatures with a strong penchant for drunkenness. And then Priapos cropped up, with his relentless erection. And, to cap it all, Pan suddenly burst on to the scene. He sported a large erect penis, vastly disproportionate to his body size, looking ready to screw anything and anybody in his path, and scattered the nymphs all over the place - and the meaning of the word 'panic' became self-explanatory.

With the appearance of these creatures, I felt a strong pull from my solar plexus to the region of my genitals, and, once again, those tendencies I thought I had put aside, returned. I was fully aroused sexually, and the mood of brutality I'd experienced earlier was also back.

But it was, somewhat, different now. The energy coursed up and down between my genitals and my solar plexus, and those proclivities fluctuated in pace with the movement. The longer the energy stabilised itself around my solar plexus, the less brutal the presence of these human-animals felt. Indeed, at a certain stage, they began to look civilised, getting involved in social exchanges with one another and, generally, showing signs of 'humanisation'.

Some even appeared knowledgeable in certain areas, and ready to offer tutelage to those who sought their wisdom - very weird! By this time, the energy was moving around my midriff, the kidneys, liver, pancreas, spleen, and three of these characters - a satyr, a silenos and a centaur - seemed to be particularly connected with the concentration of energy at those locations.

At the spleen level, it was like a whirlwind: I was spun and hurled all over the place, all over the world. I found myself travelling with a retinue of revellers, causing upset wherever I went, not because I intended to but because people did not understand the message I was spreading, a message of liberation from the shackles of so-called 'reason': they did not know that I was 'enthusiastic'. As an old man, they venerated me for my supposed wisdom; as a youth, sometimes they worshipped me as a life giver and at other times they shunned and criticised me for my pleasure-seeking and for my effeminate appearance. I journeyed everywhere and donned just about every garment known - and some unknown!

Then the energy drew me up to my heart where I was thrown into a turmoil. I was nearly burned alive by a most brilliant lightning, I was torn to pieces and thrown into a cauldron. But I survived, we survived - me and myself. I was two: one of me went to a 'place' where nobody could enter physically. There, I met, amongst others, my beloved Hermanubis, my other half, my identical self - I felt we were one and the same.....

The other me was rushed upwards, 'snatched' from my heart and taken to my head by a wonderful sibling, a sister I'd always known and loved. As I was being pulled upwards, some of my retinue followed me, others stayed behind, and yet others simply vanished. In my head, I was 'completed', 'liberated'....

I was beginning to shoot farther upwards, out of the crown of my head, when, all of a sudden, this growling started. I ignored it, and it turned into loud barking and then into high-pitched yelping.

"Whoa, whoa. Not even Athespodos could bring you back. At the risk of repeating myself, when you go, you go, my boy."

Yiannis was sitting beside me on my left, applying gentle pressure on the part of my spine between my shoulder blades. Slowly and reluctantly, very reluctantly, I began to readjust.

"What are you trying to do - kill yourself?"

"What do you mean? I couldn't possibly have died".

"Oh, yes? You have no idea," he said, and shook his head from side to side. "Take a couple of deep breaths and splash water on your face. Go on." I followed his instructions, and then he told me to walk in the stream for a few metres and return. "When you've done that, without falling into the water, come and join me," he said.

I stood up, and sat down again, took another deep breath and stood up, faltered, regained my balance and walked downstream as he had indicated. The coolness of the water was more than welcome but the fluidity made it hard for me to stay 'with it': I kept drifting back to the state I had been in earlier. I avoided falling a couple of times, but by the time I returned I was fully back on my feet.

"Why couldn't you have asked me to walk on dry ground, why the stream?"

"Because it's more difficult this way."

I couldn't argue with that!

"Now, sit here and let us go to stage two," he said authoritatively, pointing to a spot about a metre away on his left.

"What is stage two?" I asked, as I sat down.

"The re-living, understanding, and absorbing of what took place in stage one - of what you have just gone through," he said, in a statement-of-fact voice.

"Are there any other stages?"

"Yes. One more - for now."

"What does that entail?"

"Living it," he answered, in the same matter-of-fact tone.

"Living what?"

"Stage two." Not a very enlightening answer, I thought. He saw my puzzlement and expounded further. "Stage one is the journey, which is partly external, like a story, like a myth. It is also partly internal for those who are capable of grasping that aspect of it - and you did go some way towards that. It's the exoteric side of life, of religion, of science, whatever. Okay?"

"Okay."

"In stage two, you enter the essence of the journey. To an extent, you become the journey itself, the so-called myth is revealed for what it is: reality. In stage three, you live this reality. But that's for later, much later. Now: the journey again. Go back to it, and I'll guide you whenever necessary."

I went through a breathing pattern and slowly slid into the direct method. I aimed for the essence of the journey, the meaning and the reality of it. The whole thing then began to open up, but not in the order I had expected it: it came to me in what looked like a jumbled up reversed order.

I was in my head, in my 'liberated' state. My personality was different, tremendously enhanced - and it remained so throughout the ensuing journey, even on the occasions of my becoming closely identified with certain 'lower' types of consciousness.

There was a brief but powerful burst of energy in the shape of a small ball of brilliant light that shot from my head and traced a line to my genitals, my heart, my solar plexus, throat, right shoulder, left shoulder, the top of my head. It was the gesture Yiannis had made back at the cypress tree when he talked of living on light!

Next thing, I was in my feet, travelling, going through many adventures, many lives; behaving 'as nature intended', following the logic of nature, of instinct - but not as a human! When I was in my thighs, I felt like dancing again, but, in fact, I simply stood upright from a crouching position - I was a primate learning to stand erect!

As I reached the genitals and the solar plexus, I began to see an evolutionary perspective in this journey: the half-human stages of the centaurs, the sileni, the satyrs. I could see and feel the force of the sexual energy: natural and yet forceful. If it was natural why should it be forceful? I wanted to investigate this but I felt a mental nudge from Yiannis to move on - with the promise of returning to it later.

In the solar plexus itself the evolutionary scheme widened in scope. The half-human stages were not mythical or symbolic: they were real, actual. These were stages during which there was unrestricted sexual intercourse between 'higher' and 'lower' primates, even between 'gods' and other forms of life. As this understanding dawned on me, a 'myth' unravelled before me by way of illustration: Zeus creating a cloud in the likeness of Hera with which Ixion, the son of Ares, 'mates' and produces Centauros who then in turn mates with the mares of mount Pelion and fathers the race of Centauroi (Centaurs). How demonstrative a picture!

Pan was a special case. Pan, the 'universal god', the Great All, as his name indicates, the son of Sky and Earth, the principle of sexual reproduction, who seduces Selene, the moon goddess, and who is represented as a half-human with goat's horns, beard, legs and hooves, and who vanishes *into* a mountain - the perfect representation of 'nature' at its current evolutionary stage!

Then, were the 'gossamer' entities, the nymphs, the undines, and so on, who did not reproduce sexually: they were 'reverberations' of more complex Entities. These were forms of life that still exist and continue to work in their own mode. But they are indicative of forms of asexual procreation which humans also employed in the far distant past, and which they may take up again - in full consciousness!

This latter realisation shook me and caused me to move up to the heart region. It was a deliberate pull, and I was certain Yiannis had a hand in it. I found myself in the centre of my heart, reliving the lightning experience, and the tearing and the pain. But there was an understanding now: the myth and the reality.

The myth of Dionysos escaping death from the thunderbolt of Zeus. His Earth mother Semele burning in the fire, unable to survive the brightness of the lightning and the consuming conflagration. Dionysos taken up by Zeus to live another life: Dionysos the *Dithýrambos*, the "twice born". Then, the Titans tearing Dionysos to pieces and throwing him into the cauldron. Athena, born out of Zeus' head, saving Dionysos' still beating heart and taking it to Zeus. The new Dionysos, born out of the old Dionysos' heart.

There was, as with Pan and other stories, reality and symbolism, or, rather, syncretisation, here - the fate of humanity represented by one life, that of Dionysos - the Human Idea made flesh. The reality,

on the other hand, was in the intimation of an era of asexual reproduction: Zeus creating Athena out of his head, carrying Dionysos in
his thigh before giving birth to him, Dionysos being born again out
of his own heart... There were other illustrations of this form of reproduction: through the liver, the spleen....

I felt another pull, this time from the heart to the head, then back
to the heart. I was, once again, split into two. In the heart, I was
Dionysos, the 'god' who had risen from below, had reached the
solar plexus where he had been the representative of pleasure, of
wine and jollity and orgiastic delirium, and then 'died' and turned
into a divinity of the 'underworld', welcoming the souls of the dead
and helping with their purification; the god of life who became the
god of life after life....

Another pull drew me to the head once more, into the resurrection from the 'dead', to the 'completed' state - to exemplify the
way for humanity: the 'liberated' Dionysos, the link between nature
at large, mankind, and 'heaven'....

"Good, good. Enough. Enough for now," came Yiannis' voice to
bring me back from my personal Dionysian elevation. As I was
beginning to find my bearings, I reminded him that he had stopped
me from delving into the nature and activities of the genital region,
and that he had 'promised' to allow me to return to it.

"Yes, yes. But it would be better for you to tackle it through
discussion."

"Why? Why not the way I have been dealing with the rest of the
subject?"

"Because you would not be able to handle it. Believe me, I know
what I'm talking about."

I could not argue with him. I had to trust his knowledge and abilities. I knew that without him I would not have been able to enter
into those consciousness expanding experiences and attain to those
insights.

I had already begun to understand the process and significance of
the three stages he had mentioned, and had glimpses of past lives in
which I had reached the point of entering the second stage - a stage
he had just put me through! As I reflected on these matters, I came
to see that the stages were none other than initiation steps into the
ancient Mysteries: understanding the 'mysteries' of life - which is to
be found everywhere - by living its history and intuiting its nature.

"Would you please explain to me why Dionysos sometimes appeared so effeminate, and dressed like a woman?" I asked.

He laughed. "Fancy picking on that. But then, you would." He laughed again, a gentle laughter. "That was Dionysos the shaman. Something you don't read in books."

"So?" I couldn't quite make the connection.

"Did you know that some shamans would go as far as sacrificing their manhood in order to gain the ability of soothsaying?"

"What?"

"Never mind. The point is that the feminine aspect is naturally more receptive than the masculine. Becoming ecstatic and falling into trances, for a shaman is an effective way of calling on the feminine-receptive aspect of his nature. Dressing up like a woman assists in creating the psychological mood."

"But did Dionysos need all that?"

"Yes and no. As the 'completed' one, no. But you mustn't forget that he was also the example, the paradigm, the way to the 'liberated' state for all humans. As human on his way to 'completion', he behaved just like one." He paused briefly, and then continued.

"Go back to that particular female incarnation you visited earlier today, and to your experience of unconditional love at the cypress tree. See how they fit. It doesn't mean that you have to be a woman or that all women are capable of this enhancing of consciousness. It's the feminine-receptive aspect that matters. Anybody can cultivate it. But in females it's innate: it's part and parcel of the motherhood instinct."

I understood what he meant. I remembered the way I felt as a woman: the unconditional love and the giving; and the unconditional love at the cypress tree. But then I noticed that as a woman my love could also be extremely personal and demanding, and when I loved unconditionally there was always a feeling of protectiveness in the background, a feeling of personal security. I wasn't sure that this feeling was present when I experienced unconditional love as a man - any feeling of security and protectiveness I might have felt then seemed to flow out of me, out of the state I was in. Was there a real difference between the two? I wasn't sure at that point.

As I moved to a more comfortable position, the wreath on my head slipped and fell.

"Do I need this?"

"No, you can leave it off."

I looked at the wreath and picked out a vine leaf. I tried to see the connection, the real connection with Dionysos.

"Why is Dionysos connected with wine - and sex?"

"Ah, wine and sex." He smiled, a hardly discernible, sly smile, which I decided to ignore for the time being. "The two don't always feature together. But there is a connection. Wine is a means of raising the dampers of ordinary logic, of opening the doors. A small amount facilitates psychic communication with other humans, animals, plants, and other forms of life visible or invisible to the physical eye. Look at you: one grape and you were gone."

"That's not true. It was three grapes - no, four."

"Whatever."

"A small amount you said?"

"Yes. More wine will make you feel strong, especially if accompanied by incentives to carry out demanding tasks. Think of Alexander the Macedonian, for example: he would get his soldiers half-drunk to bolster their confidence before a battle."

"And if you drink a lot you render yourself useless."

"Yes. Even Dionysos himself went totally insane at first, or so we are told - he had to learn to control the effects of his imbibing in order to use it as a means of communicating with the 'divine'. It's a matter of measure. Silenos, an old follower of his, when not totally plastered, exhibited a great ability as a soothsayer."

"And sex?"

"What about sex?"

"Sex and wine - how do you reckon they fare together?"

"It's the same story. A small amount of wine relaxes your inhibitions, you become a gregarious reveller, you have sex and enjoy it. More wine, and you lose control over your sexual impulses. The sex centres become uncontrollably aroused, you indulge without measure, you turn into a sex fiend. Even more wine, and either you have an instant ejaculation or become totally unable to achieve an erection." By the time he had come to the end of this brief exposition, the sly smile had covered the whole of his face.

"What?" I asked, copying his smile.

"One way or another, you managed to manoeuvre through my hackneyed answers to your favourite obsession." He had found me out.

"You've promised - more than once."

"Yes, I have," he conceded. "So?"

"So, the basic question: what is the real function of sex?"

He leant back and looked serious.

"I'm taking on a great responsibility here, you understand, don't you?"

"What do you mean?"

"Taking you back, reminding you, guiding you and helping you to remember what you have forgotten."

"And I'm deeply grateful for that."

"That's not the point: you shouldn't have forgotten, in the first place."

"But I do remember - bits and pieces."

"Which is hardly enough. You cannot get to the truth that way."

"What *is* the truth?"

He ignored my question, and returned with one of his own.

"What is sex to you?"

"Well, basically, I'd say pleasure and procreation."

"And, procreation, as we know, hasn't been, and isn't, always connected with sex. Right?"

"Right."

"And, what about pleasure? Is it always connected with sex?" He was back to his Socratic method again.

"No. Of course not."

"We have physical pleasures of other sorts besides sexual: emotional and intellectual pleasures. And bliss, utter bliss. Maybe even more bliss in, and courtesy of, Darkness." A little facetious, but he was making his point.

"So, what you're saying is that the two, pleasure and sexual procreation, are not necessarily connected."

"Oh, no. They are connected, alright, and necessarily so." He lost me. "Look, a few minutes ago you were thinking: 'if sexual energy is so natural, why is it so forceful?'. Well, that's where your clue lies."

I was still puzzled. I knew he was nudging me to find the answer by myself, but I just couldn't see it.

"Let's say, you have a room in your house which you lock," he continued. "You put a padlock on it. Why?"

"Because I don't want anyone to get in there without my permission," I responded.

"You could just close the door."

"But that's not secure enough - somebody might just walk in."

"Precisely. That's why laws, all laws of nature, are so forceful. They're wired into the system, and they're so powerful and forceful they're unbreakable. If they were to break, the whole world would collapse - chaos. The cosmos is held together by laws. One of these laws, at the present, is sexual procreation."

"Okay. So?"

"Take pleasure away from sex and what are you left with? A black sense of humour."

"What?!"

"Look at where your sexual organs are located: centimetres away from your arse, the channel designed for the excretion of faeces. Your penis itself, the external organ of sexual stimulation and pleasure is shared by another excretory function - you screw and piss by means of the same piece of tube.

"I'm telling you, whoever designed this has a fantastic sense of humour - rubbing your face in it is what springs to mind." And on that, he broke out into a roar of a laughter. And then, trilling along, he capped his sarcastic comment with concluding irony: "Life is such a serious joke, eh?"

"But, surely, other parts of the body share functions: the mouth, the nose, the ears...

"Yes. But that's hardly the same. The location of one of the most pervasive pleasures, the location of one of the strongest instincts - that which guarantees survival of the species - is practically the same as that of getting rid of the body's most unpleasant wastes."

"The point being?"

"The point, my dear boy, is that if pleasure were not attached to this form of procreation, would you bother to fiddle around your excretory areas for the sake of producing offspring?"

His language wasn't exactly inspirational, but the point he was making was hard to ignore. I thought about it, and my answer was a clear "No".

"Reflect on what we discussed on the small island in regards to sexuality and the differences and similarities between the genders," he added. "Go back to that female incarnation again, and to your experiences with the American girl."

I did. The only important sexual difference I could discern between the genders on the physical level was the production of sperm by the male and eggs by the female. Beyond the physical bodies, even these sexual differences were further diluted and, at a certain point, vanished altogether.

In my French female incarnation, I felt extremely feminine, but in my encounter with Helen, although obviously male physiologically, my experience seemed to encompass both sides - male and female. The orgasms I experienced reached all the way from the tip of the glans to way beyond the prostate, to throughout my body, in fact - in a very similar manner to the orgasms I had in the female incarnation where the pleasure went beyond the genital/erogenous areas, reaching ecstatic proportions.

As I compared the two, I came to recognise various sensations I had felt at particular parts of my body, such as on and around the breasts, for instance, which I had experienced in both cases - sensations I wouldn't normally be aware of as a male. I also realised that the orgasms themselves were very similar in another respect: they were both ejaculatory! Yes, as a female, I had the very clear sensation of ejaculating! But to what biological purpose? Might it have something to do with facilitating a kind of 'suction' of the sperm, or providing extra lubrication? On the occasion with Helen, my multiple orgasms had been, indeed, ejaculatory, but the fluid had been discharged inwards instead of outwards - which was what Yiannis presumably meant by "retrograde ejaculations".

"Yes," he responded. "And if you were to learn to harness that energy and redirect it, there wouldn't be much you wouldn't be able to achieve."

He gave me a few seconds to contemplate the implications of such practice before moving on.

"Now," he continued, "can you see the perspective? Can you see where pleasure and procreation are placed in it?"

"Ehm...You've split them. And you've subsumed the one under the other: pleasure being the greater of the two."

"Good. Now you might remember what we have said about pleasure, happiness, bliss, being the candy that keeps all life forms in existence."

"Yes. I do."

"Pleasure, in its variety of expression, is everywhere, it pervades everything. And that brings me to the basic question: what is the primary function of sex - pleasure or procreation?"

He was now asking *me* my original question, with a slight but significant shift in emphasis. I could see that sex without pleasure wouldn't stand a chance, and that sexual procreation was only one way of propagating - albeit the prevalent one on the physical level. But pleasure, in all its variations, was clearly the driving force behind sexual reproduction - pleasure in the sexual act, in the affections involved, the parental instincts, and so on. And what of sexual deviation? He dismissed my question, saying that there was no such thing, only sexual variation.

"But why are so many myths of the creation of the world explicitly sexual?" I asked.

"First of all, there are many creation myths which are not sexual; they represent mainly a pre-sexual era and reproductive methods that still exist on other levels. Generally, though, conscious human memory is not active enough to be able to call up conditions in pre-sexual times.

"However, you are right; perhaps most myths are sexual. Why? Because sexual reproduction is the latest experiment - it's only been around a few hundred million years on this planet. And it's become the most prevalent.

"Sexual energy is a ramification of Energy in general - what forms the structure of the world and keeps it together. That's why sexual energy can by transformed, transmuted: from mundane to spiritual - whatever construction you might want to put on the concept of 'spiritual': from Earthly Aphrodite to Divine Aphrodite."

I was suddenly reminded of Helen and the enormously enhanced pleasure I had felt when making love with her, and the clarity of mind that ensued.

I sat there quietly, taking in and digesting the huge amount of material I had opened myself to. The gorge itself was quiet, too. An occasional crow or some other bird would make its presence gently felt. A few insects were flying around buzzing hypnotically. And the wonderfully relaxing sound of the gurgling stream... I felt thirsty. I bent down on my knees and lowered my head into the water and drank - like the insects, like the birds, like the fox... I splashed water on my face.

"Time," he said.

"Time for what?"

"To go. Can't you hear him calling?"

"Calling? Who--?" Yes, I heard him, just then.

It was Athespodos. I heard his bark, distant, coming from somewhere upstream, well past the walnut tree. I couldn't see him - the bend of the stream was disappearing behind the cliff; the barking was coming from around there.

"Where are we going," I asked, as I picked up the towel and the torch and followed him.

"Where I am taking you," he said, giving me an empty answer. It was one way of telling me to be quiet and follow him.

- 18 -

The Tunnel of Truth and the Cave
(We: the Amnesiacs - Remembering and not Forgetting)

We walked for some time alongside the stream which swerved left and right following the cut of the cliffs. There were buddleias everywhere in a variety of colours giving out their sweet smell, with butterflies just as varied in size and colourful patterns visiting them in their scores. I expected to see Athespodos somewhere nearby but he was nowhere to be seen. I could still hear him, although his barking was constantly receding the closer I thought we got to him.

Farther on, the gorge became narrower, with the cliffs still rising high above us. We must have walked close to a kilometre when we came to a split in the stream: most of the water ran out of a spring in the cliff to our right, the rest of it flowed from another source higher up. Momentarily, I thought I saw Athespodos rushing up the lesser of the two streams, and interestingly, that was the one Yiannis headed for. I debated with myself for a few seconds and then chose not to ask any questions; I simply followed in his tracks.

The gorge was now becoming gradually steeper to climb and so narrow we had to walk in the water. Pretty soon the top parts of the cliffs joined to form an arch, and we found ourselves walking, or rather, climbing into a crack in the earth.

I couldn't hold out any longer. I stopped for a breather and asked him where, in heaven's name, we were going.

"We're nearly there," he replied, without turning his head. "Keep going; we are practically there. And you can lose the towel - you don't need it."

I hooked the towel on a rocky jut and continued to climb. A few minutes later we appeared to reach a dead end: the crevice narrowed down to a small oval-shape slit in the rock.

"Now what?" I asked, and looked back to see how we were going to get out of there without slipping and tumbling down.

"Now we go in," he said.

"Go in where?"

"In here," he replied, pointing to the aperture in the rock. And he walked right in. I hesitated for a beat or two before following.

A few metres in, and the daylight could not reach us. I switched on the torch and walked a little farther along, keeping my balance by touching the walls. And then, that was it. Yiannis stopped and leant against one of the walls, and I saw how small the cleft had become. For the life of me, I couldn't see how we could possibly go any farther. The whole opening was now about a metre and a half high, narrowing at the top and bottom, with the middle section no more than forty centimetres wide, although it seemed to open out a little more after a metre or so. Even sideways I didn't think we could make it. And, why try, anyway?

"Because that's what we've come here for," he replied to my question.

"What - to squeeze ourselves to death in a hole?"

"Yes. Have you not heard that a man must die in order to be born?" I could hear the ringing irony in his voice. "I'll tell you what," he continued. "I'll go in first and you follow. Right?"

Was there going to be any other way? - he led and I followed. He was humouring me, but I knew he was serious. Why else would he put me through all the trekking to bring me to such a place?

"Okay. You go in first," I affected concession.

He smiled and turned his back to me, then leant into the opening, stretching his arms in front of him and lifting his feet off the ground, squeezing between the walls, hanging only a few centimetres above the water. He lay there for a minute or two, motionless, hardly breathing, before beginning to slide forward, pulling himself into the gap. He slid for, maybe, three or four metres and then crouched, pulled his feet in and stood up! He was in. In where? He turned round and crouched again to face me.

"Okay, now's your turn," he called.

I leant forward and tried to copy the manner in which he had positioned himself above the water before pulling himself in, but I found it extremely hard. Perhaps it was because I was bigger than him. I tried sideways but he discouraged me.

"No, no. Face forward, your chest parallel to the water."

I tried again, the way he suggested, but encountered the same difficulty.

"Get rid of the torch. Throw it to me," he ordered.

I swang the torch towards him as accurately as I could knowing full well that it would end up in the water - but he caught it! And switched it off.

It was dark, perhaps a faint, diffused notion of light coming from outside. But I couldn't see a thing.

"You'll find it easier in the dark. Now, relax and concentrate," he said. "It's all a matter of will."

"What do you mean? I can't will the walls to open up!"

"Of course you can." He sounded firm and certain - he meant it! "These walls are soft. They'll yield to you if you want them to. I'll guide you. Relax and concentrate. You know what to do."

I knew what to do? How? I'd never done anything like this before. But I knew about relaxing and concentrating and willing.

I breathed slowly and deeply, and relaxed. I managed to inch my shoulders forward a little but they hurt. I was now truly wedged between a rock and a hard place, as the saying goes, and could not move in either direction. I was beginning to get claustrophobic.

"No. You're not doing it properly: relax, concentrate, will. Stick to that order," he elaborated.

He was right, I'd moved too fast.

I relaxed. I let go completely, both physically and mentally. I dispersed all my concerns. Darkness was good, cool and comforting. I worked on my claustrophobia. What was there to be afraid of? In the last analysis, the rock and my body were one. I, as consciousness, could not be destroyed by a rock.

I concentrated on the periphery of my shoulders. Where did my shoulders end and the walls begin? There was no gap between them. I spread my concentrated attention on every part of my body that was in contact with the walls, and gradually felt them merging into the rock which had now become soft and spongy. There was no real difference between my body and the rock, except that *I* was in my body - which was sufficient for me to will it through the spongy walls. I began to slide forward!

As I did, I saw lines of energy coming from Yiannis and directed towards me. Some of them were simply 'comforting' lines while others were 'hooking' into me and gently winching me forward. I felt a mixture of security and disappointment: security because of Yiannis' presence, and disappointment because I realised that the feat of getting through the opening was not totally due to my personal abilities. Was this another test I was failing?

When eventually in, I was rebuked for allowing thoughts of failure to enter my consciousness.

"You've made it. Good. But, if I've told once I've told you a thousand times: thoughts of failure are themselves a sign of failure - which itself does not exist. There is no such thing as failure. You're wasting energy." As usual, he was right - irrespective of his whimsically circular logic!

"You did well, don't doubt yourself," he continued. "And don't forget that every time you make an effort, a percentage of the result is always due to some other source - it's a natural law," he added as he handed me my torch.

Was he referring to elementals - as in 'like attracts like'? Or to attracting the cooperation of a greater consciousness - in this case, himself? He had already made reference to the ancient Greek dictum which admonishes getting on with one's efforts having called upon the assistance of the goddess Athena. He was now suggesting that assistance was rendered automatically as a concommitant of any effort - without calling for it. I made a mental note to ask him to elaborate on this - later.

"Where are we?" I asked.

"In a tunnel," he said.

I switched on my torch. It was a cavernous place, with a ceiling rising on a gradient to around five metres, and a floor width of more than six. I couldn't see how far it went into the mountain lengthwise but it was definitely much more than its width. The ground was surprisingly dry and so were the walls.

"Let's rest here," he suggested.

Rest? *He* wanted to rest? That was a first. But *I* needed to. I sat beside him on the ground.

"You don't need the torch," he said.

I switched it off. There was enough light coming in through the opening to illuminate the immediate area around us but it faded into darkness farther in.

"I take it this is not our destination, then," I said.

"Yes. In a way."

"Could you possibly be more vague, please?"

He smiled at my mild sarcasm. "Every stop on a journey is a destination - and a beginning. Look back and see."

I did just that. And, yes, he was right: I'd met him at the doughnut hole which was a destination, apparently, to my 'call' and a beginning to a number of other destinations, each of which also acted as a beginning to another destination... Wasn't life, in general, the same? His reply suggested a continuity that led somewhere, a plan, albeit an open-ended one. Was that what he meant? He nearly always made remarks that were more than mere replies to my querries.

Having pondered on this, I went back to my original inquiry concerning our present destination.

"If this is a destination and a beginning to somewhere else, where do we go from here? Does this so-called tunnel of yours continue or terminate here?" I inquired, and squinted in the semi-darkness in search of another opening - which I could not see.

"Maybe it does, maybe it doesn't," was his answer. He shrugged his shoulders. Another teaser. Another poser?

I rose to the challenge. "But if it terminates here, then it is not a tunnel," I said.

"Why not?"

"Because a tunnel, by definition, has two entrances, or exits."

"Not necessarily. That's just one type of tunnel. In any case, this one too has two entrances or exits."

"Where?"

"There," he said, pointing to the way we'd come in. "That's an entrance, and an exit."

"But that's just like a doorway - it is not leading through the mountain to another exit."

"So what? It's a short tunnel that leads out of the mountain the same way it leads into it."

Was he being facetious, playing games and entertaining himself at my expense? Maybe he was tired and wanted to relax with silly wordgames.

"Well, in that case," I responded, "this is not a tunnel - it's a burrow."

That was it. Once again, I must have, inadvertently, tickled his sense of humour. He burst out laughing.

"Oh, you kill me, you do. Thank you, thank you."

I gave him time to settle down and asked him again whether the 'tunnel' really terminated there - it was obvious he was holding out on me; and I wanted to know if this was our 'final' destination on this particular journey or another resting station, as he had intimated. His answer was the same.

"Maybe it does, maybe it doesn't." And then added: "Maybe it is, maybe it isn't". He addressed both of my questions with the same degree of vagueness, and went suddenly quiet.

I didn't feel like pursuing the subject any further - it would've been an unenlightening game of definitions. Instead, I reflected silently on his enigmatic responses.

"But if you must know the truth, you must remember," he added cryptically, after a minute or two of silence.

"Remember what? I've never been in here before."

"All the same: to know the *truth* you must *remember*," he repeated.

He puzzled me. He had put extra stress on the words "truth" and "remember". I pondered. He shone his torchlight in my face.

"Truth," he said slowly, splitting the word in two.

He was speaking in Greek, of course, and the Greek word for 'truth' is *alithia*, which he split into *a* and *lithia*. Then, he repeated the same word but left out the final *a*:

"*A-lithi*," he said.

It took a little while for the penny to drop. Oh, yes, of course! The second part of the word, *lithi*, meant forgetfulness, oblivion; the first part, *a*, is a particle which when placed in front of a word negates its meaning and sometimes reverses it: *alithia* (truth), then, meant absence of forgetfulness which meant total memory!

That's what he was on about all along, telling me off for not remembering, pointing out that I would never get to the truth if I did not remember! "To know the truth you must remember" he said - not simply remember something to do with that cave but remember in general: totally. A very, very tall order.

"Yes," he said, switching off his torch, "it *is* a tall order, but then you're seeking the truth: the greatest search anyone can embark on - the search that everyone has embarked on ever since they came into existence."

"So, truth is memory."

"What else could it be?"

"Knowing all the facts?"

"Which is the same thing: complete memory possesses all the facts. Lapse of memory causes mistakes. Think of the word for 'mistake' [Greek *láthos*]: it derives from the same root as *líthi*. In other words, mistakes result from lapse or lack of memory."

"So if someone has complete memory, he cannot possibly make a mistake."

"Precisely. Although, strictly speaking, nobody makes mistakes: they simply act according to their lights, in line with their ability to remember - we've talked about this before."

Well, yes, he had touched on the subject of 'not being judgmental' on other occasions, and what he was doing now was applying his method of reiterating the point from a different angle - hammering it in from different perspectives.

"There is remembering and there is forgetting, you see," he continued; "the latter sometimes being a blessing; but, on the whole, it's no more than an incapacity to remember. However, it's not just forgetting that's the problem here, it's also the inability to hold onto the presence of an experience."

"What do you mean by 'holding onto the presence of an experience'?"

"The ability to hold the experience in your consciousness as constantly transpiring in the present."

"And this is to apply to all experiences, right?"

"Oh, yes."

"Wow. Is it really possible?"

"It's the aim."

"And how is this to be achieved?"

"By going back," he said, and gave me a knowing smile.

'Going back', the constantly recurring theme. This time I was determined to nail it once and for all.

"Going back where and how?" I persisted.

"To the beginning, to uncover the destination. By remembering."

I turned and looked at him, and he flashed another smile at me.

"There are two kinds of remembering, right?" he said, giving me a knowing look, expecting me to make the connection. And I did - he'd spoken about the two types of memory back at the hole in the rock. "We shall look at them from a slightly different, more practical, angle now," he continued. "They are the structure-dependent and the direct kind. The first one relies on associations and relationships - and it's explored by psychologists and psychoanalysts. The English verb 'to remember' is very illustrative of this sort: *re*-membering, putting back together.

"The second one relies entirely on the direct method, and it is illustrated by the Greek verb *thymámai,* or, to speak more accurately, *enthymoúmai* ['I remember'], which literally means 'to have, or to be, deeply in one's mind or heart', and 'to understand and acquire deep knowledge'."

"But this is a modern use of the Greek verb - I mean, in the sense of remembering, isn't it?"

"Partially, yes. Of course, there is the other verb, *mnemonévo,* which is better known to classicists, and which has even closer conceptual and practical associations with the direct method."

He elaborated further by offering me an etymology of the verb *mnemonévo* whose stem, as I confirmed later, derived variously from such roots as *men, man, mna* and *mne* all of which carried meanings of 'being in deep thought', of 'learning', of being a 'seer', an 'oracle', and of being in a state of *mania* (!) or 'enthusiasm'.

"Recognising is also part of memory, isn't it?" I chipped in.

My comment elicited a very approving look from him, and another smile.

"Thank you. You've, actually, put your finger right on it," he practically congratulated me. "Recognition is the quintessential aspect of the kind of memory we are concerned with here. To *recognise* [Greek: *anagnorízoh*], to know again; to go back to the original knowledge, and to know the beginning and the destination."

I was, suddenly, taken back and relived my experiences 'inside' the cypress tree and the walnut - their timeless circularity, their dynamic unfolding and growing within a frame of permanency, their 'end' being at their beginning: going back and seeing the future. Going back in order to see the future! Past and future as the present - the devil's gorge experience.

"Truth: total memory. The beginning and the destination. Memory of myself, remembering myself...." I was speaking my thoughts aloud, with half-closed eyes.

Knowing Thyself, he completed my train of thought.

Yes, of course: the Delphic edict. "And by knowing myself," I then remembered, "I know all else, since everything is within me and I can manifest everything like a hologram."

"Good, good," I heard him say. "We're going to take a look at another approach to the truth now. But watch your step - it can be slippery near the water."

His voice sounded a little distant. I opened my eyes fully and turned round to see him walking away, torch in hand, following the stream to the far end of the tunnel/cave we were in. I stood up and hurried to join him.

By the light of my torch, I saw him approaching another opening at that side of the cave. It was of a greater height than the first one and much wider. This opening was, in fact, the mouth of a tunnel which ran for a few hundred metres and was sufficiently large to walk comfortably in without stepping into the stream that flowed on one side of it. I noticed that the farther in we went the drier it became. But the real surprise came at the end of it.

We entered an enormous cave, dry and warm. At one end, there was a sizeable pool of water - more like a pond - which fed the stream we had been following. The light from my torch was not powerful enough to allow an accurate reckoning of the height of the ceiling, which could've easily been a few storeys high. The uneven floor seemed to stretch to more than half the size of a soccer pitch.

I expressed my surprise and admiration and asked one more time whether this was the end of our long trek - deliberately avoiding using the word 'destination' for obvious reasons. His answer was a repeat of the earlier one: "Maybe it is, maybe it isn't". Okay, perhaps I could extract a more direct answer some other way.

"Why are we here?" I inquired.

"I'm keeping a promise I made to you," he replied.

A promise? Which one? He had made a number of promises - to discuss or explain this, that or the other.

"You don't remember?" He sounded disappointed. "And you're actually looking for the truth...?" He shook his head and tut-tutted, feigning reprimand - or, maybe he meant it; I couldn't tell in the dark. "I promised to introduce you to some of your ancestors. Or, rather, to re-introduce you."

"Which ancestors?"

"The Greek variety." He was back to being economical with his answers again.

"When?"

"Soon. Come and sit down."

He shone the light to a small ledge, and I followed him there.

"Why in here?" I asked as I sat down.

"It's a special place. There are only a few of its kind on the planet."

He moved his torchlight around as if to familiarise me with the cave. I thought I saw flowers at the edges of the pond. I pointed my torch in that direction, and I was right: they were flowers. I turned the light round the cave and noticed other flowers in crevices and ledges - in full colour!

"How is it possible for plants to live in here, in total darkness, and flower with such brilliant colours? How is colour possible in darkness?"

"I have told you - it's a special place." Another non-answer. "You'll have to work that out by yourself."

I thought it more appropriate to deal with that later. For now, I wanted to explore the cave. I stood up and walked a few metres over to my right, casting the light all round, looking for the continuation of the tunnel. In my excitement, however, I tripped and nearly fell; Yiannis called me back with a mild reproof and a cryptic remark to the effect that if I were not careful I would be tripping over myself in more ways than one. I declined to respond to his comment, but on my way back I noticed the faint outline of what looked like an opening at the far end of the cave, opposite the part of the tunnel we had come in.

"Is that where the tunnel picks up from here?" I asked, as I sat down again.

"No. That's another cave."

"Ah. Are we going in there, too?" I asked, with unconcealed excitement.

"Oh, no. That's out of bounds."

"Why?"

"Because it houses the history of the planet. Leave it alone. Not now - some other time. Perhaps."

The history of the planet?! He was casting tantalising morsels of thrilling possibilities of investigation before me and then denying me access to them. And "perhaps" didn't sound very encouraging. I wanted to probe the issue further, I wanted to visit that cave.

"You can try, but you won't be able to get in," was his response. "You'll be wasting your time, and mine."

"Why?"

"Why, why, why? You are back to that again, are you? You

know very well why."

The only thing I could think of that would have prevented me from getting into that cave was some kind of 'barrier', a 'guard' of a sort. And, given the psychophysical environment I was dealing with, that would be a highly efficient elemental constructed for the purpose by humans or other beings infinitely more capable than me.

I turned the torch to see the knowing smile on his face. I had to drop the issue - for now. But only for now. My curiosity - no, an intense and genuine interest - had been aroused. I had to get into that cave, somehow. Also, as with the first cave, I wanted to know if there was a continuation of the tunnel - leading out to some exciting side of the mountain, perhaps? I checked around with my torch but, again, the light was too weak to detect any obvious openings from where I was sitting. I would have to walk around and investigate from closer quarters, later.

"Did you say we were going to take a look at another approach to the truth?" I reminded him.

"Yes. The diamond approach."

"Diamonds?! Oooh, great." It was my turn now to be facetious. I cast my eye around as if looking for diamonds on the ground. "Where, where?!"

He smiled at my silliness and shooshed me gently. "Shshsh. Be quiet."

He turned the beam of his torch to the ceiling and then moved it around, as if stroking the walls and the surface of the water.

"A good place to nest here, don't you think?" he remarked in low voice and in the manner of an actor throwing away a line.

"Yes," I said, "a very good place - if you're a bird or a bat."

He did not respond to my comment. He remained silent, and I wondered why. He should have said something. But his silence acted as a prompt - and he probably meant it to be that way - that led me to reflect on the expression he had used: "to nest". One of its main meanings was the one I had responded to, but, as in English, it had other, related, meanings too: a nest also meant a den or a lair or a hideout.

Instinctively, I looked around for wild and dangerous animals - not that there would be any in that part of Greece, and I'd seen most of them earlier during our trek. Looking around, however, I noticed how clean and tidy the place was. There were no traces of habitation either by humans or animals; and yet it looked neat, too neat, as if it had been tidied by someone.

I watched Yiannis' light as he moved it from wall to wall, from the ceiling to the water. In the darkness of the cave it became hypnotic - he did not stop it anywhere in particular, he kept moving it around slowly, in a measured way, and I followed its mesmerising undulations. Then the movement became gradually faster and faster, and I tried to keep up with it. My head was spinning....

After a while, it slowed down and came to pause on a small flower at the edge of the water. It was a beautiful, if strange, flower that stood at the tip of a slim half a metre tall stalk, and resembled a sunflower in shape and colour - golden and round, with distinct segments that looked like petals. It reminded me very strongly of an earlier experience I'd had in which I had identified myself with one such a flower.

Yiannis asked me to switch my light off - I'd forgotten I had it on. He switched his off too. The flower continued to be visible in the darkness. In fact, its colours intensified and began to radiate throughout the cave, emanating a delicate, but emotionally powerful, scent.

The identification I had felt with a similar flower in the past now became overpowering, and I found myself, once again, taking on that form - the flower from the pond sliding inside me - but only momentarily. I felt that, had I remained in that state for any considerable time, I would have vanished, dissolved, disappeared. I had the inkling that that was a state to aim at but that I was not capable of attaining and retaining it - yet. Something hurt inside me. It was a pain of two kinds: the pain of disappointment for not quite making it, and a more 'surgical' pain, like the cauterising of a wound with disinfecting spirit.

As the flower withdrew from me and retreated to its earlier position by the pond, I started to experience a different feeling regarding the cave: it was not so much a cave now as much as a temple - a 'holy' place. Visually, it remained a cave but the feeling was one approaching religious awe.

And it was dark, pitch black. And quiet. I'd been in dark places before, in rooms and other caves, but this darkness had a different feel about it - a lightness I hadn't experienced on any other occasion, a lightness that was practically a substance in itself, and which

I felt spreading inside me and causing my body to lose its heaviness and solidity. It was pleasant, elating, and made me feel a little light-headed. The quiet, too, was unique. I had heard of people talk of 'hearing' the silence, but I hadn't understood what they'd meant until then - it was as if quiet actually 'existed' instead of simply being absence of sound.

I sat there listening to the quiet and watching the darkness - watching the sparkles which began gradually to fill the darkness, watching the darkness giving way to clouds of swirling colours and shapes.

Before long, whole scenes were passing by: landscapes with animals and humans engaging in all kinds of activities, a great variety of forming and dissolving objects - some of it merely psychological flotsam and jetsam surfacing from my gradually unconstrained subconscious, as the Teacher might have put it. The cleansing stage of the passive-receptive method of intuiting - certainly not the one he would have advised me to pursue throughout. But I knew I could use it as a preliminary 'opening-up' to lead to the 'concentrative' stage.

I allowed it to unfold without my interfering with it and let it peter out without becoming involved in it. I ignored all the perceptual and emotional claptrap that was thrown up, and resisted all the 'imaginary' digressions.

The problem here, however, was that there did not seem to be a concentrative stage - I hadn't planned this situation and, therefore, had no objective to concentrate on, had no clear idea where it was leading to. The last two things Yiannis had spoken of which were worth noting, and perhaps pondering on, were the diamond approach to the truth and this cave being a good place to "nest" in. The second of the two I decided to leave alone as it did not sound relevant at the time, it might have been just a way of speaking.

The first was the really significant one. The diamond approach to the truth. I pondered. That would be my concentrative stage. I engaged in a breathing exercise while concentrating on the idea of a diamond, visualising a diamond hanging in the air a short distance from my face. The quiet and the surrounding darkness proved highly conducive to focusing my attention and visualisation. All the same, it took me a while to construct the image of a diamond, and even then it was a simple one with no more than half a dozen sides.

I rotated it slowly, continuously correcting the sides that kept slipping and spoiling the shape. I made the sides reflect an imaginary light.

And then, just when I thought I could hold the image fairly comfortably, it began to take on a life of its own. It grew increasingly bigger and moved away towards the centre of the pond where it hung high up above the water and close to where the ceiling must have been. Its sides also multiplied enormously, with some of them being very obviously bigger than others; and it possessed a light of its own - radiating from inside as opposed to the light I had imposed on it from the outside, which had now disappeared. The overall shape of this gigantic diamond was that of an egg - an egg which radiated, through the multiplicity of its sides, a glorious iridescence....

The Cave and the 'Ancients'
(The Diamond Approach to Truth)

Yiannis remained silent throughout this development, and I had almost forgotten he was present - until I raised the query in my mind regarding the significance of the diamond and its connection with the truth. Then he 'spoke', although I could not be certain whether he spoke physically or merely projected his thoughts. He reminded me of his promise to re-introduce me to my Greek ancestors and the necessity on my part to 'remember'.

He had hardly finished 'speaking' when the diamond sides turned themselves into 'doorways' through which human figures began to emerge - a great variety that seemed to cover all epochs and races, many of whom I felt strongly attracted to. But there was a selection process which I sensed Yiannis was operating - picking out the ones he wanted me to pay specific attention to. They were all from ancient Greece. And I began to recognise them, some because of past personal acquaintance and others by simply 'recognising' who they were. They stretched back to pre-Homeric times, to the era of the heroes and beyond.

First, they came to their 'doorways', one by one, as the diamond egg revolved slowly on its axis. They were all kind of 'priests', but not in the modern sense of the word. They were Initiates in the ancient Greek Mysteries, people who had gone through lengthy processes of Initiation - lengthy in terms of years and lifetimes. By means of training and devotion to their search - and a great deal of psychological pain - some of them had overcome the 'human condition', had become 'completed'. Not all of them had come out of the same type of Mystery School, nor were they all of the same level of Initiation, but they all shared the same source of knowledge. And they had a duty: to disseminate.

I became deeply involved in these 'revelations' and wanted to understand what the process of dissemination entailed. Yiannis was not forthcoming with explanations, he simply guided me mentally and left it to me to prod and unravel my intuitions.

After a while, I began to pick up threads, but it was a complicated unravelling. The idea of dissemination was wrapped up with a
drastic change of approach to the understanding of the world, an
approach which was being introduced as a shift to enable consciousness to develop in a new direction - before temporary balance
was restored at another level.

It was complicated because it implicated more than just human
consciousness. The scheme included the Earth as a whole, the Universe, the world of Existence in general.... I felt Yiannis pulling me
back and stopping me from moving into a wider field; he wanted me
to stay within certain limits; and to make sure I remained in his
target area, he drew my attention to Omeros (Homer).

I was not made to see the details of Omeros' work, only his approach. Omeros was a great Initiate who disseminated symbolic as
well as semi-mythical events in the history of creation and of human
consciousness. Many of the myths he 'created' or perpetuated were
just that: pictorial ways of depicting events of creation; others, were
literal accounts. He presented them in ways that his contemporaries
were capable of experiencing, indeed *were* experiencing, and therefore able to understand - according to their individual lights. In
many instances, giants and monsters and gods were not symbolic or
mythical but actual existing beings.

I saw Hesiodos (Hesiod) standing next to Omeros, as if in support, expounding his *Theogonia* in which he traced the birth and
adventures of the gods. As with Omeros, these were representations
of cosmic, and prehistoric human events: a display of semi-human
and 'semi-divine' beings engaged in an evolutionary scheme.

But what really grabbed my attention was Omeros' great epic,
the *Odysseia*, one of the most potent depictions of the journey of
human consciousness ever written. It was constructed to work on
many levels: heroic for the general public, representational but also
real for the various degrees of Initiation, and schematically abstract
for those who were practically 'completed'. The last two aspects
were the ones that interested me most: the adventures as real events,
and the abstract.

As I dwelt on them, Yiannis guided my attention to individual
pieces and their meaning. Each adventure was acted in 'real' space,
that is, it took place in an objective world - albeit non-physical; but
nonetheless real. The adventures, as the Initiate went through them,

were experienced in objective space and elicited normal reactions - indeed, the perception of the events was more powerful than if they had taken place in physical space. I was reminded of the fear I had experienced in the rock and the pain I had felt when I concentrated on the woman's broken arm back at the cypress tree - but also the elation I had felt on various occasions.

Each incident was an adventure with specific meaning for each individual Initiate, in accordance with their level, and each adventure was specially constructed to emphasise and develop a particular feature of consciousness - the whole enterprise being a shortcut to consciousness expansion carried out at a non-physical level; an often painful journey, with the experience of pain decreasing as intermittent feelings of elation increased towards the stage of 'completion'.

I watched a 'speeded-up' version of the epic, and participated in some of the experiences. I could see and feel the sufferings of Odysseus as he resisted the temptations thrown in his way, sacrificing earthly pleasures, breaking the illusions, trying not to deviate from the path, developing one-pointed concentration: aiming for the goal.

And, again, there were many levels to accommodate different degrees of Initiation. I had a taste of the experiences of many acolytes who had gone through the adventures at a literal level and experienced first hand the actual existence of Cyclops and of Circe, to mention but a couple, and reacted to them on a one to one basis in real space. And then I was 'pulled up' to another level at which the very same experiences were meanings.

I wanted to stay with Omeros and Odysseus much longer, as they had started to draw me into a world of reminiscences, but the old man pulled me back with the warning that I should remember but not indulge: "be in the world but not of the world" - I knew, however, that I would go back at some point to revisit the *Odysseia* scene by scene, adventure by adventure, experience by experience.

As I was being 'pulled away' from Omeros and Odysseus, I had the sensation of being in the middle of an earthquake. I'd had experiences of this sort as a child back on my island home and I knew that the best thing to do on such occasions would be to run out into open space - a cave would be just about the worst place to be in. I expected Yiannis to make a move, but he didn't. There was also a loud hissing noise which I took to be coming from the spring which fed the pond.

I was baffled when I realised that both the 'earthquake' and the hissing were, instead, coming from the diamond egg - and my own body! At least the place wouldn't be caving in on me. But why all the shaking and hissing? The latter I half-recognised as the sound I'd heard sometimes when getting out of my body - but the shaking? I had no answer to that, and it did not concern me for long, as it soon settled down to a gentle shimmer - a very pleasant shimmer, in fact.

The shaking and the hissing of the diamond egg was accompanied by a number of 'special' looking people stepping out of 'doorways'. As before, they appeared to be of a variety of cultures but I recognised in particular those from India, China, Persia and Greece. Once again, my attention was directed to the Greeks. I resisted that and made an attempt to see why all these people, with their racial differences, were grouped together and pointed out. And it was worth the effort. They were the Axis people. I remembered that from around the middle of the 7th century to about the end of the 5th century BC - down to Plato and Aristotle - there had been a sudden flourishing of intellectual and artistic creativity in these countries - and, as I now intuited, also in other parts of the globe.

In Greece, in particular, later scholars spoke, and still do, of the birth of philosophy and science and mathematics, besides the inventions and achievements in art, literature and history, to mention but a few areas in which they undoubtedly excelled. But why were these people shown to me, apart from the obvious fact that they were indisputably great in all those areas?

I was then back to being shown that they were Initiates of varying degrees and that they had a task to carry out - all of them, including those that were not Greek. What task?

"First, you need to bear in mind the great impulse," the old man spoke at last.

He had mentioned the "impulse" up on the hill in relation to a new race - he had called it "new" then. Was he now referring to the same thing? I waited for him to expand.

I heard him take a deep breath. "It's like a deep breath the planet takes periodically; it rejuvenates itself and inaugurates a new cycle. Everything and everybody is affected. It reverberates throughout the

Earth for centuries. For humans, it ushers in a new era, developing a new characteristic of consciousness. You have remembered that, haven't you?" he said, more in a confirming tone than questioning.

Yes, I had. I had seen and felt and been made aware of the fact that there had been a change and that there had been a task to be carried out. But what change and what task exactly? I asked.

"So, you have not really remembered, have you?" he sighed. "You see and yet you don't see, one minute you remember, the next you forget. Go back."

And on that, the diamond egg projected a most brilliant display of colours from its innumerable 'doorways'. Those 'doorways' out of which people had come most recently emitted a golden radiance - a radiance which also emanated from the persons themselves. I'd never seen so many hues of golden yellow before. I watched in amazement, and thrill. And gradually I began to understand.

It was a process of revisiting a distant memory and coming to see what I had already seen but only half-understood and allowed to be obscured by inattention: the diamond approach to the Truth, a many-sided diamond in which every side revealed an aspect of the truth, all aspects being true. No contradictions, no falsehoods. But with every 'impulse', a new way of looking at the world is emphasised, and consciousness becomes 'judgmental' as the emphasis shifts - the aim of the Initiate being to see all aspects and cease to be judgmental... A long journey, a long cycle...

I was pulled back to the task at hand. What was it? Ah, the shift from the intuitive to the rational, from the direct method to the logic of objects, of things outside of us which must be observed and 'judged'. The objectification of the world, the need to develop discrimination and a 'three-dimensional' logic in order to eliminate the pitfalls of confusing personal fantasy, unchecked gullibility and superstition with real intuition and knowledge.

The shift to objectivity, logic and scientific method - a shift to observing the 'external', physical world. A long and arduous process aiming at gaining and strengthening individuality - restricting consciousness in order to enable it to expand with accuracy at the stage of 'completion'....

"But haven't people always viewed the world as an object - as in hunting for survival and fighting for control and supremacy, for example?" I wondered.

"True," the old man retorted, "but that has been at an instinctual and emotional, low-emotional, level. Fear - remember? 'Objectivity' in the instinctual sense has been around for a very long time - since the inception of sexuality, in fact. A much earlier 'impulse' towards the formation of individuality."

He sensed my readying myself to ask about "the inception of sexuality", and intervened. "Don't go there, it is not relevant at this juncture. We are dealing with another impulse here: a push towards observation and the application of a more objective logic - an intellectual approach."

I pondered. If this was a concerted effort, how could we account for the discrepancies? I knew from history that practically all of those early Greek philosophers - collectively known as Presocratics - had put forward ideas which competed, and often contradicted one another. Perhaps with the exception of Pythagoras--

"Ah, but you're wrong," Yiannis cut into my thoughts. "The contradictions were apparent, not real. And they were only due to personalities and degree of Initiation. Look," he said, and drew my attention to one of the figures that was already standing in front of one of the 'doorways'.

It was Thales, a genius of a man whose name appeared consistently on all the lists of the seven sages of ancient Greece. His life and exploits unfolded before me, but Yiannis wanted me to pay special attention to two things about him: his arguments that everything in the world had its source and sustenance in water, and that "all things are full of gods".

" 'All things are full of gods' - a most misunderstood and misinterpreted pronouncement if ever there was one. Scholars take it to mean that there are little gods in everything around us, which is not too far from the truth, but they forget that Thales, and those that preceded and followed him, also believed that nature on the whole was divine, that 'God' was everywhere, that nature was 'full with God', 'full with life', 'alive' - *hylozoein*. The 'gods' he referred to were directive agencies. You know what I'm talking about, don't you?"

Yes, I knew. I'd seen and experienced those wonderful entities who worked selflessly through their bodies to create and maintain the world. And it seemed to me that the figure of Thales was nodding in agreement (!).

"What about his theory in regards to water?" I asked.

"Another misinterpretation. Thales *knew* that water had special qualities - besides being essential to life and turning to steam or air and becoming solid, as in ice. Also, there was another thing that has never been brought out: it was not just *physical water* he talked about - it was also liquid in general. In the case of us humans, it was the liquid in our nature and our liquid nature: the fluidity of the psyche. You may see that coming up with the others later."

Once again, Thales nodded his approval. I decided to coordinate with him and get direct confirmation. Which I did, and 'asked' him to expand on the comments made by Yiannis. He did, not by way of literally speaking but by means of 'formulating' thoughts which I could 'see'. However, he added nothing new, apart from giving me a longer explanation - and he sounded as if he had rehearsed the whole thing. Yiannis chortled.

"Why are you laughing?" I asked

"Because I could see what you were doing."

"What do you mean?"

"You posed your questions with twentieth century expectations. You know very well that the Thales you've just been communicating with lived over two and a half thousand years ago. You have been talking to what Thales left behind - a shell, a ghost, a computer record, not an actual living person. The real Thales has incarnated and died many times since. Come on now, get with it."

True, logically and experientially the evidence was there, but I got carried away - the imagery was so 'alive' and convincing.

"What am I doing here, then - talking to ghosts? What for?" I responded in half-serious protest, beginning to suspect that Yiannis was setting me up for a practical joke.

"The knowledge is still there - all that's required of you is your understanding," he continued, ignoring my reaction. "There," he added, drawing my attention to another figure, "coordinate yourself with Anaximenes."

Anaximenes was a younger contemporary of Thales, about forty or so years younger, and living in the same city of Miletos (Miletus) on the coast of Asia Minor (present day Turkey). He pointed out air as the principle of life, what started and maintained the world. And, as with Thales concerning water, he pointed out that air changed with condensation and rarefaction, becoming liquid and solid, that air was necessary for life, that it was pervasive and divine - the breath of 'God'. I could see that it was a matter of emphasis.

Then Anaximandros (Anaximander) - an imposing figure, lying between the other two in terms of age - made his presence felt. The three of them, from the same city, stood close to one another and put on a show of arguing. It was rather amusing, and I wasn't certain that it was not the work of Yiannis. But there was a serious side to this: it was an illustration of the fact that these three men, and especially Anaximandros, had introduced the practice of *rational debate*, in which one person puts forward a theory which another person criticises and in turn proposes a new one, and so on - something which we are all used to now but which was first practised in Miletos at the beginning of the 6th century BC.

Anaximandros, like the other two, as well as a number of his contemporaries and those that followed him, was what we might call a Renaissance man - interested in everything and writing about everything. But, again, Yiannis drew my attention to four arguments this Greek had put forward.

First, he proposed that everything rose out of what he called the *Apeiron*, that is, the Indefinite, the Boundless and Indefinable - not directly, but by a process that resulted in the hot, the cold, the dry, and the wet or moist, and out of these four conditions the whole world was created. Second, he argued that the Earth floated freely in space, third, that life began in the sea, and fourth that the world as a whole came into existence and disappeared periodically.

"Ignore the last three for now," Yiannis suggested, "and let us look at the first proposition. What do you make of it?"

I could see straightaway that the *Apeiron* was none other than Darkness or Non-existence. In the context of the two previous thinkers it could also be the divine that pervades everything, which is the beginning and principle of all things and into which everything returns.

"What of the hot, the cold, the dry and the wet?"

I had a real problem with this one. For a start, these 'things' were not substantives, they had no substance, they were features, adjectives, qualities. But qualities of what? If I said 'the coffee is hot', the word 'hot' would be describing the coffee; these 'things', however, were describing nothing.

"Precisely," he said. "You've put your finger right on it. They're describing something that does not exist: substance."

"You mean Darkness."

"No. I mean substance. Darkness is beyond description."

"But substance exists. It's all there is."

"Not really. Substance is an illusion. It is something that appears to be but it isn't."

"What?!"

"Look. When you are describing something, what are you describing if not qualities? Your body, as you very well know, is nothing more than a bunch of vibrations which perceives other bunches of vibrations. These vibrations are perceived only because a bunch of vibrations you call a sense organ is so arranged as to respond in a particular way. But, in the last analysis, vibrations are not substantives: they're activities, which give rise to illusions you call things, substantives."

I had to give it to him. His short-cut logic left nothing to be desired - except the truth.

"But, at a further analysis, everything is light - is it not?" I said. "Including illusions."

I'd thrown the ball back into his court: he could not say that light did not exist - to say that, he would have to deny consciousness. He could, of course, say that consciousness was an illusion, but then he would be admitting that he was conscious that consciousness was an illusion, and then that..... Mind you, he had said in the doughnut hole that consciousness was a psychological conglomerate, that it....

He did not answer my question but, instead, I suddenly found myself surrounded by the walls of a ten metre high pyramid of equilateral triangles as its sides. The diamond egg that lay beyond was partially obscured by the exceptional brilliance of the pyramid side which stood facing it. Like the last people who had come out of the diamond, that side of the pyramid glowed in vibrant golden yellow. It was a living energy. I felt it pouring itself into the pyramid and flooding me.

Something inside me responded, something that was golden yellow within me: it responded in recognition and reverence - it vibrated at the same wavelength as that side of the pyramid. I stood up automatically, crossed my arms over my chest, and bowed - in reverence and love. This was no ordinary energy - it was alive, life-giving, creative. And it was directive: it had intelligence and purpose. Suddenly, I realised I was in the presence of - and inside - a great entity, greater perhaps than the ones I had encountered on the hilltop. I was certain that I owed my life to it - it was inside me, an essential part of me, I wouldn't be alive without it! - not only physically, but also emotionally, intellectually and at the intuitional level.

I saw a strong connection with many of those personages who had come out of the diamond egg - and I felt that a special case was being made regarding those Greeks, perhaps for my benefit and at Yiannis' suggestion. The connection with the Greeks was at an intellectual and intuitional level. I saw them ushering in a new era but also holding onto an older one - emphasising the logical but also holding onto the intuitive, applying 'three-dimensional' logic but being 'esoteric' in their knowledge and evidence.

And then, just as one side had come to life and poured itself into the pyramid and me, another side, the one to my right, did exactly the same - only this was in the richest red. And, again, I felt the penetrating connection and the urge to respond reverentially and with love, which I did by turning round and bowing - except that, as I turned and took my position opposite the red triangle, I was also still facing the golden side. I had kind of duplicated myself so that I ended up facing both sides.

And that was not all: the same thing happened with the side opposite the golden triangle. This appeared in all the shades of blue, but primarily in a deep electric blue. Like the others, it circulated throughout my bodies - physical, emotional, mental - and was recognised and acknowledged for its essential presence. As I left a 'duplicate' of myself and turned to the fourth side of the pyramid, I was flooded by the most glorious purple which electrified me with its magnificent healing energy. I bowed in reverence and love and turned to my original position, facing the golden yellow.

I was now standing in the centre of a pyramid with the 'four of me' facing its four sides and totally immersed in colours. I could feel those different-coloured energies coursing throughout the pyramid and me and knew they were the creators of the world, the principles of existence; the four qualities of Anaximandros. They were qualities of themselves which appeared substantive! The real substance, however, was the *Apeiron*, which was beyond Existence!

Through the golden triangle I then saw another man, a flamboyant figure, stepping out of the 'doorway' he had been standing in. This was Empedocles, who pointed to the four sides of the pyramid and named them as gods and as "roots" or elements responsible for the creation of the world - fire, air, earth, water. And, by way of illustration, he affected the four sides one at a time, causing them to predominate in turns - and, in effect, causing me to feel hot, cold, wet, and dry, according to the way he influenced them.

But there was something else he did not affect which acted of its own accord and brought about a balance amongst the colour agencies: it was a silvery energy which rose from the floor like a mist and spread throughout the pyramid and me. I felt its coordinating and 'reconciling' influence inside me, the balancing of the colours and of the sensations of hot, cold, wet, and dry.

I knew of Empedocles, the inventor of rhetoric, the philosopher and great physician who, like Pythagoras - whom he followed in many respects - was credited with performing medical miracles, and who rightly taught that in order to cure diseases one must understand nature as a whole. Who--

Yiannis pulled me back, and the pyramid was gone. I resented that but he responded with his usual comment that I should not indulge. I was standing before the diamond egg with Empedocles receding to his 'doorway', and the three Milesians continuing to 'argue'.

But Yiannis' main intention now was to show me how these early Greeks who were connected with the Mystery schools were not simply the initiators of the new approach, that of looking outside and arguing using logic - and thus inventing rational debate - but that the overlapping in their teachings pointed to the source of their common knowledge and that the emphasis in their individual teachings was just that, emphasis and nothing more. The real interest of those who had gone up the rungs of Initiation was the original meaning of philosophy: the love of wisdom, not just knowledge.

And, to drive his point home, Yiannis indicated Heraclitos (Heraclitus) who was standing in one of the 'doorways'. Heraclitos has been both admired and dismissed by the ancients as obscure, enigmatic, oracular, haughty and supercilious. But when I coordinated with him I found all those epithets totally misapplied. The man was a beautiful human being who simply did not care to 'popularise' his knowledge. He came from a royal and priestly family and what he wrote was mostly for the eyes and ears of those who were ready and able to understand, that is, those who were on the path of Initiation - just as, a few years later, Parmenides and Empedocles wrote for their disciples and those who were already on the path.

"You can see that Heraclitos emphasises fire as the main element, the essence of the world," Yiannis began to expound. "But notice, too, how he talks of the finest aspect of fire as ether, the directive principle of which the souls of men are also constituted. And how this soul-intelligence of man is part of the cosmic intelligence which, at a deeper level, is the *Logos*, which, as you know, embraces the meanings of account, reason, proportion, measure, balance, directiveness, as well as speech."

Yes, I could see that. I could also see how ether featured in the accounts of all those early Greeks as the finer aspect of nature, of the world in general. In some accounts even, it was an extra element that balanced and organised all other elements. I was powerfully reminded of the sparkling silvery mist which rose from the ground and 'balanced' the colours in the pyramid.

"The *Logos* is the backbone, so to speak, of the structure of the world, its hidden and essential aspect - its apparent aspect being the continuous movement or war of the opposites," Yiannis further elaborated on Heraclitos' idea.

"Is this why he calls the warring, ever moving opposites, 'same', and the other way round, the 'same' he calls 'opposite'?"

"Yes, because of the unifying function of the *Logos*. Opposites are on a continuum: cold is the other end of hot, for example, with gradations in between. Day and night are opposites that form a unity in which neither can exist without the other. Also, because something that's bad for one form of life could be perfect for another, such as sea water: poison for man to drink, absolutely necessary for fish to survive."

Coordinating with Heraclitos, I could see how the basic 'elements' of water, fire, earth and air were working, and how predominance of one or the other was seen as war, but also how the ethereal aspect of fire, the *Logos*, held them in eventual balance. I could also see how Empedocles later spoke of Love and Strife and that Love was basically and ultimately the real creator and sustainer of the world. Further ahead, I could see Parmenides' denial of the world of multiplicity, and his follower Zeno coming up with his paradoxes of time and space to illustrate the illusory nature of the world! - there was definitely an underlying current here.

And then I saw something specific that engaged my attention further. It was Heraclitos' idea that the soul, which, in his terminology, is itself 'fire', after death turns into 'water', but that the souls of virtuous men become guardian daemons before, eventually, joining the cosmic 'fire'. This I found very intriguing because, when translated into another terminology, it fitted very comfortably into the Teacher's system!

After death, according to the Teacher - and to my limited experience - most souls end up in the world of desires and emotions - signified by water. Those who are morally 'advanced' stay in that world to help others disentangle themselves from their 'watery' attachments. Eventually, they die a second death which takes them to another level where they join the 'spiritual fire' - and there are, also, those who 'die' while still alive in order to carry out the same task.

Heraclitos, who had given up his royal title, privileges and political position in order to devote himself to the Mysteries, eventually left his home town of Ephesos (Ephesus) to live in the mountains, spending the rerst of his life in meditation.

By this time, I'd begun to remember directly, my memory was slowly and gradually being restored. The cave was, indeed, a temple because of the way we had used caves a long, long, time ago: to "nest", to leave our physical bodies and 'travel' to other worlds. Later, we used special rooms in temples and pyramids for this purpose....

These Greeks were now being set in a clearer light. Empedocles, the philosopher, physician, eloquent speaker, miracle worker, was a mystic - occultist or Magician would be better words to describe him if only for the public exhibition of his 'secret' knowledge of nature. And so was the great Parmenides who changed the course of Western thinking. They were Pythagoreans... And so were many others of their contemporaries and later searchers after the truth....

Parmenides, the mystic, stood at his 'doorway', ready to elaborate. I did not need the details of his journey: the fasting, the meditating, the incubating - the 'nesting' - nor how the goddess guided him to a state of understanding Truth. But I loved to remind myself of how he had brought out the idea of stringent abstract reasoning to prove to the world - to those who were 'listening' - that reality as we know it in everyday life does not 'exist'.

I coordinated with him to hear the two 'choices' one more time: (i) reality *is* and exists, (ii) reality *is not* and does not exist. Choice (ii) he rejects on the grounds that only that which *is* can be known. Reality *is*, and it is uncreated and ungenerated (it cannot come about from non-being), it never perishes (it cannot turn into non-being), it is continuous, indivisible and unchangeable (nothing can come into existence and impinge on it or change it), it is homogeneous, motionless and balanced in perfect equilibrium, it is like a sphere and occupies all space because there can be no void 'inside' or 'outside' of it.

Later scholars called this kind of inquiry a 'second-order' intellectual activity, totally missing the two points of the exercise: one, demonstrating how the application of 'three-dimensional' logic can lead to abstract conclusions, mistakes and illusions, and two, that the constant concentration on this method can lead to a 'breaking through' the logic itself, to transcending it by way of affecting consciousness along the lines of the practice of a *koan*. All that was got out, by most people who studied Parmenides, was the application of his logic in the three-dimensional world. Indeed, Parmanides' closest follower, Zeno, who was now standing next to him in the 'doorway', illustrated very forcefully this point with his famous antinomies and paradoxes of space and time.

Anaxagoras then came out of his 'doorway' to put forward the idea of Mind as the eternal reality lying behind all creation - infinite and self-ruled, in the world and yet apart, the motive force of all things that exist: Heraclitos' ether-logos, the fifth element that balances the other four - agreeing with Parmenides and Empedocles in his central argument, and pointing out that everything in the world contains everything else in it, and that there are many 'worlds' not just one.

Then, Diogenes of Apollonia showed the intrinsic connections between macrocosm and microcosm, and how the creation of the world is purposeful. He then leant forward to point out something of particular interest to me, namely, that perception can only take place in the presence of attention - which I had already equated with a core aspect of consciousness.

Next to Anaxagoras I then saw Democritos (Democritus), the

much-travelled 'atomist', the Laughing philosopher, the Magician, the alchemist - being ushered in by none other than the Pythagorean Philolaos (Philolaus). Atoms: the 'irreducible shapes' of Nature - 'reducible', and explicable, only as non-three-dimensional 'etheric' vibrations.Was there anything this man did not know or write about? If only his works had survived.

What a picture! A series of great men, all pointing out aspects of the Truth in their individual characteristic ways, in accordance with their level of Initiation, even appearing antagonistic to one another at times, but bringing in a new and powerful means of individualising, of honing consciousness by way of rational debate.

And then, as if to crown it all, the Master himself, Pythagoras, with his long flowing hair, more resplendent than Empedocles, made his appearance in a large glowing 'doorway'. And it all came flooding back:

The School: the public 'listeners', the inner groups, the innermost groups. Membership: men, women, slaves, foreigners - no discrimination, all equal, all human. The healings, the 'miraculous' healings, the 'miracles' performed as tests of Initiation. The edicts: "Teach by healing" and "Heal by teaching". The disciples having to find their own way, their inner selves. The 'teachings': abstinence, self-control, control of wild desires, thoughts and emotions... Reincarnation... Techniques for remembering past lives... The numbers... Many universes.... The central hearth.... The music... The sounds: constructing and deconstructing... Pherekydes.... Abaris and the 'flying machine'... The persecutions, the murders, the arsons... My old school, my beloved Pythagoras... Everydody was touched and influenced by his presence and by his 'teachings'... *Τάδε έφη Πυθαγόρας* = 'thus spake Pythagoras'....

And, close behind Pythagoras, practically inside him, stood the powerful figure of Orpheus holding the *kratēr*, the chalice, the mixing bowl filled with the *kykeón,* the drink which contained all the elements of creation and which, when drunk, caused confusion to those who were not ready and enlightenment to the initiated.

Ah, hadn't Yiannis said something to me along the lines of "we'll make a Pythagorean out of you yet"? I should ask him to explain, seeing that I had now remembered my ancient connections with the School. I asked, but there was no reply. I repeated the request, but there was still no response. I fumbled for my torch and turned it on.

Yiannis wasn't there. His bag was lying on the ground where he had placed it earlier, but he himself wasn't there. I shone the light around the cave calling out to him. Nothing. Not only that, but the diamond egg also began to fade away. Soon, the cave was back to its normal quiet and darkness - except for my torchlight.

I sat down and switched off the light to make it easier to concentrate and evaluate the situation. But not for long. The darkness was lit again by a white brilliance that seemed to come from the direction of the out-of-bounds cave. I couldn't make out the actual source until it subdued itself somewhat - or I adjusted myself to the brilliance perhaps - and then, I recognised Yiannis. He was young, very young, and he was in a Body of Light. No, no, - he *was* a Body of Light! I felt it, I felt the difference: to be *in* a Body of Light means that you construct one and inhabit it, to *be* a Body of Light means that you have abandoned your physical body and now live as a Body of Light!

And then, he began to change. He lit up like a Christmas tree. Spinning wheels and globes of many different colours suddenly appeared all over this Body of Light, which itself gradually became more of a tenuous outline of a human form. It turned into a delicate and yet complex structure of revolving concentrations of energy, all interconnected by 'streams' of light. There were times when flowing energies gave the impression of wings - on the ankles, the sides of the body, the sides of the head - while at other times it looked very much like an array of stars, a constellation, a galaxy! It retained the personal touch of Yiannis - his love and connectedness with me - but, at the same time, there was something 'objective' and awe inspiring about it which conveyed a sense of kin with those wonderful entities in the pyramid and at the hilltop.

It was a *transfiguration*! And it brought back clear memories of similar events with other consciousnesses, such as Pythagoras and Empedocles - and chants of being the "child of starry sky", and existing "in his own image". It was a triumphal display, and it filled me with love and joy - but also with a strange feeling of hope and sadness. It was as if my best friend, my father, my protector, were leaving, returning home years and years ahead of me. I was almost in tears, but I checked them back - it would have been indulgence. "Be happy", he always said. It was easy, with all his outpouring of love. He was intimating what I should be expecting if I continued my search and my practices - he had, of course, spoken of having to become Light in order to survive Darkness.

There was a sudden and overwhelming emanation of light from 'Yiannis' which illuminated every nook and crevice of the cave, accompanied by a most uplifting music. Then, just as suddenly, the Light 'collected' itself towards the roof of the cave and shot through it, making a hissing and shaking noise. Momentarily, I thought the roof was about to cave in, but, as before, the shaking and the hissing was a psychic sensation I experienced through my connection with the activity of light.

– 20 –

The Medallion and the 'Lecture Hall'
(Humans, Non-humans, and Gods)

Back to darkness and total quiet. What would I do now? I was torn between staying in the cave a while longer - perhaps to ponder, reflect, meditate - and getting out of there and into daylight right away. I'd always been a day person, fond of sunlight. I had to get out of there. But which way? I didn't particularly want to return the way I had come in. I was not sure I could squeeze through that narrow opening again without Yiannis' help. And if I didn't make it, I would have to come all the way back to find another exit. I decided to go for another exit there and then; I felt certain that when Yiannis first said we were in a tunnel he meant it the way I understood it, that there was another way out.

I turned on my torch and went for his bag; I would need his torch and whatever else was in there. There was hardly anything: the torch, an empty bottle, and a little dry bread. Ah, and the chain with the medallion. He'd certainly been travelling light!

I picked up the medallion to examine it. It was light in weight; it felt nice and comfortable. I'd been intrigued by the fact that it was blank, just a blank disk. It was also sharp - I nearly cut my finger on its edge. I turned it carefully over to check the reverse side. That was more interesting. Engraved on it were three concentric circles, and in the inner circle there was a version of the caduceus-cum-Hippocratic emblem - a vertical rod with a small globe at its top and outstretched wings on either side of it. Entwined round the rod were two snakes which ended with arched heads facing each other just below the wings. The heads of the snakes and most of the two wings were within another circle.

The symbolism of Hermes, the messenger god - speed of travelling and communication, among other things - was obvious. Hermes was, also, known as the "guide of the soul", that is, the god who guided the soul into the underworld, the Greek counterpart of the Egyptian Anubis - hence Hermanubis, as I had been already reminded up on the hill. The Hippocratic part of the engraving was clearly linked with healing.

As I dwelled on it at a deeper level, I came to realise that it did not stand simply for healing, that is, piecemeal, occasional healing, but for a state of health that did not allow illness to appear at all. I could not see any further than that, except for my recognising the entwined snakes as the two columns of energy on either side of a person's body, and of the middle column. The whole engraving had a powerful symmetry about it that went beyond the mere representation. It was gripping!

I turned the medallion back to the obverse side and took another look at its blank surface; only to become aware, after a short while of staring at it, that it wasn't, in fact, blank! Faintly engraved, was a circle just inside the edges of the medallion. From the centre radiated lines that reached the periphery of the circle. I counted twelve. The overall picture was one of a circle with twelve segments. As I continued to stare at it, the image of the 'sunflower' began to develop through it like an image on photographic paper.

There was definitely a great deal to this medallion that needed unpacking. One immediate puzzle was which side was the front and which was the back - the way it was constructed and hung gave no indication. But it felt nice, and friendly. I decided to wear it - as a present from Yiannis, and, maybe, as a talisman. It was when I was putting it on that I realised how short the chain was; much shorter than when I had last seen it on Yiannis. The medallion hung just above my heart.

Since I had no idea how long it would take me to get out of there, I thought it a good policy to strengthen myself with whatever nourishment was at my disposal before setting off on my search for an exit. All I had was the little dry bread left behind by Yiannis. I walked to the pool and filled the bottle and then soaked the bread and ate it - it was only a few mouthfuls. I also drank to slake my developing thirst. I placed the full bottle in Yiannis' bag, along with his torch, slung the bag over my shoulder, and made for the 'forbidden' cave. I was still very keen to investigate, and, since I could not see any other opening in the cave, this, I thought, might perhaps lead to some other passage and to an exit.

The opening was small but wide enough for a person to walk through. Three or four metres in, the passage seemed to open out into something much wider. I decided to go in. But as I approached the opening I was gripped by inexplicable fear and felt sick; my stomach began to turn and my bowels were about to open. There was clearly something 'guarding' the entrance. I withdrew and took a couple of deep breaths. Having restored myself physically, I concentrated on creating a strong Body of Light, and then made another attempt.

The same thing happened, except that the attack of fear and nausea was much weaker. I withdrew for the second time, now feeling confident that I could make it. As I approached the opening for the third time, I was surprised that I did not feel nauseous. I was relaxed and casual - except that the medallion began to feel hot on my chest. I stopped and retreated a few steps, and the medallion started to cool down. On my next attempt, something really weird took place: I lost interest - more than that, I found the very idea of going into that cave repulsive. I pulled away and sat on the ground. I needed to recover and decide what to do next.

Yiannis was right. Trying to get in there would be a waste of time, even dangerous as I had just found out. I should concentrate my efforts on finding another exit.

I was about to move away when I had second thoughts. Who felt fearful and nauseous? Who was repelled by the idea of going in? My bodies: my physical, emotional, intellectual bodies - not me. *I* was not my bodies. If only I could hold onto this for a short while, I could get in there.

I stood up and prepared myself by strengthening that sense of I-ness, the consciousness I called *I*, and by dissociating myself from my bodies. And then I began to move in.

My physical body was attacked by pain from all sides, inside and out. It felt like breaking up, every joint and every sinew hurt, the blood was like boiling water in my veins. My emotions ran wild: fear, anger, depression - emotional turmoil. My thoughts were totally disorganised, now going in one direction now in another. Dark brown and grey piercing and tearing energy clouds were attacking relentlessly.

I had to hold onto that sense of being conscious - being conscious, and nothing else - dissociating, jettisoning all baggage and simply holding onto that sense. I knew this battle wouldn't last: either I would disintegrate under it and be lost as a unit of consciousness or survive it and come out stronger. It would not last, I was sure of it. I *had* to be sure of it.

And I was right. It did not last. I was inside - with my bodies intact. My confidence was, naturally, raised by this 'victory', but I was disappointed by the location. It was just another cave, smaller than the previous one. Where was the history of the planet? I expected to see artifacts, evidence. There was nothing. There were various openings all around which could be passages leading to other caves or chambers. Or, OR, Yiannis had tricked me into this as a test!

In any case, whatever Yiannis' veracity or intentions were, I had to continue looking for an exit - and if, in the process, I came across the 'history of the planet' I would consider it a bonus. But I had to move on, the batteries in my torch were showing signs of dying. I set about checking the walls from close quarters, slowly and methodically. Every now and then, I would come across a shallow entrance that led to a small dead end cave - but no chamber of artefacts. Then I would retrace my steps and carry on. It wasn't long before my torch packed in altogether. I took out Yiannis' torch and continued.

Eventually, I went into a passage that seemed to stretch for ever, with other passages branching off left and right. It was a maze, a labyrinth. I could've called it a warren but for the fact that there were no rabbits or any other form of life down there. And Yiannis' torch was now dying on me, too. I veered off to the left into a sizeable cave and decided to rest for a while and take stock. There were a number of small flat areas around the cave which were slightly raised off the ground and formed a series of ledges. I couldn't tell whether they were natural rock formations or artificial constructions, such as benches. It was a strangely warm and comfortable place. I sat on one of the ledges and pondered.

There were two major tasks requiring my attention. One of them was, naturally, the immediate problem of getting out. The other was the reflecting on and analysing and digesting the experiences I'd had in this underground maze.

By comparison, the latter should've been the least pressing; and, yet, I found myself drifting irresistibly into those questions of consciousness and existence that had dogged me all my life. Would it be appropriate - indeed, an intelligent course of action at all - to try and tackle them at this point in time when getting out of there was becoming increasingly a matter of life or death? But I coud not shake them off. How wonderful it would have been to ponder on such things and discuss them in the company of like-minded friends on the beach as we watched the sun go down - perhaps over a glass or two of Greek wine....

I was feeling ever so tired. I could not concentrate properly. Maybe I should rest. Yes, I needed to rest, just for a while, before resuming my search for an exit. I let go and entered that in-between state of wakefulness and sleep, sometimes called the Fourth State, which I had used on many occasions in order to slip into conscious dreaming, and other altered states of consciousness. Right then, however, all I wanted was to rest. But I could not get rid of the issues.

So, I switched off the torch and made use of the darkness to relax and allow some of the more persistent questions to raise their heads - a practical 'trick' for inviting inspiration. I thought of the fragility of Man, something which my father seemed to be constant-ly reminding me of; his intention being to draw my attention to the fact that life was precarious and that a person could drop dead any-time, whereas for me the fragility of Man was deeply important at a different level - that of existence in general, not merely the death of the physical body.

We walk around being perfectly confident of the unity we call Self, Individuality, 'I'. Yiannis had shown me how illusory that 'belief' might be, and I had experienced that possibility myself - although I had also experienced the 'solidity' and constancy of the 'I'. But how often is this 'I', this unit, a unit? - 'we' are constantly pulled this way or that by whichever physical organ or function or psychological complex happens to be predominating at the time; with each one having its own logic.

These 'bits' we are made up of, however, don't seem to be al-together random. They appear to be held together as if by a magnet, apparently according to 'laws' which govern their activities at a variety of levels. What is an even greater puzzle is why there exist such 'laws', whose operation gives rise to the impression we call unity. And, what is it - if there is anything - that causes these 'laws' to facilitate the coming into existence of the units, in the first place?

I was back to the basic question: *Are* we before we *Exist*? One part of me was saying that the units themselves were innate, that they simply were, and that they served their own purpose. Another part was saying that they were only constructions brought into existence by some power or other - the 'magnet'? - for its own purpose or benefit: 'It' creates, and dissolves or re-absorbs its own creations according to, and for, its own 'needs' and 'desires' - if such words be appropriate to use here.

I became aware that I was dangerously slipping into the realm of theology. Whether I was willing to posit a purposeful, self-directing 'It' that creates, orchestrates, and 'destroys' its own creations, or a multiplicity of 'eternal' units, it wouldn't make that much difference. Were those ancient Greeks getting to me? I knew that the Teacher would have certainly argued for an eternal, directive power which he would have called 'God', as well as for eternal units. Yiannis, on the other hand, would have gone for 'possibilities' not certainties - positing an underlying 'eternal' nature against which he would allow the possibility of the development of powerful units, of individual consciousnesses....

Whichever way I looked at it, it all boiled down to individual consciousness. After all, it was 'I' who had perceptions, concepts, experiences. But, given that there was this sense of 'I', what was the status of the experiences? Perceptions could be illusory, concepts were no more than metaphors of the 'understanding' in its efforts to capture the 'knowing'. The 'mind' was a sieve, an eclectic sanitizer whose function was mostly to keep the 'logics' of the parts - physical organs, psychological complexes, and so on - from monopolising the terrain or coming to blows with one another: it kept schizophrenia at bay.

Moreover, I, now as 'mind', am restricted by the opiates of thoughts, habits, beliefs: the beliefs in free will, continuity of existence, God, were all wired into me for the purpose of 'survival', they enabled the unit to exist. Happiness, too, as it touched the emotions, belonged in the same category - even the happiness derived from the thought of dissolving into Non-existence; for that happiness, as I'd tasted it in the rock, was still experienced by a person, a consciousness which was conditioned into existence.

Yiannis had suggested, on a number of occasions, that the only way out - and the only way to find out - was to become '*dis*-illusioned'. Which implied stopping the flow of perceiving, believing, feeling and thinking from asserting itself as the only 'reality' by either placing it on a perspective and rising above it or by refusing to ackowledge it altogether. I understood that the first option had been the one taken up by most researchers. The latter, if at all possible, would take one totally out of 'humanity' - something that had been tentatively hinted at by Yiannis but only as a final stage, perhaps even after 'completion': a most exciting suggestion, nonetheless, which implied amazing ontological changes!....

I held the medallion between my right thumb and index finger and rubbed it gently, absent-mindedly, like a child holding a doll or a comfort blanket. I wondered why Yiannis - or whoever had forged it - hadn't made it clear which side was the obverse and which the reverse. An apparently trivial thing to dwell on, but it held my attention for a while until the penny dropped. I understood it.

Up to that moment, I would have taken it to be a 'symbol', something that stood for a concretisation of meanings, of being a representation, a 'generic' concept. Now, it was an object that took the meaning of 'symbol' apart. It was not standing for something else: it was a correspondence, a group of correspondences packed together - the original meaning of 'symbol'. And it was imbued with tremendous energy.

Suddenly, I realised why I thought of it as a 'talisman'. For some peculiar reason - ever since I saw Yiannis wearing it at the taverna - I did not use the everyday normal Greek word for it, which would simply have meant an object for protection against evil, an amulet. I, consistently, used the English word 'talisman' - which now I recognised as an originally Greek word which had got into English via the Arabic language! The original Greek - *télesma* - carried the meanings of Initiation, of magical ceremony, of 'paying one's dues' and being free by means of 'completing' oneself; it was also a blessing.

It felt like a message left by Yiannis for me to wear and ponder on, a clue and intimation of a deeper consciousness. And 'wearing' it had wider implications than simply having it hanging round my neck. It contained correspondences which I experienced strongly in myself: as with the pharaonic sceptre, I felt the Hermes staff of the medallion transferring itself to my middle column, and the wings at the top spreading out from the crown of my head. The two entwined snakes identified themselves with my two side columns wrapped round my middle column with their heads facing each other towards the top of my spine, just below the cone that sat at the tip of the staff. This was not a 'symbol' standing for something outside itself: it was a direct correspondence, and wearing it meant having it within myself.

The 'symbolism' seeped through to the other side of the medallion. There was continuity moving in both directions. The power of the serpents on one side also contained the calm 'completeness' of the twelve empty segments on the other side, which themselves were a declaration of freedom: Yiannis telling me that he was free to come back, if he so wished, in whatever shape and form he chose to - the prerogative of a 'completed' individual consciousness.

Once again, I was filled with love and happiness, an outpouring, a blessing from a great consciousness. I felt a touch of nostalgia for his physical presence. His response was to bring out of my middle column the rod of Hermanubis. I felt a breeze on the sides of my head, as if the wings on either side of the tip of the rod were fluttering. The tip itself, the cone, was at the centre of my head, enclosing within it my pineal gland. I felt a surge of energy, and found myself standing before Hermanubis. As with Yiannis, when I first met him at the rock, he exuded a mixture of gentleness and severity. But it was the latter that really hit me. Despite his smiling at me, I felt a penetrating pain of regret.

At first, it was the sheer sense of it, and then it opened out into individual cases: friends and relatives, colleagues, even apparent strangers, whom I had wronged, some knowingly some unwittingly. It was a replay in minute, excruciatingly painful, detail. I felt their hurt the way they had felt it - I changed places with them, I was totally in their shoes. My god! I had always thought I was a nice person. It had never occurred to me that I was the cause of so much pain. I saw how I had nearly always justified my behaviour while the other person was in turmoil. And it went on.....

I could not stand this any longer. I broke down and burst into tears. I cried and cried and cried, and begged for forgiveness. I fleetingly thought of Yiannis' usual ticking off whenever I let myself 'indulge' in wasteful emotions, but this time he was definitely keeping out of it - I had to go through it, and make a promise to myself never to hurt anybody ever again. The vision of Yiannis at the cypress tree flashed before me - when he had said that he was incapable of hurting anybody. A flash, no more, but it was sufficient for a glimpse of understanding.

Then my grandmother turned up. She was a loving and caring person who had always looked after us kids whenever we fell ill, and cured us with her pagan rituals and chants to the sun, the moon and the stars. She flooded me with her love and repeated whisperingly her constant advice, as she passed by: "Don't mock the afflicted lest they find you out." An advice with deep karmic implications, which I hadn't always heeded. Now I could see how wide the ramifications were: it was not merely the mocking that was being pointed out here, it was more generally the attitude of insensitivity, of not feeling with those in pain or at a disadvantage. It was an advice to open up to other people's conditions and points of view, to be in their shoes.

Hermanubis gave me a guarded look of appreciation for my glimpse of understanding, but his whole demeanour was still one of severity and disapprobation. As I probed for the reason, I was taken back some years.

I was in my early teens and I was lying in a bed in hospital nursing a minor foot injury. In the bed opposite mine was a very old man, all skin and bone, on his last legs. I felt for him and sort of looked after him for the last few days. He was quiet, and needed very little attention, but I liked sitting and chatting to him.

One morning, I woke up at around four and felt the urge to see how he was doing. When I went over I found him awake. He smiled and squeezed my hand. I sat at the edge of his bed and smiled back. There was nothing to say. A few seconds later he made a small rasping noise as he breathed out - and died, still looking at me and smiling. I couldn't move. The nurse chided me mildly for being up so early, and took me back to my bed. Needless to say, I did not go to sleep. I had just witnessed death for the first time. Was death that easy? Just breathe out and.... and what? He was with me one minute and the next he was gone, gently, quietly....

A few days later, I was out of hospital and playing with my friends in the street. Suddenly, this young Turk raced by us on his bicycle, heading for a middle-aged woman who was sweeping the pavement in front of her house. When he reached her, he jumped off his bike and lunged towards her wielding a knife which he plunged into her neck and chest again and again until she dropped dead on the ground. He then threw the knife away, mounted his bicycle and rode off. He was that woman's son who disapproved of her abandoning his father and taking up with another man.

I was horrified. I walked over to the woman's blooded body to take a look but my stomach was not strong enough. I vomited, and went home looking white like a sheet.

In the space of a few days I had witnessed two deaths, and I felt as if I were going to witness a third one: mine. I accepted the first as natural, but the untimeliness and violence of the second haunted me for a long time.

Why was Hermanubis looking so stern? - and waiting? What for? The answer came in the experience of dying - my dying. I underwent a series of deaths, my deaths, from one incarnation to another. Some, like the old man's in the hospital, were quiet and expected, others were violent and seemingly untimely. Some were important, even famous, others were insignificant. Some I had already visited in the present life.

I was guided to see, once more, the repetition and continuity of life. Death was the end of physical life but not the end of 'life'. Life continued. The idea of 'resurrection' was a misconstrued and distorted memory of continuity of life. There was no end to life while in Existence. Physical death was always followed by a shift to another form of life, like ice turning to water, water turning to steam. There was not even a gap.

What was happening here was a reiteration of the purpose of socalled 'death' and 'rebirth': the creation of consciousness, of individuality, of a core that would survive Darkness - having expanded to include everything in it. All this I already knew. What else? There were other insights to be gained at this juncture.

All incarnations were seen as important and yet not so important. They were important for their individual contributions but when viewed on a perspective they were no more than stepping stones to the creation and expansion of consciousness. There was a sense of the end justifying the means, which surprised me, seeing that Hermanubis himself was involved in the judging of the actions and intentions of developing consciousnesses.

However, on this perspective, judgment was not to be seen as 'judgmental', that is, judgment was simply the application of the

Law, which, according to the ancient Greeks - as I knew - even the gods could not evade. In the end, through 'mistakes' and constant adjustments, consciousness would expand. On the way, the 'guide of the soul', Hermanubis, could become a personal acquaintance or merely a representative of the Law, depending on the individual's approach.

One other penetrating insight was the survival of the fittest. Not in the purely physical Darwinian sense but in terms of conscious-ness: the greater, the more expansive the consciousness the more likely it was to 'survive' Darkness.

To gain a better perspective, I was shown a brief history of the planet. Was this what Yiannis had meant? Maybe. But I was still fairly certain that there were artefacts to be found somewhere in this labyrinth. For now, I was more than content to be enlightened in another direction.

The history of the Earth I surveyed contained both physical and psychological aspects. On the physical side there were great land masses moving around over hundreds of millions of years, the shape of the planet being nothing like what it is now; there were seas where there are now mountains and vice versa and changing con-tinuously, the magnetic poles shifting many times so that the tropics could be found practically anywhere, including the arctic and ant-arctic regions. The fauna and flora, too, varied enormously, with species disappearing irretrievably and new ones appearing. Climatic changes ranged from freezing to scorching.

'Modern' humans appeared on the planet much much earlier than is calculated at present - there are fossils to be found to push the dates so far back that anthropologists will have a real problem re-evaluating their data.... Humans in general - and some 'strange' ones - have appeared and disappeared a number of times.... There have been periods when gigantic humans roamed the Earth - the structure of their nervous system being so simple that they would be unaware of sustaining severe injuries to their arms and legs as they ran through the forests trying to escape ferocious predators.... The Earth itself is a garden/laboratory in and through which experiments have been taking place for innumerable ages.....

As I viewed all this, I became aware of the similarities with my own experiment in going back to my birth. There was a strong par-allel and an intimation of symbiosis.

On the psychological side, too, there were parallels between the planet and humans in general. All animal life as well as all the species of vegetation, with their own particular logics and agendas, have always been pushing and pulling the consciousness of the planet in one direction or another.

And just as the seas and the land masses and everything that comes and goes inside and on the surface of the Earth contributes to the formation and life of the planet as a whole, so do the parts and organs of a human body influence its functioning as a unit.

The human form is loose - apart from a sketchy outline, everything in it is experimental. The organs and all else are on a drawing board from where they take living shape through numerous 'virgin' cells which act as raw material - and, every now and then, they return for 'reshaping'. Nowadays, occasionally 'deformed' humans - 'mutants' - are born: conjoined twins of all sorts, children with four arms, cyclops, and so on - the range is endless. But for millions of years there have existed naturally 'beings' with organs and body parts growing in the 'wrong' places: humans with animal parts and vice versa, and so-called mythological gods and animals.

As human consciousness expands, it becomes global, that is, it begins to relate more closely with the consciousness of the planet, which itself is incalculably enormous. The survival of the fittest is thus achieved not by fighting but by expanding and becoming increasingly more inclusive....

The scene that followed was what you might call a dream within a dream: waking up to find that you are in another dream from which you wake up to find that you are in another dream... Except that I was not dreaming - unless the whole of life is a dream (!). I was in another state of consciousness.

The cave was fully lit, and full of people - and I'm using the word 'people' very loosely here. I quickly picked out four categories. There were 'dead' people and 'living' ones, the latter group comprising people who were still alive but out of their physical bodies. There were also humans with some animal features, and there were those who resembled humans but were mostly light within which I could perceive vague human outlines - mainly energies irradiating from what looked like human faces. Those who were distinctly human - the 'dead' and the 'living' - were sitting on the ledges, the others were either standing or hovering in the air.

There was an atmosphere of loving and caring together with a keenness to learn. The cave was, in fact, a kind of lecture hall, but not in the usual university lecture hall sense. The thirst for knowledge which was strongly present was indistinguishable from an accompanying devotional feeling. All those people were there to learn in order to serve, and to learn how to serve.

While I was being warmly welcomed I realised that a lecture had already been in progress. Indeed, practically all of my reflections and experiences since I entered that cave were common knowledge to all those in there. My thoughts were being studied - and my intuitions were none other than my personal 'notes' from the ongoing 'lecture'! I had been listening/seeing, interacting, and absorbing a 'lesson' all along without being aware of a 'lecture' taking place! I had been to similar 'lectures' before but only during sleep. This was different.

As I settled in to the new awareness, I began to recognise people I knew who were now dead, and I was delighted to see also a number of 'brothers' and 'sisters' of the Teacher's school, as well as of other schools from around the world. Some of the 'half-humans' - themselves guardians, teachers, instructors, guides - were from way back. Those 'of the light' were not, strictly speaking, human - they were, however, closely connected with human evolution. And it was one of this particular group who had the floor, so to speak, at that moment.

I soon noticed that whatever was being 'said' I could take in in more ways than one. I could hear it, if I so wished, but I could also see it in concrete visual terms or in abstract shapes and colours, or comprehend it in totally abstract or intuitive terms. I also noticed that the 'speaker's' countenance kept shifting and changing, exhibiting features from different human races - including that of Yiannis and the Teacher.

It didn't take me long to realise that all these varied ways of making the lessons available and the various 'personalities' through which they were being delivered were, in fact, the different ways in which those listening were receiving the material. The message was the same but the manner in which it was being received varied according to culture and individual personality - perhaps also level of Initiation.

I reflected on how people in everyday life misunderstand one another in spite of the fact that we all live in the same mental space: we misconstrue meanings and intentions, we prepare an answer while the other person is still talking, we ignore a great deal of what is being said. I wondered--

The 'lecturer' picked up on my thoughts and continued:

"Listening: what is it, how is it done?"

It was amazing: he - or she, there was no gender distinction - sent out the thoughts of what he was saying and the rest of us surged towards him and immersed ourselves in his 'light'. I knew the theory and, up to a degree, the practice, but what he was doing was not simply reiterating: he was pushing the point to the extent of not only causing the loosening of our ego boundaries but also of softening our centre, our core.

It was a delicate operation: you could lose your bearings, you could go mad. But he was acting from authority: "You absorb yourself in the other person's thoughts, you identify. You don't criticise; you make his/her thoughts and feelings your own, you become that person." I knew the theory of 'no judgment', and had seen it practised, and had had a go at it myself . Now I was experiencing it fully: discrimination without judgment. Within his consciousness there were no limits, no boundaries - and no centre. The vastness... And then each of us returned to our respective core, to re-establish our individualities. It was a taster, an intimation of possibilities...

And he continued. I couldn't tell whether he was working from a plan or doing it impromptu but he was using many of my questions and inquiries and turning them into lessons. Was I that important? No, of course not. These were questions raised by all those like-minded people - why else would I be drawn to that particular gathering? He continued with mostly pithy, laconic, statements - kernels we were required to prise open and follow the unfolding of their meanings as they flowed out of him.

"Creation is imbalance."

As he said that, everything and everybody just vanished, the place was plunged into total darkness. Then there was a great explosion, and the cave was filled with intense light. But, even though light was everywhere, darkness lay lurking somewhere in the background, not seen but sensed. And the meanings began to unfold: "Light exists, light is Existence itself. It comes out of Darkness and expands - the creative impulse which is found everywhere. Continuous movement without which everything will collapse into Non-existence, into Darkness. Darkness *is*, Light *exists*."

"The objective world is your creation."

On this utterance, I felt all the light being drawn into me, being sucked into what I am as consciousness. And then coming out of me, being projected out of me, but in that projection I felt everyone around me participating: "I am part of the created world, but I have played, and still do, a part in its creation and continuing existence. What's more, nothing exists in the world which is outside my own existence."

"Existence in space and time."

With this, I was temporarily confused - too many 'times' and too many 'spaces'. I took a deep breath and concentrated on him as he continuously irradiated shapes, colours, movement. They all existed in many different kinds of spaces in each of which time was also ex-perienced differently:

"Consciousness participates in, and contributes to, the creation and perception of space(s). All dimensions - spatial and temporal - are, in the last analysis, consciousness-based. While some experi-ences take place in *no time* and are remembered *in time*, others unfold in space-and-time and are forgotten - until they are resur-rected. Numerous spaces and times exist simultaneously, and they criss-cross. A person can be conscious in more than one space-time set simultaneously; also, other space-time sets may impinge on a person's current set uninvited."

"Life is a dream."

This was a teaser, at Yiannis' suggestion. I could see Yiannis laughing through the light of the 'lecturer'. I was glad for the light relief. All the same, meanings reeled out of the 'lecturer': wave upon wave, layer upon layer. I decided to offer my own interpret-ation: 'Dreaming is a series of states, and if life is a dream, then life is a state of dreaming. Many people think that, by definition, if there is dreaming then there must be waking, having erroneously assumed that dreaming is the opposite of waking, and that a person must fall asleep in order to dream.' I was more than glad to hear Yiannis laugh at my response.

"Training the mind to understand what we already know."

This took me back to 'knowing' and 'understanding'. Something like tiers appeared to come out of the 'lecturer'. They were tiers of understanding, functioning in a variety of universes all of which are spatially co-existing - each with its own type of comprehending. Knowledge is memory which is accessed by understanding through training.

"Love is all-pervasive."

Once again, light was emphasised. But this time it was gentler, and it shone out of everybody and everything in that cave - even the walls exuded light, they were light. Everything was light. "Love is light. It's everywhere and in everything, and everything is love. We are in it and we are conditioned by it. No matter what we do we do it in love. It is through love that we become the light that survives Darkness. We survive Darkness by becoming love-intoxicated."

The whole cave was an astounding sight. Everything was scintillating light, and all the people in there were giving out wave after wave of vibrant energies in indescribable colours. Momentarily, I felt that a discord had been introduced by a floating thought. It was the thought of a selfless deed being a reward in itself, that is, in performing a selfless act a person feels good and therefore the act is not selfless because it is rewarded. But, immediately, the thought dissipated in view of the understanding that existence was light and love and so feeling good and being happy were innate and natural states.

"Memory is what makes a *person*."

The 'lecturer' turned into a lotus bud which then began to open slowly and, apparently, unceasingly, giving forth rows and rows of petals. Each one of us dipped into the open lotus to get our share. But then, at some stage, we all 'claimed' the whole lotus for ourselves, which we proceeded to 'wear', and in that process turned ourselves into a multi-petalled lotus - the selfsame lotus multiplying and yet remaining the original one. "Connected, individual memories create and hold together a person in existence. Total *personal memory* frees a person from individual existence. *Universal memory* releases a person from Existence."

As a footnote, there was a scene in a Greek church - presumably for my benefit - in which the priest was chanting at someone's memorial service and praying that the memory of the deceased be kept alive forever and ever, thus declaring the belief and intention of his religion to keep a 'departed' person chained by means of their memories of him - a frightful thought!

"There is no mercy."

It was now the turn of those 'of the light' to play their part. They took over the cave and shone in every nook and crevice. And they multiplied. Like the 'lecturer', they gave out a sense of gentleness and severity. They took it upon themselves to represent Laws. "The world is governed by Laws, immutable and unyielding. There is no such thing as mercy - this is an infantile human conception springing from weakness and the need for parental support. You are never given anything you have not earned."

Under this apparent harshness there was a caveat, an explanation, to the effect that acts of mercy were good, in fact, necessary and natural in the process of consciousness expansion - but these were actions on the part of individual consciousnesses, not of the Laws. As this explanation was being 'given', a tremendous surge of compassion rose within all of us in that cave - a powerfully empathic feeling for all and everything in pain and other forms of suffering or 'disadvantage'.

In the middle of this, I saw the 'lecturer' advancing towards me and showering me with his love-light. As he stood in front of me, a hand came out of his light and touched the medallion hanging round my neck, and then went past the medallion and into my chest. I felt a great thrill radiating from that spot and coursing throughout my body - it was as if my whole body were being cleansed and filled with energy.

While he was doing this, his appearance changed - as if he'd turned into somebody else. For a brief moment, I thought it was Yiannis, a young Yiannis, 'within' the 'lecturer'. Then, he changed again, and a tall imposing figure appeared 'around' Yiannis. Immediately, I recognised Pythagoras. He was young, very young, his face beaming with his usual captivating smile. But even he was 'overtaken', so to speak, by another figure who appeared behind him, 'enclosing' within himself all the others.

This new figure surpassed the others in brilliance. It was as if I were looking directly into the sun. I shut my eyes instinctively, afraid that I might be blinded. But it made no difference: this was not physical light and I could not avoid it. The light was then dimmed slightly and I saw a young man standing there with the famous 'archaic' smile hanging on his lips. It was a *koúros*, recognisable from representations in ancient statues. But why? What was the significance of his presence? The moment I formulated the question, I recognised Apollo. I also realised why Yiannis and Pythagoras stood within the god: they had become 'Apollo', they had reached the stage of 'completion' and become the god.

"And what is a god?" I heard the 'lecturer' ask.

Again, I wondered why this visitation. But before I'd finished my mental query came the answer:

"*You* are a *god*."

I became aware at that moment that perhaps this was the point at which many great investigators into the 'mysteries' of life become rather unhinged, overwhelmed by the belief in their uniqueness. Fortunately for me, however, I was quick to understand that all that statement meant was that I, as a human being, had the potential - perhaps, I was 'destined' - to become god: eventually. My interpretation was confirmed when I turned round and saw that all my 'fellow students' were in the same boat: they were all undergoing the same experience...

It was a 'common' experience in which the meaning of 'consciousness' merged with that of 'conscience' - in Greek, in fact, it's the same word. I understood at that point why Yiannis had been going on about morality being informed by consciousness, indeed, flowing out of it: 'common experience' and 'common knowledge' - meaning both that all the senses were involved simultaneously (synaesthetically) and that 'knowledge' and 'awareness' were in the nature of collective ownership, that is, contributed to and shared fully by everybody - leading to Superconsciousness!

And then, suddenly, the 'lecturer' pulled his hand out of my chest and, to my horror, I saw him holding a piece of flesh, my flesh! Strangely, though, I felt no pain. And then I realised he was not holding anything 'real', only an *image* of a part of my body - two small lobes - which he proceeded to replace; and, as he did that, I felt the same surge of energy I'd experienced earlier when he had first placed his hand there.

This time, my attention was drawn more forcefully to the spot, and I found myself being sucked into it. I went right into this little organ, which now loomed enormous. It was the thymus, a lymph gland central to the organisation of the body's immune system, and which in ancient times was considered to be 'the seat of the soul' and a 'fiery fighter'. I wanted to know why. I was not given a purely and solely 'physical' explanation but instead was taken through a complex series of functions and images.

First, the thymus itself, in which I was now practically swimming. It is at its peak of activity in youth - childhood to puberty - during which time it builds its defences against sources of infection, and it reaches its full growth and potential in puberty. Indeed, it is so aggressive in carrying out its task that it produces excessive amounts of 'defensive' cells most of which it destroys to prevent them from turning against the system itself! While this information was being spelled out, I was also shown Yiannis, Pythagoras and Apollo as young men, and reminded of two of Apollo's important characteristics: those of the destroyer and the healer, the Apollo *oúlios* (ούλιος) who destroys and makes whole.

The whole of the gland, with me inside it, was then flooded with the effulgence of the Sun-Apollo. While pleasant at the beginning, this brilliance, and the heat that came with it, gradually became unbearable. I was on fire, I was burning! There were flames everywhere, it was a veritable conflagration! I don't know how long this situation lasted - my sense of time was totally obliterated, I may have passed out. At some point, the fire disappeared and the heat abated. What remained was the brilliance which was now healing and comforting, and a feeling of cleanliness and exhilaration. I basked in the light, and found myself going back to a scene that had taken place a few years earlier and had moved me a great deal:

I am on Mykonos, sitting on a rock by the sea, facing the island of Delos as the sun is making its way down to the horizon. I am drenched in sunlight, and reflecting on my experiences at Delphi past and present, on my memories of Delos, the island of Apollo, where Theseus had danced with his companions after the killing of the Minotaur, where Pythagoras had come to nurse his beloved teacher Pherekydes... The sun is at its point of setting, dressed in its multi-coloured royal robes of glory... I am filled with emotion by the beauty of the sight and the memories it has brought to the surface... Then, that magical time of day glides by and darkness prevails. Cool darkness that ushers in the starry mantle of night....

In Search of an Exit
(The Abandonment and the Way Out)

And then I was back at the cave, and nobody was there, except for scintillating specks of light-energy and the atmosphere of thirst for knowledge and love-impulsion-need to serve. If I had to choose between the two, knowledge or service, which way would I go, I wondered. The words of beloved Buddha rang in my ears: "To do a little good is better than accomplishing a great task." But then, accomplishing the great task of becoming Light in order to enter Darkness implied becoming loving and caring and doing more than "a little good" - which appeared to be the central meaning and essence of 'consciousness expansion', and which satisfied both ends of the polarised counsel.

I was lying on a stone slab, reminiscent of the old days when we lay on a slab in the dark for long days and nights, going through practices and experiences for the expansion of consciousness. I felt hungry and wondered how long I'd been in there, or if, indeed, I was in the same cave. If the experiences in the rock and the Cove of Love were anything to go by, time and location would be irrelevant, as Yiannis would have said - and I could almost hear him saying just that. All the same, I switched on the torch to check my watch and the cave. The batteries had gone flat!

Right! There I was in total darkness, and starving, and not knowing where exactly I was, and, more importantly, not knowing how to get out of there. I fumbled and took out of the bag the bottle of water. At least I had the water. I drank and rehydrated myself, and then sat back to work out a plan. What plan? All I could do was stand up and walk carefully, holding onto the walls and taking care not to stumble and fall. Which was what I did.

I managed to find the opening that led out of the cave and into the long passage. I knew that if I were to continue the way I had set out earlier, I should be turning to my left, but I hesitated. For a few seconds, I wished I'd gone back out of this tunnel the way I'd come in with Yiannis. But it was probably too late now. I'd walked for so long before coming to this last cave that I was almost certain I couldn't find my way back in that direction - I had turned left and right so many times....

I decided to stick to my original plan and turned left. I walked slowly and carefully, following the turnings of the passage and ignoring the occasional openings which, very likely, would have led me into dead end caves. I was determined to follow this passage to the end and see where it would lead me. I meandered for what felt like hours - and came to the end of the passage: literally to the end! As I followed the walls with my hands, I realised I was simply turning round at a dead end wall! I nearly collapsed with exhaustion and frustration.

I sat on the ground tired, angry and frustrated. I took a few deep breaths and relaxed. Surely all this experience must be part of a test. I should keep my cool. Where was Athespodos when I needed him? I concentrated on him calling for help. All I needed was a faint bark, enough to orientate myself to an exit. Nothing. Worse than that: I suddenly realised I couldn't switch to the direct method, I could not 'see' or 'hear' in any other way besides my usual physical senses. True, I was tired and could not keep my mind focused properly. But what kind of test would this be if I were to fight for my survival in an emaciated physical body and without the ability to 'see' and comprehend and make decisions by means of the direct method?

I began to feel depressed. A sense of emptiness descended on me. A feeling of having been cut off from everything and everybody. I was abandoned. Not long ago, I was filled with euphoria, of happiness, of health and vigour. Now I was a mere shadow of myself. Where were those wonderful people I had spent time with in the 'lecture hall'? They were my friends - supposedly.

Yiannis had said that there would be a time when I would be totally abandoned, left entirely to my own devices. I had taken this to be something like a theatrical play or a film in which I would play the part of the abandoned 'hero', knowing all along that it was only a play, a pretense. This was not like that. I was alone - and lonely! My physical body was failing me, and my 'psychic' abilities had taken a hike. What would I do? Fight. But how? How would I do that in a debilitated body? How?..

I was, suddenly , plunged into a strange and indescribable fear of total existential annihilation. It was not a fear of dying: it was a sudden awareness of the real possibility - no, certainty - of being obliterated. I had nothing to grab onto, and nothing with which to grab onto anything, in order to retain the sanity of existence; no hope of surviving as a unit or even as a fraction of anything. The fear that had gripped me at the rock faded into insignificance by comparison. I was utterly paralysed: physically, mentally - totally....

Then, I had the vague impression of closing my eyes to gather my thoughts but, instead, I fell asleep! or, at least, it felt so. It was a dark, empty sleep, devoid of awareness, the kind of sleep I had never had before. How long did it last? One hour, two hours, a day, a night? All I felt when I came back was that it must have been long in terms of clock time, and that I had fallen into a black hole as far as consciousness was concerned. When I opened my eyes, I found myself back at the exact psychological spot at which I had been before the 'sleep' - thinking about my inability to deal with my predicament whilst in a debilitated, delapitated, body....

Then it hit me: *in* a dilapitated body! *In*. That was it. *I* was *in* a dilabitated body. Dissociate. That was what I had to do - dissociate. *I* was not my body, and the state my body was in at that moment - weak and exhausted - it should not be difficult to control, to order it about.

And then it hit me: the realisation that I could dissociate, as I was doing at that very moment, was new. I had forgotten that I had used dissociation before, that I was capable of doing it all along. I had lost this connection together with the loss of my 'psychic' abilities.

But I was making a reconnection now. I took the bottle out of the bag and drank some water - I should go easy with it, it was running out.

I stood up and began to walk again. This time I would get off the passage by following my nose, orientating myself towards an exit by sniffing the air around me. I had done that as a kid in order to find the sea - a game I had played with my friends. Granted, there wouldn't be a sea nearby to smell the sea air, but that should not matter - it was the orientation I was after. I was taking a chance because in the absence of sea air I always relied on some extra element which bordered on the 'psychic', and perhaps it was. And now with that aspect blocked out.... I had to try, anyway; I had no other choice - short of lying down and giving up altogether.

After some time, I turned to the left through an opening and, to my delight, it was not a cave, it was a passage! I was right to follow my nose. Encouraged by that success, I decided to make use of some other, common sense, means of orientation. I started to concentrate on possible draughts and changes in temperature around me. Soon, I was on autopilot, feeling my way forward with confidence. My body was hurting but I was ignoring it, there was no way it would stop me. For the first time since I had entered that tunnel, however, I wished there were animals living in there - and I would not care if they were wild and dangerous: their presence would have at least indicated that there might be entrances and exits.

And then, I thought I heard Athespodos! Or maybe I was hallucinating. I wanted so much to hear him that it wouldn't be surprising if I had created an elemental of him. But, anyhow, I had nothing to lose in following his bark. I stopped and waited for a while. I was disappointed. Nothing. I resumed my search, and, not long after, I heard him again. It was him, surely it must be him. His bark was faint, very faint and distant. I decided to follow the direction where I felt it was coming from. It turned out to be a long way away, and it stopped after a while. But I continued to walk in the general direction. For how long? I had no idea. I just walked and walked....

And then there was light! Yes, there was light! Not much, a glimmer. I dismissed it at first, but it was there. I felt like rushing towards it, like a man in a desert rushing to a mirage. But I had to control my impulse and watch my step in the dark. I walked slowly and carefully as before. As I got closer, I realised that the light was not coming from a source directly opposite but from somewhere above. When I arrived at the spot, I saw it coming down a high and very narrow chimney. A small opening, but it was an opening, and that was all that mattered at the time. I needed to sit down for a rest but I decided to take a look around first.

The passage continued for a short distance farther on before coming to an end. Around where the light reached the ground there were desiccated carcasses of small animals, probably fallen down the chimney and killed by the fall. Some of them must have survived for a while because there were dried up faeces scattered around. I cleared a little space on the ground and sat, and then took the bottle out and drank the rest of the water. I needed the energy for the climb.

The chimney was high, vertical and narrow but didn't look impossible to climb. I simply needed a little rest before embarking on this new labour. I sat there for a while pulling myself together and reflecting on how I let myself fall to pieces earlier, how I lacked belief in myself and in the purpose of the task. When I felt I was ready, I stood up and set about to climb. As the chimney was so narrow I decided to discard the bag, together with the torch and the empty bottle. Travelling light was not a choice, it was a necessity.

I started to climb by grabbing at small protrusions and pulling myself upwards while securing against falling by resting my weight on whatever foothold I could get. The chimney proved more difficult to scale than I had thought. Not only was it vertical but also far too narrow - I could hardly fit my shoulders across it. My shirt and shorts started to tear against the jutting bits of the walls - not to mention the cuts on my arms and knees. The opening I'd come in with Yiannis was, at least, horizontal and the rock smoother - and, of course, Yiannis was there to help.

I persisted a while longer before stopping for a rest. I looked up and then down and calculated that I hadn't climbed more than a third of the total height. And I was already too tired to continue - if I fell I would probably die from tears and wounds before hitting the ground. I considered my choices. And decided to climb down, have a real good rest, and then attack the chimney with more determination. And so I did, and in the process acquired some extra cuts I could have done without.

I sat on the ground, amongst the dried up carcasses and excrement, and tried to relax and re-energise myself. I was, obviously, going about it the wrong way. But what else was I to do? I had tried all that was possible. I even dissociated myself from my body, which was definitely a right move. But still not enough. What else was there? I began to fall into depression again, and felt the need to sleep. I quickly shook myself out of it - falling into a black sleep again might prove fatal, I might not come out of it. I turned away from the small heap of animal waste and remains and took a few deep breaths.

Dissociating was a right move but it did not go far enough. Fear was what was motivating me. I had dissociated myself from my physical body but I was still concerned with survival - even my dissociation was not complete, as I was still too conscious of the cuts and tears. I had to re-evaluate the situation. I soon realised that I had been far too concerned with my survival as an individual consciousness. But wasn't that the point of the whole enterprise - to create a strong individual consciousness to survive the Darkness? No, not exactly.

In my absorbing concern for survival, I had ignored that all-important further stage: the expansion. Had I retained my other abilities, I wouldn't have overlooked it. And in my efforts to survive physically, I had also allowed the psychological unity to fall apart - with anger, frustration, depression and so on splitting away and claiming importance. I would now have to reclaim the psychological unity, make myself whole, and then expand. Without the direct method I had no idea how successful I would be, but I had no real alternative - except the application of my will.

I relaxed and concentrated, first on my body: I could control it; hunger and exhaustion and cuts and pain were irrelevant; I could ignore them without the batting of an eyelid, they were under my control. Then, the mental parts: to be angry was a totally daft reaction, a waste of valuable energy and a hindrance to concentration; frustration was only the result of paying too much attention to nuisance conditions; depression was the result of physical exhaustion and repeated failures in my efforts to get out of there - it was also indulgence. I dismissed the demands of all these conditions for attention, and claimed unity and individuality of consciousness by sheer will.

Then came the harder part: the expansion - without the use of the direct method. All I could do was fall back on the technique. How did I get into the tunnel through the first opening? By feeling the walls of the opening as part of me, and by willing them to soften and give way. That was what I had to do again now.

I stood up and began to clamber. I kept my concentration: my body and my psyche were tools at my command, the walls of the chimney were no more than an extension of my bodies, and they were soft and yielding. And I clambered on. As if in a dream, I felt my sandals falling off my feet. I continued. Not much of my clothes were left on my body, and the cuts had multiplied, but, amazingly, the jutting bits of the walls were both tearing and balmy, cutting and healing. No pain, just tearing and healing.

And then, and then the singing of birds! Yes, I heard birds singing! It sounded like a dawn chorus, or it could have been dusk - who cared? I was close to the top. I could see shrubs across the opening. I pulled myself up to the edge and scared a few birds away as I pushed through the small branches of the plants. And I was out, amongst some of my favourite aromatic bushes, and a basking lizard! I was at the top of a mountain, on a small plateau surrounded by cliffs. It was dawn.

I stood up straight, barefoot, in my tattered shirt and shorts, my body cut, torn and bloody, and stretched out my arms to greet my friend, my brother, my Sun, my Apollo. I saw the 'tube' and the pouring of energy, the travelling light, and the radiating colours that vibrated and caressed and embraced the planet! I was back, I'd been restored! I could see beauty again! Whoever said that beauty was in the eye of the beholder, forgot to explain that, when the eye of the beholder was properly opened, it could see that beauty was everywhere.

I heard Athespodos in the distance, and saw him standing close to the lip of a cliff in the line of the rising Sun, wagging his tail, greeting me - inviting me to join him? An enormous eagle flew towards me from the direction of the Sun - as if it had come out of the Sun itself - and glided close above me in a circle quietly, confidently, authoritatively, regally, before heading back where he had come from, right into the sunlight, his outstretched wings producing a sound resembling that which had been made by Yiannis' Light as it shot through the ceiling of the cave....

Athespodos barked again. He was definitely inviting me to join him. Surely, he would guide me down the mountain, help me find my bearings, and then... Meet Yiannis again in the flesh perhaps? Join other fellow travellers on our way to becoming Light to enter the Darkness in full consciousness?... Life is such an open-ended enterprise....

Appendix
Exercises

The following exercises - mostly gleaned from the book - are graded in terms of complexity and purpose. Concentration and visualisation are essential, along with the cultivated ability to relax, physically and mentally, and become perceptive/receptive.

In visualising, we also incorporate all the other senses in order to create the feeling of being present.

We always take a few deep breaths before each exercise.

Etheric Energy in the Air: This exercise is best carried out in the open, preferably in good sunny weather. We concentrate in a relaxed manner at the space about half a metre in front and slightly above us. Soon, we'll be able to see silvery-metallic and squiggley white sparks flying all over. The longer we concentrate the denser the space becomes with this energy. When sufficiently relaxed and concentrated, we begin to breath in this energy both through our nose and through our skin.

Swirling Clouds of Colours: Similar to the above but carried out indoors. We sit in front of a blank wall, or some other flat surface, about a metre away and concentrate on the space between us and the wall. Soon clouds of swirling colours will begin to form before our eyes. When sufficiently absorbed in this activity, we shift our attention to the flat surface and watch the unfolding scenes and figures. These are images surfacing from our subconscious and may or may not carry any significant meaning. We can, however, pose questions to this process and receive surprising responses.

Psychometry: This is a process well-known to psychic circles. We pick up an object, hold it gently in our hand, relax over it, and perceive impressions relating to it. These could be visual, auditory, tactile, and so on. More actively, we pose questions regarding the history of the object and/or the character, physical and mental state and concerns of the owner of the object. When dealing with people, we always seek consent, before delving into their personal life by means of this practice. An extension of this technique could be used to allow us to 'soak in' the atmosphere and history of a building, an ancient site, and so on.

Hypnagogic Images and Impressions: When relaxed as we prepare to go to sleep we enter into a state which is very conducive to having all sorts of sensory and mental experiences. If we allow ourselves to relax enough and simply prevent ourselves from falling asleep, we can pose questions and receive answers which could be visual, auditory, and so on. But we can also pose questions and receive answers purely on the intellectual level, that is, we can gain clear intuitions. And if we train ourselves to stay on this border between wakefulness and sleep we can further initiate and fully participate in wakeful dreams. These could be just that, that is, dreams, or they can develop into contacts and conscious communications with departed humans or other forms of life.

Relaxation, Visualisation and the Body of Light: We sit upright with our spine straight and our eyes shut, and relax. We begin by visualising our toes. We see them as clearly as possible, and then move our attention through the arches, the ankles and the legs to the knees. We visualise and relax all these parts. We relax the knees and move through the thighs to the base of the spine. From there we continue the journey through as many of our internal organs as we can visualise, taking in the spine as well. We reach the shoulders which we relax, and move down to the arms, elbows, forearms and fingers. We relax the neck and the whole of the head, paying particular attention to the forehead and facial muscles. Now, we see the whole body relaxed, as a unit.

Next, we see white energy emanating from every cell of our body and coursing through it and cleansing and envigorating it. That done, we remove our attention from the physical body and concentrate exclusively on the white energy itself which has now taken the shape of the physical body - like a duplicate. We concentrate on this with as much attention as we can muster and stay with it as long as possible: this is a Body of Light which, with special practice, we shall inhabit and use as our vehicle to move around at will.

The Vortex: We do this sitting down. We visualise a column of white energy rising from the ground in direct line with our spine. It reaches the spine, which it encases as it continues to move upwards. It passes through the head, as it leaves the top of the spine, and shoots out above the head turning itself into a V-shape cascading fountain of white energy. We pursue this for a while and then see this column revolve like a vortex - clockwise, from our left, to our front, to our right, to the back, to the left, to the front, to the right, and so on. As the vortex rises and spins, we identify with it, spinning and rising within it. This exercise must always be carried out while sitting, as dizziness and small spasms may occur.

The Hermanubis Columns: We do this standing upright with our feet slightly apart. We visualise a column of white energy rising from between our feet, encasing the spine and terminating in the centre of the head turning into something that resembles a small pine cone. From our feet themselves we see two other columns of white energy rising and coursing through our thighs and crossing over at the level of our genitals; they move up and cross back at the solar plexus; having moved higher up they cross again at a point just above the sternum; then they move farther up and cross at the base of the throat, thus finding themselves back on their original sides. They move along vertically just above the shoulders and curve in turning themselves into the heads of serpents and pointing to the cone at the centre of our head. There are two small fluttering wings right behind the heads of each of the serpents. We hold onto this for as long as possible.

Opening up and Expanding: This involves an opening up type of meditation similar to that applied in psychometry, except that no questions are posed. It is a progressive exercise and it's best done gradually. We begin with inanimate objects and plants or trees. The latter are not only easy but most pleasant. We sit in front of a tree, relax, and open up to it, that is, we move ourselves as consciousness into it, connect with it. We bypass the intellectual questioning about its nature and we merge with it. We shall soon begin to experience the tree synaesthetically, that is, smell it, taste it, hear and see its sap coursing in it, and so on. It is a game of love.

We can apply a modified version of this method in order to understand people directly. We can do this if, for example, we want to understand a person when they are talking. In which case, we need to learn not to argue mentally, not to engage in preparing an answer while the other person is talking. It's a game of love. We decide to connect with that person and understand them, and the easiest way to achieve this is by merging ourselves with them. Again, it's a game of love. Another variation of the method can be used to 'see' and 'feel' health problems in a person for the purpose of healing.

The same general process - not criticising, not being judgmental, but simply wanting to be one with our object of attention - can further be extended to the whole of humanity and to the whole of nature. It's a game of love, which leads to an ever increasing, expanding, consciousness.

The Temple of Light: This exercise can be carried out on one's own or in a group. In the latter circumstances it is more potent.

We sit and relax as usual. We imagine ourselves standing at the edge of a cliff. Behind us lay a forest with lush vegetation, in front of us and a long way down below stretches the sea. We are in a Mediterranean or subtropical country; it is late afternoon in the summer. We are wearing a thin white gown, and we are barefoot. We feel the warmth of the flat edge of the cliff under our feet. Seagulls and other seabirds are flying around with some of them coming to roost in the face of the cliff.

A welcoming breeze rises from the sea and glides up the tall cliff and reaches us, causing our gowns to flutter. We smell the sea air as it caresses our face and our hair and gently lifts us off the cliff. We are weightless. We rise up from the cliff and straighten into a horizontal position and glide ahead. We look down to see the base of the cliff far below. Ahead is the open sea. We glide for a while and fly over a small 'island', a rocky outcropping, barren except for a couple of trees. We see the water lapping all around it, a few seagulls flying. We look ahead of us to see the sun about to set. It is a glorious sight! We absorb the wonderful colours as they spread in the sky and the sea.

Then we see the outline of land in the distance. As we approach, we find ourselves looking at a cliff very much like the one we have left. It's enormous. We glide close to its face and see the seabirds flying around us and into their nests. We rise up to the lip of the cliff and land gently on it. It feels warm to the feet. A short distance away, we can make out a big classical-looking building. We walk towards it on flat slabs and approach it. It is circular, and it is supported on columns all round. We walk up the seven steps to its floor. There is no doorway, no specific entrance - just columns.

We see light somewhere inside it, and walk towards it on a flat, smooth, seamless floor that feels like marble. As we approach the light, we see people and other 'figures' coming out of the darkness and into this pool of light. The columns form a perfect circle in the middle, an area where the light pours from above. As we get closer, we see people of all races and ages getting into the light and rising up towards its source, only we cannot see an actual source - it 'feels' like a translucent dome but we cannot actually see it.

We move into this pool of light and float upwards with the others. We begin to swirl around clockwise as we rise. Like the sourceless light there is also sourceless music which spreads around with the light. As we swirl we begin to lose our human form and gradually turn into shades of colour which mix with the others and separate and mix again. Occasionally we change our original hue altogether. Slowly, we begin to realise that each one of us is not only a hue but also a note. It is - we are - a wondrous symphony of colour and sound, feeling our affinity with all other entities and our innate connection with the sourceless light.

The Cave: This exercise can be done either sitting or lying down. It is very simple but can lead to a wonderful experience.

We are in a big Cave, sitting on stone ledges along with other people whom we perceive only vaguely. There is a small pond at one end of this Cave and various entrances/exits around. It is comfortably warm and quiet. We sit there and wait in the darkness and the quiet.... We know there are going to be visitors at some point, and someone will give a talk... We sit and wait....

The Cave exercise, along with the Temple of Light, if they are carried out on one's own, will be most beneficial if they are done in bed at night and the person falls asleep while visualising. In such case, individuals could compare notes regarding their experiences of a particular night. It will be most rewarding. See you there.

For comments on

HYPNAGOGIA:
The Unique State of Consciousness
between Wakefulness and Sleep
(New Edition in paperback 2010
by Thyrsos Press
ISBN-13 : 978-0-9553052-1-4)

please turn over

▶ **More comments on Dr Mavromatis'** *Hypnagogia*: ◀

"An extremely important book...intellectually exciting and emotionally satisfying....lavishly illustrated....a book of outstanding quality."
Professor Peter McKellar, *Journal of Mental Imagery*

"Mavromatis' notion of the loosening of ego boundaries is not only right on the money, it's also reinforced by modern neuroscience's understanding of the brain. ...Mavromatis found that during hypnagogic sessions, he and his subjects could pass around mental images like telepathic hot potatoes."
Jeff Warren, *Head Trip*

"I cannot imagine anyone interested in the human mind who will not find things of interest here...I recommend this book very highly."
Changes

"Here is a book to feast upon. ...The sweep of Mavromatis' ideas can be seen from first to last. Whatever the highway or byway he takes, he holds our attention...Mavromatis has succeeded admirably in bringing the subject to life."
Bulletin of the British Psychological Society

"It is not often that one can recommend a book without any reservations at all."
Guy Lyon Playfair, *Light*.

"I consider Mavromatis' work to be fundamental and groundbreaking toward a unified understanding of the mind."
Sirley Marques Bonham, PhD (*Consciousness and Hypnagogia*)

"Mavromatis links hypnagogia to dreams, schizophrenia, creativity, meditation, mystical experience, and, most strikingly, paranormal experience... (he) relates hypnagogia to what is described in Tantric Yoga as the 'Fourth State', the junction of waking, sleeping and dreaming... his study of hypnagogia is the most thorough to date, and it is difficult to see how it will be surpassed as the standard work."
Gary Lachman, *Fortean Times*

" 'Hypnagogia' makes fascinating reading...It also serves as an encouragement to the reader to initiate his own personal investigation."
Alyson Bond, *The British Journal of Psychiatry*